AMERICAN BUILDING ART

THE NINETEENTH CENTURY

# AMERICAN

NEW YORK

# BUILDING ART

### THE NINETEENTH CENTURY

CARL W. CONDIT

OXFORD UNIVERSITY PRESS • 1960

© 1960 BY OXFORD UNIVERSITY PRESS, INC.

Library of Congress Catalogue Card Number: 59–11752

PRINTED IN THE UNITED STATES OF AMERICA

*TO ISABEL*

# PREFACE

A comprehensive history of structural forms and techniques in the United States has never been written. This work is designed to treat a subject which very much deserves to be explored. Building techniques may be regarded as a part of the history of architecture, but by and large they do not constitute the aesthetics of architecture. They form part of its physical substance or raw material, so to speak; they are the data out of which the aesthetic object is created. Much of the interest in building technology arises from the organic dependence of architecture upon it. The architect and engineer fashion in good part what they must by virtue of the strict limitations imposed upon them by structural demands. Further, in a highly industrialized and mobile culture there is an enormous volume of utilitarian construction—bridges, dams, highways, railway structures, power plants, factories, warehouses, isolated walls, piers, abutments—which requires considerable practical skill and inventiveness to build and maintain. Very little of this construction has any aesthetic character, although this need not be the case.

Nevertheless, whether building techniques are part of architecture or merely serve utilitarian needs, they have an independent history of their own. It is with the history of those techniques as they developed into the structural basis of modern building that this book deals. Originally my intention was to cover the whole of the American development, but I soon realized that this would be impossible. I early decided to set detailed treatment of the seventeenth and eighteenth centuries aside, partly because building techniques showed little range and diversity compared to the immense radiation that occurred in the nineteenth, partly because the subject is fairly well covered in other works, especially Hugh Morrison's *Early American Architecture*. As I got further into the nineteenth century it became apparent that I would have to treat it separately. My hope is to cover the twentieth century in a subsequent volume.

An explanation of the arrangement of material in the text might be useful. The fundamental narrative of need, invention, and practical application constitutes the text proper. In addition to this, a large number of notes are appended at the end of the book. They serve a variety of functions: detailed analytical descriptions of particular works, especially those containing dimensions, loads, stresses, and other quantitative material; explanations of technical terms; explanations of the kind of structural problem and general mode of solution associated with various types of structure; descriptions of the chemical and physical properties of structural materials; and subsidiary examples necessary for rounding out the historical narrative. The science of structural mechanics has never been presented in nontechnical terms suitable for the general reader and yet adequate to this extremely important branch of scientific technology. I have tried to give such a presentation in general descriptive terms in the text and in more detailed technical terms in the notes. The history of technology ought to be written analytically, with a clear statement of each problem, its solutions, their failure or success, as the case may be, and the reasons therefor. Any other presentation does not do justice to the nature of the subject.

I am indebted to a good many people and institutions in the preparation of this book. I have indicated all sources of quotations in the notes and of illustrations in the list thereof. I have relied so extensively, however, on the McGraw-Hill Company's *Engineering News-Record* and its predecessors that I owe special thanks to that organization for their permission to use the material that I have taken from their publications and files. I was assisted most kindly by the staff members of many libraries and other institutions, chiefly the Burnham Library of the Chicago Art Institute, the John Crerar Library of Chicago, the Technological Library of Northwestern University, the public libraries of Chicago, Cincinnati, Boston, New York, Philadelphia, and Baltimore, the Avery Library of Columbia University, the Baker Library of the Harvard Business School, the Railway and Locomotive Historical Society, the American Antiquarian Society, and the historical societies of Rhode Island, New York City, and South Carolina. The large expenses involved in a project of this scope were borne mainly by generous grants from the Committee on Research Funds of Northwestern University and from the American Philosophical Society of Philadelphia. Without their aid the task would have been hopeless. A number of people gave generously of their time and knowledge in reading the manuscript and making many valuable suggestions for its improvement. Mr. and Mrs. James Wishart and Professors John Dundurs and Carson Webster read various chapters, while Professor Macklin Thomas took on the formidable job of reading the entire work. The final result owes much to the patient day-to-day reading and intelligent criticism made by my wife, Isabel. The major part of my final chapter, "An Architectural Appraisal," was originally published in the *Bucknell Review*. I wish to thank the editor, Professor Harry Garvin, for his kind permission to reprint it here.

CARL W. CONDIT

*Morton Grove, Illinois*
*November, 1959*

# CONTENTS

# LIST OF ILLUSTRATIONS

AMERICAN BUILDING ART

THE NINETEENTH CENTURY

# INTRODUCTION

The nineteenth century was unique in the history of the building arts and hence in the history of technology itself. The period saw not only the greatest number of structural inventions but, even more important, the transformation of building from an empirical and pragmatic art to an exact science. The explosive progress of building techniques produced in one century more innovations in material, structure, form, and method of construction than the whole previous history of the art. New materials as well as new techniques enormously extended the range of buildings and bridges in type and in size. As a matter of fact, all the basic structural elements of contemporary building had been developed and given practical demonstration by the end of the nineteenth century essentially in the forms we know today. It is true, of course, that the traditional methods of construction in wood, brick, and stone flourished throughout the century and continue to do so at the present time, but these were increasingly submerged under the outpouring of technical inventions in metal and concrete which were new creations of the age.

In spite of their number and diversity, however, the whole body of invention for the most part represented variations on five basic structural types: (1) the interior building frame (including rigid frames), which may consist of wood, metal, concrete, or combinations thereof; (2) the truss—the assemblage of members, beams, and the like, forming a rigid framework—flat, polygonal, or arched, usually of wood or metal, although on occasion of concrete; (3) the reinforced concrete slab, flat as in a floor or bridge deck, or curved into a shell or dome; (4) the arch rib of metal or concrete; and (5) suspension by wire cable. The cantilever, almost as old as building itself, was elaborated into a variety of forms and sizes, but these differed only in details from the common truss or beam. The built-up girder was an enlargement for wide spans of the simple beam.

But invention, even in so revolutionary a time, was not a matter of spontaneous generation but rather an organic development out of older techniques. None of the fundamental types that we have described, if we consider their archetypal forms, was original with the nineteenth century. Some, indeed, can be traced to pre-classical antiquity. To point out that such structural techniques go back to medieval or classical origins, however, is not to say that they had in all cases a continuous history. The record is so defective in places that it is impossible to state a definite generalization one way or the other. Bridge construction in wood, for example, is particularly perishable, and to claim an unbroken sequence between Roman truss bridges and the late medieval is a highly speculative matter. In other kinds of construction, especially masonry, there can be no question of continuity. There is generally sufficient evidence to warrant the view that the evolution of building techniques, like other inventive and creative activities, is an organic process. When the historian surveys the past, all that he really sees is an ever-branching continuity extending through all the aspects of culture. Technical invention reveals the same characteristic. It produces a long series of mutations rather than a few original creations. For every apparently new thing there is a precedent. What appears to be a form without relation to anything that has gone before is usually a new pattern or *gestalt* made up of elements previously developed to a lower stage of refinement. The nature of invention in the nineteenth century and the requirements which motivated it were such as to exhibit to a striking degree the organic interrelations within technical processes and between such processes and utilitarian demands. This characteristic was perhaps more marked in building techniques than in any other field, if only because of the greater extent of their practical necessity. It is this pattern of interdependency which constitutes the central theme of the present history.

What distinguishes the basic structural forms of the nineteenth century from their classical and medieval ancestors is not only the extent of their adaptive radiation but also their appearance in what ultimately came to be two dominant and universal materials, iron and concrete. For all buildings other than residences, barns, and pens, for all bridges, trainsheds, and structures of waterway control, wood and traditional forms of masonry virtually disappeared as structural materials. There has been a surprising revival of them in recent years, but at the end of the last century it looked as though they had gone into permanent eclipse. A number of causes associated with the explosive growth of industry combined to bring this about. The need for an immense volume of large and durable buildings, the requirement of fireproof construction, the need to erect buildings and other structures rapidly, economically, and efficiently, to adapt them to uses in a crowded urban environment, to provide housing for the new processes of manufacture, administration, and transportation—all these combined to present the builder with demands previously unknown in such variety and dimensions. Materials and structural elements which could be manufactured in mass and rapidly erected displaced traditional techniques.

Most of the fundamental inventions in nineteenth century construction, such as the iron frame, bridge truss, and arch, were European accomplishments. American work, with some important exceptions, consisted of adaptations of the original forms rather than innovations. On the other hand, the proliferation of structural forms probably reached its greatest extent in the United States because of the builder's more pragmatic and individualistic approach to his art and the sheer variety of geological and topographic features that he had to face. The new metropolis offered him challenges enough, but for the great range of structural types other than city buildings the most decisive and influential factor was the railroad. This, together with the physiography of the American continent, stimulated most powerfully the ingenuity of engineers and builders. In bridges alone the railroad demanded every conceivable type. The wooden pile-and-beam and the wooden truss served well enough for a time, and continue to do so for short spans on branch lines. But iron soon commanded attention. It was used in simple post-and-lintel construction for signal bridges, more elaborately in girder spans, through and deck trusses, cantilevers, arched trusses and ribs, and suspension bridges. Stone masonry was used throughout the century for bridges, ranging from small culverts to immense viaducts, larger than anything that had been built before. The engineers eventually saw the advantages of concrete and used it first for bridge piers, then shortly for arch spans and later for girder spans. As the weight of trains increased, many bridges had to be demolished and replaced at regular intervals. And often with every replacement a new form appeared.

The variety of railroad buildings was even greater. They ranged from tool sheds and switchmen's shanties to immense structures which were among the largest and most complex buildings ever constructed. They included way stations; passenger, mail, express, and freight terminals; office buildings; warehouses; shops; engine terminals; yard service buildings; hotels; and dormitories. The trainshed was a special type that taxed the ingenuity of designers and erectors. There were so many solutions that the history of the shed almost reproduces in microcosm the whole evolution of wide-span enclosures in the nineteenth century. The operation of trains and the servicing of locomotives involved still further additions to the variety of structures. While steam power was still dominant, it demanded multiplying coal and water facilities along the railway lines. Coal elevators and docks, dams, reservoirs, pump houses, tanks, and distribution systems sprang up at every terminal and division point. The modern highway is indebted to the railroad for such special features as separated grade crossings, interchange systems without interfering traffic, fly-over junctions, tunnels, traffic signals, by-pass routes, and separation of different types of traffic. Most railroad buildings were strictly utilitarian structures, untouched by any premeditated art and usually blackened with smoke. At the same time, they included an ever-growing number of distinguished works of architecture. In the face of such demands the architect had to rely to an increasing degree on the engineer, and the engineer in turn on the scientist.

The progress and multiplication of building techniques would have been impossible without a parallel advance in theoretical and experimental science. In construction the age-old dominance of an empirical and pragmatic approach was at last giving way to a scientific technology. The symbiotic relationship between engineering and science which distinguished nineteenth century technics is nowhere more apparent and dramatic than in building. Large and elaborate systems of trusswork and column-and-beam framing required the precise determination of the most efficient shape of members and the most thorough exploitation of the properties of materials. Both could be achieved only through the advanced methods of scientific inquiry which the age had mastered so effectively. The introduction of iron, whose behavior was little understood, required a predictive and experimentally verifiable science of strength, internal structure, and elastic properties. Further, it was necessary to know the alterations of these characteristics that might occur under static and moving loads, impact, vibration, fatigue, and temperature change. The scientific progress depended in turn on technical inventions such as testing machines, load-measuring gauges, and the instruments of metallurgical analysis. In 1800 builders knew practically nothing of these matters; a century later accurate knowledge of them formed the core of engineering curricula and handbooks.

The science of structural materials began with the publication in 1638 of Galileo's *Dialogues on the Two New Sciences*. Shortly afterward Robert Hooke established the basic law of the relationship of load and internal stress in an elastic body, namely, that stress is proportional to strain. The vigorous development of the subject in the eighteenth century was often characterized by a separation of theoretical and empirical components. While the mathematical approach was followed by mathematicians like Euler and the Bernoullis, testing machines were being introduced by the scientists Réaumur and Musschenbroek and the engineer Perronet, but it was not until the work of Coulomb that a union of the two areas began to emerge. With the publication of Gauthey's *Treatise on the Construction of Bridges* (1809–13), the stage was set for a productive synthesis of engineering, scientific, and mathematical talents. Progress in the field was long dominated by the French, with their vastly superior technical schools, but as the century passed, British and other Continental investigators played an increasingly larger role. The American builders, while ingenious in practice, had no native body of scientific inquiry to guide them.

This rapidly expanding field attracted the talents not only of specialists but of creative scientists and mathematicians of the first rank. Its development fell into three broad areas, which in the early part of the century often continued to be pursued separately but which were gradually merged into a unified science of structural materials as the age progressed. The oldest and most highly developed in theory was that concerned with the strength and elastic properties of materials. After it came the analysis of stresses in arches and framed structures, and finally the experimental investigation of the properties of materials in the forms and under the conditions of actual use.

After Euler's initial work on the deflection of loaded beams and columns (1744), the theory of elasticity lay relatively fallow until the beginning of the nineteenth century. An attempt was then made in France to found the theory on the assumptions of classical mechanics, namely, the atomic nature of matter and the existence of forces of attraction and repulsion among its particles. The pioneer in this movement was the mathematician Poisson, who in 1812 proposed that the elastic properties of materials are a consequence of these inter-molecular forces. But this was highly speculative, and for all Poisson's brilliance, it could not lead to immediately fruitful results. What was needed was the more empirical approach of directly investigating the elastic properties of members under deflection. Thomas Young, in his *Lectures on Natural Philosophy and Mechanical Arts* (1807), initiated a mathematical formulation of elasticity on an empirical basis, but his own countrymen showed little interest in the theoretical development of the subject until the mid-century, in spite of their pre-eminence in industrial technology.

Further progress was the achievement of French theorists and engineers. By 1830 Louis Marie Navier, Jean Poncelet, and Gabriel Lamé had put together a fairly comprehensive theory of compressive and tensile deflections and the effects of impact and vibration, and had begun the attack on one form of indeterminate structure, the continuous beam.[1] No iron trusses had yet appeared, but the rapid spread of chain and wire-cable suspension bridges provided the chief empirical basis for their work. Navier investigated English and American suspension bridges, and Lamé was consultant on the design of the earliest European bridges of the wire-cable type, which were built in Russia.[2] The initial phase of the science was rounded out by the work of the Russian engineer D. J. Jourawski, who was the first to deal with the hitherto neglected subject of shearing stresses in connection with his design of wooden railroad bridges in the 1840's. Lamé was the leading figure of this highly productive group. The publication of his *Mathematical Theory of the Elasticity of Solid Bodies* (1852) may be said to mark the coming-of-age of structural science.

The peculiar problems associated with indeterminate structures—continuous beams, redundant trusses, fixed and two-hinged arches—presented a formidable task, which engaged the attention of some of the best scientific talents of the age.[3] Navier, the thermodynamicist Clapeyron, and the Austrian engineer Rebhann attacked the subject of continuous beams. Rebhann was the first to use bending-moment diagrams, which appeared in his *Theory of Wood and Iron Construction* (1856).[4] By this time iron railroad trusses were being built in growing numbers in Europe and the eastern United States. On the basis of the pioneer work of Coulomb, the most thorough investigation of deflections and stresses in fixed and two-hinged arches was carried on by Jacques Antoine Bresse from 1850 to 1865. By the latter date iron arched trusses of great size had been introduced in British and French trainsheds. Bresse also made the most general analysis of continuous beams, extending it to beams with unequal spans under non-uniform load. The complete solution of all problems of indeterminacy was the achievement over two decades, from 1858 to 1879, of an international group—the great English physicist James Clerk-Maxwell, the Italian physicists Ménabréa and Castigliano, and the German engineer Otto Mohr. The man who may be said to have completed the transformation of building art from simple empiricism to mature science was Barré de Saint-Venant. In a career that extended over half a century, from 1835 to his death in 1886, as mathematician, experimenter, engineer, and teacher, Saint-Venant achieved the vital synthesis of theory, experiment, and practice that henceforth made structural engineering an exact science.

The analysis of stresses in the members of trusses and other structures was a uniform, step-by-step process characterized by the extension of basic techniques to an increasing variety of forms. Contributions to this development came from men who represented an even wider range of nationalities, among them the American engineer Squire Whipple. The German mathematician August Möbius founded stress analysis in trusses in 1837 when he established the mathematical relationship between the number of joints and the number of members necessary for statical rigidity. After him it was a matter of orthogenesis, in which each solution led the way to the next.[5] Thus the great railroad bridges at the end of the century—like the Firth of Forth and Memphis cantilevers—could be analyzed in exact and final detail, even to the number and spacing of rivets.

But however valuable theory might be, without the adjunct of controlled empirical investigation it was severely limited. As a matter of fact, the introduction and rapid expansion of iron construction made experimental inquiry a matter of desperate necessity in view of the disasters that accompanied the vast building program of the century in Europe and America. It was necessary to determine exactly the nature of elastic deformation, the elastic limit, and the ultimate strength of the metal. While the English trailed behind the French and Germans in mathematics and scientific theory, the rapid spread of the British railway system compelled the engineers to devise methods for the direct observation of the properties of iron. Wooden beams and wire cable had been tested experimentally by Dupin and Lamé in France before 1825, but the testing of large-scale cast and wrought iron members was initiated by Eton Hodgkinson and William Fairbairn in England. Hodgkinson not only tested columns and beams but also wrought iron plates, the last in connection with the building of the Britannia and Conway tubular bridges.[6] The union of talents in this enterprise was prophetic of what was to come. The bridges were required for the railway lines that Robert Stephenson was then building. Realizing that he was faced with problems for whose solution there was no precedent, Stephenson turned to Fairbairn, iron manufacturer and ship-builder, who in turn sought the assistance of Hodgkinson, mathematician and scientist. Although the results of these tests were published in 1846 and 1849, the systematic testing of structural members on the part of manufacturers did not come until 1858, when David Kirkaldy established machines in the iron works of Napier and Sons. While pioneer work in the German states began as early as the 1830's, the state-owned testing laboratories of the new nation were not founded until 1871. Meanwhile, the German engineer Wöhler had initiated experiments on the fatigue of metals in 1858. By 1865 testing machines appeared in the United States and three years later played a vital role in the preparation of the steel for Eads Bridge.[7] By 1870 exact specifications for performance and quality of metal could be prepared by engineers with a reasonable expectation that manufacturers could meet the requirements.

Two scientific achievements at the mid-century proved of great value in the progress of strength of materials. One was the development of micro-metallography and its application to the examination of the internal structure of iron and the alterations of structure under conditions of actual use. The earliest work in the field was done by P. R. Hodge and Robert Stephenson in England about 1850. The second was the discovery of the double refraction of polarized light in transparent materials under stress. A number of physicists were involved in this activity, but those who first applied it to stress analysis were Franz Neumann in Germany (1843) and Maxwell in England (1850).

By the last quarter of the nineteenth century a close symbiosis of science and technology had evolved, in which every technical problem was eventually treated as a scientific one and the resources of theory and experiment were brought to bear on it. University training on an advanced level, supplemented by widely circulated publications, at last took the place of rule-of-thumb. After the Civil War the growth of American technical schools and the study of European work made the new theory increasingly available to American engineers. The pragmatic habit of mind, often scornful of abstract theorizing, at first obstructed the acceptance of such work.[8] But the sheer magnitude of the problems involved in long-span railroad bridges and framed skyscrapers eventually compelled the engineers to master the scientific and mathematical tools. The day of the carpenter-builder was over once and for all.

# WOOD FRAMING

## 1. THE COLONIAL BACKGROUND

The high level of aesthetic excellence in American colonial architecture rested on a very simple and thoroughly traditional structural base. For the most part it grew directly out of medieval origins. During the seventeenth century the colonists used medieval timber framing for every kind of building that required any elaborate construction, such as churches and large residences. The techniques were derived from the vernacular and utilitarian structures of the late medieval village in England, Holland, Germany, or the Scandinavian countries. The early colonists lacked the time, skill, architectural knowledge, wealth, and even the desire to imitate the newer forms of Renaissance and Baroque building art. In the Puritan mind of New England many of the proudest achievements of seventeenth-century architecture were associated with the Anglican or the Catholic faith, toward which they felt the bitterest hostility.

Building in the early colonies grew from urgent practical necessities. The colonists relied on what they knew from their former life and what skills had been preserved among them. The structural techniques of the late Middle Ages, maintained without change through the Tudor and early Stuart period, were carried over to New England by the first permanent settlers. When the eighteenth century undertook excursions into the grander architecture of the Baroque and Neo-classic, construction with brick and masonry according to relatively careful designs began to supersede the older work of the carpenter-builder. Yet the venacular building of the century continued the previous tradition. Thus one can trace an unbroken line from medieval framing, through the New England braced frame and trussed roof, to the iron framing of the mid-nineteenth century. And the same is true of bridge construction, where the line extends from the medieval wooden truss to the long-span steel truss of the modern railroad.

The primitive character of the first colonial shelters would hardly suggest the antiquity and previous high development of framed construction in wood. Timber framing in the form of a simple repetition of post and beam is astonishingly old. It was apparently first used in two- and three-story houses at Knossos as early as 1700 B.C.[1] Thirty-four centuries later, the American colonists, with little money, few tools, and inadequate skill, had to learn again the techniques which Mycenaean builders first brought to the mainland of Europe. The earliest buildings on the East coast were unbelievably crude. On Roanoke Island the original shelters were huts whose walls were made of stakes driven into the ground, the space between them being filled with interwoven branches and clay daubing. At New Amsterdam they were even worse. The settlers lived in pits dug in the ground and roofed with spars covered with sod or bark. An old Anglo-Saxon technique was employed at Jamestown for the church and the stockade: the palisade wall of sharpened logs reinforced with wattles and clay. The medieval "cruck" method of bending trees into a vault and thatching it with twigs appeared at Jamestown and Massachusetts Bay. In the latter colony Governor John Endecott adopted an Indian variation on the cruck: he drove a circle of poles into the ground, bent them toward one another, lashed them together with bark, and covered them with mats of reeds except for an opening at the top to allow smoke to escape. Eventually Endecott added a door, window, log chimney, and stone fireplace.

The log house appeared first in Delaware, chiefly of Swedish and Finnish origin. It was perhaps the earliest example of the fully constructed shelter. Actually the log house is not a framed building, since it is composed of solid bearing walls. The techniques employed in its construction, however, were widely used in other kinds of structures. The wall was built up of hand-hewn logs with chamfered ends, the logs interlocked at the corners by notching. The Swedish settlers of Delaware and New Jersey kept their log houses throughout the colonial period. They grew in size and elaboration. A second story was added, sometimes cantilevered out from the wall at the ground floor. Eventually a third floor appeared, providing a loft under the pitched roof. In a few cases porches were added, of simple post-and-beam construction. The practice in the two-story log house was to leave the logs exposed on the lower half of the structure and to cover the upper half with clapboards. The roof was usually shingled.

Fortunately the rude beginnings at New Amsterdam and Massachusetts Bay lasted only a short time. By the 1630's houses of framed construction began to appear. The establishment of the power-driven saw mill about 1633 made it possible to cut heavier timbers quickly and exactly. Much improved hand tools began to be made or imported in quantity. The colonists rapidly acquired the skill in carpentry which was to reach extraordinary levels of refinement in the early years of the Republic. The heavy timber framing of

11

posts, beams, and (later) diagonal braces with plaster infilling again revealed the medieval origin of seventeenth century colonial building. The most important American invention was that of exterior sheathing or covering, usually of very nicely cut butted planks, overlapping clapboards, or shingles, a protective covering necessitated by the rigors of American weather. The same technique, for the same purpose, was later applied to bridge construction. By 1675 materials other than wood began to appear abundantly in the thriving towns of the seaboard. The brick bearing wall, the stone chimney, the roof of slate or tile in the larger cities and on the wealthier plantations of the South gradually replaced their wooden counterparts. But it was the braced timber frame —New England frame, as it came to be called—that best represented the ingenuity of the colonial builder and that became the precedent for the many types of framed construction that dominated modern building.

By the mid-eighteenth century the wooden frame of posts, beams, and rafters reached the stage of development which it was to retain until the invention of the balloon frame in 1833. And it was destined to survive in mill construction until well past the middle of the last century. The material of the New England frame was usually oak, a hard wood of relatively high strength but sometimes excessively brittle. The timbers were generally hand-hewn with an axe but sometimes either hand- or power-sawed to square or rectangular section, the exposed surface smoothed with an adze in the case of hewn timbers. Joining was at first accomplished either by a straight butt joint with wooden pins, or by fitting the beveled end of the beam into a notch cut in the post. Later the mortise-and-tenon joint with wooden pins became nearly universal (in this joint a slot, or mortise, is cut in the post to receive a tongue, or tenon, of the beam end). Members of the wall frame were joined into units on the ground, as large as two men could handle, and raised into position. The finished portion of the frame then provided support for the remainder of the construction.[2]

On a foundation of fieldstone, laid up dry or in clay mortar (lime was at first rare), the wall was built up. Its framing consisted of a series of light studs, set about 2 feet on centers, framed into the sill and girt. At window openings the studs formed the side jambs, and the head and sill were mortised into the studs. The infilling between studs was originally of clay and straw, or wattle and lime daub, later of sun-dried or kiln-dried brick. The studs and filling were covered with horizontal plank or clapboard siding nailed to the studs. The clapboards were overlapping wedge-shaped boards of oak with beveled ends, usually about 5 inches wide and 4 to 6 feet long. Sheathing as a nailing base for the clapboards appeared in the early eighteenth century. As a consequence, the clay or brick infilling gradually disappeared during the late colonial period. Shingle wall covering was first used by the Dutch at New

Amsterdam about 1640. It spread to New England within the next ten years. Plaster wall covering appeared here and there around 1700.

Roof construction was generally of two types. One was the purlin roof, in which the purlins were placed above the rafters and the sheathing was laid on them at right angles to their lengths. The other was the rafter roof, where the top face of the purlins was below the rafters and the sheathing was laid on the latter in horizontal rows, parallel to the purlins. By the end of the seventeenth century shingle, slate, and tile covering had become common in the better houses. There was a variety of roof shapes, which could be reduced to four main types: the gabled or pitched, the gambrel (with a double pitch on either side of the ridgeline), the hipped, and the rainbow roof (a gabled roof with a slight convexity of the sloping planes). These roof forms are still standard in most residential building today, but they disappeared quickly for large structures during the nineteenth century in favor of the flat roof. The gabled roof, however, was retained for covered wooden bridges, and it persisted to the beginning of the present century in the railway trainshed. Conical and pyramidal roofs appeared in some Dutch and German building in New York, New Jersey, and Pennsylvania. Such forms had only special uses in later building, most notably in the railway engine house or roundhouse about the middle of the nineteenth century.

The French introduced another variant of medieval timber framing in New Orleans and the Mississippi valley. Their earliest buildings were of a primitive palisade construction known as *poteaux-en-terre*. A series of heavy upright posts, spaced a few inches on centers, were driven several feet into the ground, the spaces between them being filled with clay and grass or Spanish moss. The enclosure was roofed over with simple beams. Later the log posts were set on a stone foundation topped by a timber sill. An example of this construction still survives in the courthouse at Cahokia, Illinois, built about 1737. Shortly after 1700, however, the French had brought to New Orleans a kind of timber framing which had originated in medieval braced construction and which was well adapted to relatively large multistory structures. In this system a heavy wooden sill was laid upon a stone foundation. The sill, in turn, supported a series of posts spaced about 3 feet on centers. A continuous beam running over the tops of the posts provided the base plate for the framing of the next story. Between each pair of posts there was a single diagonal brace, extending between opposite corners of the panel. In a few cases there was double-diagonal bracing. The space enframed by post, beams, and diagonal brace was filled with a nogging of soft brick, the whole then covered with plaster. The best example of this kind of construction is the three-story Ursuline Convent in New Orleans, built in 1734.

In other colonies the methods of timber framing differed in no essential respect from the techniques introduced in New England and New Orleans. The early settlers of Virginia brought with them a knowledge of Tudor half-timber construction and were using it regularly by the latter half of the seventeenth century. Again, however, clay or brick nogging was never exposed. In Virginia the covering of clapboard siding or other varieties of sheathing was called "weather-boarding," a term later applied to the covering of structural members in a timber truss bridge. Brick walls appeared earlier in Virginia than elsewhere, having been introduced in 1611. Larger buildings had massive brick walls and correspondingly heavier and more elaborate framing. The most famous example dating from the seventeenth century is Newport Parish Church at Smithfield (1682). The church has massive brick walls at least 2 feet thick at the base. The original interior construction has disappeared, but it is very likely that the roof was supported on a series of king-post trusses spanning from wall to wall.[3] By the end of the century the largest, costliest, most sophisticated homes were being erected in Virginia. They were always of brick, the walls revealing the elaborate brickwork of the highly skilled English masons, with curving gable ends, multiple-stack chimneys, and Tudor beamed ceilings. The Virginia houses formed most of the American examples of Jacobean architecture, of which little remains today.

The framing and wall construction of the Dutch buildings in the New Amsterdam region was like that of New England except for the employment of unusually heavy joists, almost as massive as the New England summer beam. Hand-hewn shingles nailed directly to sheathing laid across the studs came to be the favorite wall covering. Aside from their famous brickwork, the major Dutch innovation was stone masonry construction. At first the stone walls were irregular rubble masonry laid in straw-bound clay. Later tooled stone blocks were laid up in lime mortar, prepared either from oyster shells or natural cements. The combination of stone or brick bearing walls with interior wood framing—common in warehouses, taverns, the larger barns and farm houses—provided a precedent for the construction of textile mills throughout the first half of the nineteenth century. All the colonists, of course, gained familiarity with stonework through the construction of chimneys. Chimney foundations offered an introduction to reinforced masonry through the practice of imbedding timbers in the stonework. Here, too, lime mortar gradually superseded clay as a bonding material.

Wood framing with masonry bearing walls appeared in the work of the German settlers in western Pennsylvania. They came to rely generally on the solid bearing wall and partition of stone with simple beams spanning from wall to wall, but in the early eighteenth century they made many excursions into timber framing. Their most unusual innovation was the use of diagonal braces which extended across two or more panels of the wall frame. This con-

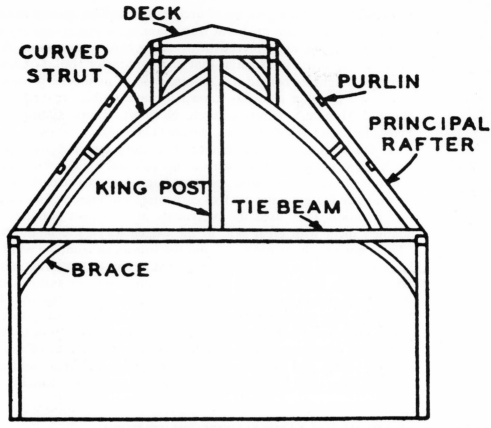

DECK

CURVED STRUT

PURLIN

PRINCIPAL RAFTER

KING POST

TIE BEAM

BRACE

1   Old Ship Church, Hingham, Massachusetts, 1681. Cross section of the nave showing the roof truss.

struction characterizes the Moravian Meeting House in the Oley valley, Pennsylvania (1743–45). Here one recognizes medieval German antecedents.

Roof framing in the form of trusses was rare in colonial building, but where necessary, as in the nave of a church, for example, the colonists were able to learn the technique. The beginning of truss framing in America was undoubtedly the interior construction of the Old Ship Meeting House, Hingham, Massachusetts, 1681 (fig. 1). It still stands today, one of the classics of early American structural ingenuity. The building proper is 45 × 55 feet in plan, its hipped roof rising above clapboard-covered walls about 20 feet high. The roof is carried by a true system of truss framing, the elaboration of which betrays the empirical, rule-of-thumb approach of its builders. Each truss spans the narrow dimension between a pair of the 20-foot posts.[4] The trusses, with their curved members, look like the inverted framework of a ship's hull, a resemblance which gave the church its name. This system of construction was derived from late medieval truss framing, which frequently had curved members, but the exact precedent would be hard to determine. A vault with hammer-beam trusses, such as that of Westminster Hall, London (late 14th century), might lie behind it. Combinations of members in truss-like forms were used in other churches known to have timber framing, for example, Richard Munday's Trinity Church, Newport, Rhode Island (1725–26), or Peter Harrison's King's Chapel, Boston (1749–54).[5]

At the beginning of the nineteenth century building art depended fully upon the structural achievements of the colonial builder. New European inventions of the coal-and-iron age came later. And to a remarkable degree this dependence fell upon the work of carpenters and masons following a vernacular tradition. They used the precedents of their own national origins and adapted them with great skill to the exigencies of life in the New World. "Thus, gone to the world's end, did the European combine what he already knew with what the New World suggested to him or forced upon him," as the art historian Oliver Larkin summed it up.[6] New inventions in the early Republican period gave the builder an immediate advantage over his colonial forbearer. The most important of these were the nail and spike-cutting machine, introduced in 1777, and the circular saw, 1814. Yet in the basic forms of framed construction the enormous adaptive radiation of the nineteenth century—mills and other factories, commercial buildings, bridges, whether wood or iron—had a small number of simple ancestors behind it.

## 2. WOOD FRAMING IN THE EARLY NINETEENTH CENTURY

The chief importance of wood framing in this history is that it provided the precedent for framed construction in iron and concrete. Since the use of timber framing belonged largely to vernacular tradition, it was seldom associated with works of architectural distinction. And the same was true of iron framing until the last two decades of the century, when the skyscraper began to be designed with some architectural and structural sophistication. Thus an investigation of the history of building techniques immediately confronts us with one of the great basic facts of nineteenth century building, the dichotomy with respect to structural character between serious architectural work and strictly utilitarian construction. Nearly all structures designed as monumental and hence symbolic art were built according to long-established techniques of masonry construction and were thus structurally conservative though artistically most effective. If we recall the leading American architects of the past century—men such as Latrobe, Strickland, and Mills among the Greek

Revivalists; Renwick, Upjohn, and Richardson in the medieval enthusiasm of the middle period; McKim and Burnham of the last phase of classicism; even Sullivan, a pioneer of the new movement—we are immediately struck by the fact that the best architecture usually lay outside the main stream of technical innovation, while technically advanced work seldom showed any aesthetic merit. When we follow the development of internal framing from wood through iron and steel to concrete, we shall find little that would stand among distinguished works of architecture. Timber framing in particular belonged largely to the world of strict utility.

The heavy braced frame of colonial building began to evolve in two different directions at the end of the eighteenth century, as it was variously developed to meet different structural demands in the rising commerce of the new Republic. In one direction it continued to be used for domestic architecture with little modification until the present time—it still flourishes today—although much of this later use was associated with rather arbitrary revivals for sentimental or aesthetic purposes. The main stream of this development, however, was arrested and given a radically new turn with the invention of balloon framing in 1833. The other line lay in the direction of commercial and industrial construction, at first in mills, later in stores, warehouses, railway stations, and office blocks. This line, which led to iron framing, consisted essentially of a repetitive post-and-beam form that could be multiplied without change for any size of structure.

The continued reliance upon wood for commercial buildings until the middle of the century arose from a number of obvious virtues not shared by other materials. In the first place, until the introduction of concrete and of mechanized techniques into the building process, wood was always easier to handle and very much cheaper than stone or iron. Second, mills and other factories, warehouses, and freight stations had to have open interiors for the unobstructed distribution of machines and the handling of goods. Interior bearing partitions would have been intolerable. The need for light often required that the exterior walls be opened to their maximum extent, a possibility on which masonry construction places a serious restriction. Finally, wood possesses a considerable tensile strength, stone hardly any, and thus the use of wood for beams was mandatory. Its great disadvantages are its combustibility and the slow growth of forests, but until iron and concrete could be readily used as substitutes, there was nowhere else to turn.

The beginning of large-scale timber framing occurred in the textile mill, which was first established along the rivers of New England around 1800. The records of mill construction are scanty, but it seems clear that wood was the dominant, if not exclusive, framing material for the first fifty years of its history. For about two decades the mill building was constructed wholly of wood, from interior beams to roof and exterior siding. About 1810 stone walls were introduced as a fireproofing measure, but unfortunately this sometimes had the result of turning the building into a furnace, so that interior destruction was more nearly complete than it might otherwise have been. The early mill was a modest affair, a plain wooden box usually from one to three stories in height and about 50 × 150 feet in plan at the outside. The height increased to five stories shortly after 1800. The wooden frame and clapboard siding showed clearly its colonial vernacular ancestry. Its plain unadorned form indicated its sober utility, but its proportions and the rhythms of its openings and roof lines frequently revealed the hand of a careful designer relying on the classical examples of his architectural surroundings.

The first cotton textile mill in the United States was the Slater Mill, built in 1793 along the Blackstone River in Pawtucket, Rhode Island. The building still stands as a historical monument, its original structural character unchanged, although various members have from time to time been replaced. The construction of the Slater Mill provided a standard for timber framing that was followed undeviatingly for the next sixty years. The building is three stories high and has a gable roof. The entire floor, roof, and wall load is carried by a complete system of wood framing, the outer members of which are covered with clapboard siding. Stone foundations carry heavy horizontal, or sill, beams which in turn support the columns. The floor and roof beams are framed into the columns and thus form the familiar cage of serial post-and-beam construction.[1] At some later date the owners of the Slater Mill installed a horizontal mill wheel. The special roofing above the upper end of the vertical shaft is supported by a king-post truss whose vertical member is a wrought iron rod.

The simple construction of the Slater Mill was so exactly suited to requirements that there was no need to change it for better than half a century. If the mills grew larger and the machinery heavier, it was necessary only to increase the number and dimensions of posts and beams. The classics of the period of all-wood construction were in Rhode Island—the Lippitt Mill at West Warwick (*c.* 1810), for example, or the first mill at Woonsocket (*c.* 1820), designed by J. C. Bucklin, one of the architects of the Arcade in Providence. Repeated fires, however, turned the mill builders to the possibility of substituting stone bearing walls for wood framing and sheathing as the exterior envelope. The transition occurred about 1810. The original Georgia Mill at Smithfield, Rhode Island (1812), was one of the first to be built with stone walls. The Georgia Mill was twice enlarged before Zachariah Allen, Providence's foremost mill owner at the time, took it over and completely rebuilt it. The new mill (1853–54), two stories high and 70 × 250 feet in plan, represented the culmination of the wood and masonry form. It followed the traditional method of interior framing except for the introduction of triangular trusses to carry the gable roof. Iron members had been in use in British mills for better than half a century by this time, but Allen seems to have distrusted the new material. An iron water wheel at the mill at Plainfield, Rhode Island, broke in 1856. Allen concluded that the material was not as safe as wood, at least for wheels, and there is no record that he ever used iron structural members.

Combinations of wood and iron construction do not seem to have appeared in American mills until about 1850. The introduction of cast iron columns in conjunction with stone or brick walls was in part a fireproofing measure, but it was also dictated by the necessity for stronger bearing members to sustain the constantly increasing load of machinery. Thus by 1850 the new standard of mill construction included brick or stone bearing walls, interior columns (compression members) of cast iron, and floor beams and roof rafters or trusses (in part, tension members) of wood. The Pemberton Mill at Lawrence, Massachusetts (1853), was thought to be the representative example of sound construction for the big multistory mill. Its structural system and its short history summed up only too well the state of the building art at mid-century. Its wooden beams, carrying the plank floor, rested on hollow cast iron columns at one end and in openings in the brick bearing walls at the other. They were secured in the openings by wrought iron plates imbedded in the brickwork. The under, or tension, surface of the beam was reinforced with wrought iron tie rods. It appeared to be very sound construction.[2]

On January 10, 1860, with a full shift of 650 operators on duty, the Pemberton Mill collapsed. More than 200 people were killed. The inevitable *ex post facto* investigation gradually uncovered the causes. In the first place, before the mill was in production, there had been repeated difficulties with outward spreading of the walls while machinery was being installed. The iron plates and tie rods were added to keep them in place. Accounts of witnesses and the nature of the collapse itself revealed immediately that this weakness had not been fully corrected. The walls fell inward partly as a result of insufficiently massive construction for the total machinery load. But this was only the beginning. Careful examination of a fractured column disclosed a casting so defective that one wonders how the member survived as long as it did. An eccentric core in the column mold allowed nearly all the metal to be concentrated on one side of the column, leaving a thickness of only $\frac{1}{16}$ inch on the opposite side. The eccentricity of the core was a consequence of the questionable practice of casting columns horizontally. Even in the case of sound members, however, the distribution of the load was so unequal that it was impossible to calculate the column stress. Finally, investigation by a correspondent of *Scientific American* proved that the timber beams were also inadequate to carry the great weight of machines, without any defects in the wood. The Lawrence jury charged with establishing guilt in the disaster ultimately indicted Albert Fuller, foreman of the Eagle Iron Foundry, which cast the columns, and the architect, Charles Bigelow, who had underestimated the wall thickness. The jurors, unfortunately, missed several culprits—the mill owners who overloaded a building obviously inadequate from the behavior of the walls during construction.

The problem of assigning causes for this once typical item of weekly news had many ramifications. The conclusions of the jury in the Pemberton case were acceptable enough as far as they went, but they represented immediate causes which in themselves were the effects of much more extensive conditions. In the first place, the new material, iron, involved many variables which could not be accurately determined. Its exact physical properties under various conditions of load and temperature and its internal structure were largely unknown, and thus its reaction under stress was highly unpredictable. The method of stress analysis for framed structures had been developed only a few years before the Pemberton Mill was constructed. Applicable at first only to determinate bridge trusses, it was some time before it could be reliably used for the framing of large buildings. Methods of inspection at places of manufacture and on the site of construction were primitive, if they existed at all, and there were many restrictions, both natural and arbitrary, on what it was possible for an inspector to discover. Legislation fixing standards of performance was either nonexistent or inadequate. And finally, the irresistible pressures of a ripidly expanding capitalism tended to promote carelessness and dishonesty. Repeated disasters like that of the Pemberton Mill ultimately forced the adoption of sound methods of inspection and testing. The insurance companies played an important role in these improvements: by the 1860's they were beginning to set structural and fireproofing standards that were decisive factors in the rapid progress of building techniques during the latter half of the nineteenth century.

The construction of mills pointed the way to the use of wood framing in relatively large buildings of many different kinds, chiefly warehouses, public buildings, churches, and shops. Most of these exhibited simple repetitive post-and-beam construction. The original Temple Building in Chicago was typical of standard New England braced framing in larger structures. Two stories in height, with a gable roof, it was erected at the corner of Franklin and South Water streets in 1833, the largest building in the town at the time (four years before Chicago received is charter). The main structural elements or its heavy frame were long familiar—sills, posts, beams, girts, braces, and roof rafters. It was the old New England prototype in a raw new town on the prairies.

The Arcade Building in Providence, Rhode Island (1827–28), provided an important innovation in the wood-framed building. Designed by J. C. Bucklin and Russell Warren, this masterpiece of the Greek Revival still stands in a narrow block between Westminster and Weybosset Street. It is a true arcade, consisting of a wide central passage through the building flanked on both sides by two floors of shops. The side walls and the colonnades at the ends, the chief bearing members, are of stone masonry. Most significant for subsequent building, however, is the skylighted gable roof. The glass openings are set between the sloping roof rafters, which are spaced about 4 feet on centers and slope upward from the stone side walls to the ridge beam. The rafters curve downward at their lower ends to meet the upper edge of the walls. The clear span under the skylight is about 32 feet. The simple construction of the glass roof is a forerunner of the elaborate systems of glass-and-iron framing that were used to cover the interior courts of later office buildings.

The familiar king-post truss of the mills was repeated in many other buildings and has enjoyed a continuous history up to the present day. A common variation was the insertion of a pair of diagonal struts, one on either side of the post. From time to time there were experiments in other forms, but few of them bore fruit in the later history of construction.[3] Most roof trusses spanned the transverse dimension of the building, at right angles to the ridge beam. In a few cases trusses were used to span the length of the structure, thus acting like greatly deepened purlins.[4] The introduction of iron rods as auxiliary tension members in the wooden truss appeared in the 1840's. At times they were simply added to the under or tension surface of the wooden member, but later they replaced it entirely. A particularly fine example still survives in the Inbound Freight House of the Illinois Central Railroad on South Water Street, Chicago (fig. 2). The original building was completed in

2   Inbound Freight House, Illinois Central Railroad, Chicago, Illinois, 1855, 1872. Cross section showing the roof truss.

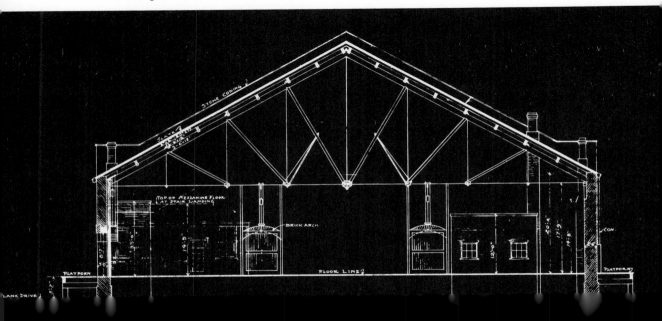

1855; it was partially destroyed by the fire of 1871 and rebuilt substantially along its former lines in 1872. The wood-and-iron trusses carry the gable roof between masonry walls.[5] Although timber framing for urban buildings other than residences and small commercial buildings was almost entirely superseded by iron, the wooden roof truss or combinations of wood or iron never wholly disappeared. These forms enjoyed a surprising revival during the building boom following World War II in small structures that required unencumbered interior space, such as garages, bowling alleys, churches, and the like.

## 3. THE BALLOON FRAME

The revolutionary invention in wood framing lay not in the direction of the braced frame or truss but in a wholly new method of radically lighter construction. The balloon frame, as it came to be called, was the first of Chicago's many contributions to the building and civic arts. Its inventor was an architect and builder from Hartford, Connecticut, with the pious name of Augustine Deodat Taylor. He arrived in Chicago in June 1833 and was within less than a month commissioned by Father John M. I. St. Cyr to build St. Mary's Church. Construction began in July 1833 and was completed in October of the same year. Taylor built the church on a balloon frame, an idea that he undoubtedly derived from the studs that formed the wall supports in the New England house. A contemporary description refers to the church as having been built "of scantling and siding." Its distinguishing characteristic was the use of a large number of light, closely ranked studs and joists which, along with the horizontal sills and plates, were framed together at the edges of the floors and roof. Taylor abandoned entirely the heavy members of the New England braced frame. It was hardly possible to devise an easier method of permanent construction.[1] The need for cheap houses in rapidly growing Chicago led to the immediate adoption of balloon framing for residential building. The nail-making machine and the power-driven saw were the decisive inventions that made the new technique practicable on a large scale.

In its strength, simplicity, lightness, and ease of construction the balloon frame was a masterpiece of vernacular building. Within a few years it was adopted throughout the prairie West for most of the building requirements of town and farm. Its strength arose from the fact that the floor and roof loads were spread over a large number of light, thin members of no more than three or four different sizes. Its enormous advantage over all previous methods of building was the simplicity of its construction, which could be reduced to a few of the most basic hand-and-tool techniques. An energetic man with moderate skill in carpentry and a saw, hammer, and a bag of nails could build a house or barn in little more than a week. A small crew could build a town, complete with railroad station, general store, court house, and tavern. Within a generation the balloon frame dominated the West and produced a vast number of architectural progeny. Without it the towns of the prairies could never have been built in the short time that saw the establishment of rural and urban society in the region. The invention was enthusiastically hailed by practical men—builders, manufacturers, engineers—who saw in it another example of that empirical ingenuity of the American which grew as much from an untrained pragmatic temperament as from material necessity. Like the wooden bridge and the mill frame, other products of the carpenter's skill, the balloon frame suggested analogous modes of construction in iron and thus helped to lead the way to modern steel framing. The light frame and the bridge truss revealed how much more Americans were at home in wood and iron than in masonry. Thus framed construction advanced rapidly in the nineteenth century, while work in concrete depended on traditional cumbersome forms of stone masonry until the end of the century.

The first architectural publication to describe balloon framing was Gervase Wheeler's *Homes for the People* (1855). A little later the new system came to international attention when two models were exhibited at the Paris Exposition of 1867. The American entries were the only examples of such construction at the Exposition. In spite of this reputable publicity, however, the professional architects for the most part ignored the new technique. It was true, of course, that most balloon-framed houses were architectural atrocities, but that was a consequence in part of the architect's own neglect. Calvert Vaux's scornful condemnation may have been justified on immediate aesthetic grounds, but he did not see that the artistic failure was partly a result of his own practice, typical of the major architects, of designing buildings always in terms of traditional modes of construction. Paradoxically enough, Vaux, like others who were beginning to theorize on the subject, urged the development of a native style on functional and organic grounds. He was most seriously concerned with raising the standards of American taste, but in fulfilling this mission he seems to have distrusted the new techniques and social demands as bases for the creation of a reputable art of architecture.

Two utilitarian innovations of great architectural consequence were either stimulated by the balloon frame or grew directly out of it. One was the open interior plan, spread out around a central utility core. It was achieved by building the house in four narrow, often balloon-framed wings in a cruciform plan. The later addition of the movable partition gave the open plan a maximum flexibility and adaptability. The Chicago architects made effective use of this device when they developed the modern apartment and hotel. The possibilities of the open plan were first systematically presented in Catherine Beecher and Harriet Beecher Stowe's *The American Woman's Home* (1869). It offered two great advantages: the central location of utilities, equidistant from other parts of the house, and the possibility, through the cruciform plan, of three-way exposure of all rooms except the core. The influence of the open plan and the balloon frame on contemporary architecture has been so profound as to be virtually synonymous with the modern house.

The second innovation was prefabrication, a revolutionary technique that was literally made possible by balloon framing. It was another anonymous outgrowth of the vernacular building tradition. By 1860 several firms in Boston, New York, and Chicago were prepared to ship prefabricated sections of framing, walls, floors, roofs, and partitions to any rail terminal in the United States. At their destinations these sections were assembled on the site into houses, barns, cribs, and even small stores. The various pieces were numbered and could be joined together by nails or bolts. One of the two entries at the Paris Exposition of 1867 was a prefabricated balloon-framed farm house shipped in sections to Paris and assembled on the grounds. Prefabricated stores, as well as houses, were manufactured by the Chicago millwork firm of Richards, Norris and Clemens, beginning in 1872. All portions of the frame, walls, floors, and roof came in prefabricated sections. Doors and windows were assembled complete in their frames, ready for installation. All connections could be made by nails and screws. The claims of the company's brochure were neither exaggerated nor flattering. "Any man of ordinary intelligence," it said, "can put up a house, by simply following printed directions accompanying each, and to be found in another part of this book. No more ingenuity need be called into requisition than that which is used in putting together a farm wagon."[2]

Prefabrication expanded to include school houses, barns, and railroad stations, and during the Civil War the New York firm of Skillings and Flint manufactured prefabricated hospitals and barracks for the Union Army. By 1880 the manufacture of ready-built structures had become a major industry in the building trade. They included domestic and farm buildings up to three stories in height, railroad stations, warehouses, cribs, bathing houses, stores, fruit stands, summer kitchens, and outbuildings of every description. By 1897 another New York company was prepared to ship prefabricated houses to Alaska for use in the Klondike Gold Rush. Thus by 1900 a considerable segment of the building art was industrialized. It was probably the greatest social consequence of the balloon frame; yet in the twentieth century this valuable technique was nearly lost by the resistance of pseudo-cultivated taste and by the opposition of architects, building trades unions, and the entrepreneurs themselves. Today it is slowly returning, but mainly for the curtain walls of skyscraper office buildings.

# IRON FRAMING

## 1. THE BEGINNINGS OF IRON CONSTRUCTION IN THE UNITED STATES

Iron has a greater antiquity and a more continuous use than has generally been supposed. By the fifth century B.C. the manufacture of wrought iron was sufficiently advanced to warrant its use for auxiliary members in large buildings. The huge temple of Zeus Olympios at Akragas (c. 470 B.C.), for example, had iron beams of considerable size included in the stonework of the architrave for additional support to the overhanging entablature. Once they had learned to use the material, Hellenic and Hellenistic builders repeatedly took advantage of it. The Romans acquired their knowledge of it from the Greeks but generally preferred bronze for metal beams and trusses.

The material used during the Middle Ages was wrought iron, although cast iron was a medieval invention. A large variety of cramps, stays, tie-rods, and dowels in the window frames, spires, and pinnacles of Gothic cathedrals were made of wrought iron. The medieval builders were so well aware of its importance in their structural system that they were at great pains to protect it from oxidation. The usual expedient was to boil the iron member in a bath of tallow, thus getting some penetration of the surface as well as a protective coating. The medieval use of iron had Byzantine and Islamic precedents, and the latter in turn may have been partly derived from Indian techniques. All these lines of structural development converged in Renaissance and Baroque building, when iron tie-rods and beams became common.

The new Iron Age began in the eighteenth century. Even before the revolution that gave birth to modern industrial technology, the builders of the period had begun to employ iron on a large scale. The first great engineer to use cast iron extensively was the Englishman John Smeaton. In a long career that extended from the mid-century to his death in 1792, he made the material familiar to builders in a wide range of machines and structures. The decisive step in the direction of iron framing was the application of the material to columns. St. Anne's Church, Liverpool (1770–72), was the first building in England with cast iron columns, and may have been the first anywhere.

Various forms of roof framing in cast and wrought iron appeared in France during the decade preceding the Revolution. They influenced the extremely important structural developments in England at the end of the century. William Strutt of Derby combined all the new techniques in iron to build the first multistoried, iron-framed, fireproof building, the Calico Mill at Derby (1792–93). Two other mills followed before Matthew Boulton and James Watt began the construction of their iron-framed mill buildings in 1801. It was from this basis that the vast proliferation of iron and steel construction in the nineteenth century evolved.[1]

The need for fireproofing provided the initial impetus for the use of iron in buildings. The desire for more light, with a consequent demand for greater openness of wall construction, was a later factor. Certain works of masonry construction which sought to realize these aims helped to suggest the possibility of more satisfactory solutions in iron. The most notable early attempt to achieve total fireproofing was Robert Mills's Public Record Office (now called the Fireproof Building) at Charleston, South Carolina (1822–23). Mills was at that time Commissioner of the South Carolina Board of Public Works. The Record Office still stands, a somewhat tarnished but still beautiful survivor of the Greek Revival. Mills's aim was to produce the most durable and incombustible structure possible at the time. His success was revealed by the fact that the Record Office withstood unharmed the Charleston earthquake and resulting fire of August 31, 1886.[2] The basement, cornices, stairways, and porticos of the building are stone; the walls and interior vaults are brick; the wooden roof is sheathed in copper; and all sash, frames, and shutters are iron. Aside from the roof, which is well protected, only the interior furnishings are combustible. Mills would not hazard the use of iron for structural members in the Record Office, preferring to rely on the familiar materials of brick and stone, but the union of sound engineering and architectural form gives the building an importance that looks well ahead of its traditional construction. When he came finally to use iron, for the interior columns of the Patent Office in Washington (1839), he was able to integrate it perfectly with his functional classicism.

At Boston Alexander Parris tried his hand at a kind of framed construction in stone when he designed the warehouses and market buildings along opposite sides of North and South Market streets, facing Quincy Market, about 1826. In these buildings Parris sought to open the walls so as to bring in more light than anyone had done before with the solid bearing wall. Instead of laying up blocks in the traditional way, he set a series of long, narrow slabs on end to produce a row of piers, then capped each opening with another slab acting as a lintel. Thus the serial post-and-lintel system defined a succession of narrow bays filled with glass.

The work of Mills and Parris represented essays in the direction of iron-framed construction. They were attempts to deal with problems that could be solved satisfactorily only with the new material. A more important influence, of course, was the growing number of multistory English mills and warehouses in which iron had been successfully used for interior columns and beams. In the United States the iron column made its initial appearance in Philadelphia. The iron industry of eastern Pennsylvania had, by 1800, reached a pre-eminence that was not to be challenged until the mid-century. It had originally been established at Colebrookdale, near Pottstown, in 1720, and a century later the older New England furnaces could hardly meet its competition. The manufacturing capacity was there, and it remained for an enterprising builder to take advantage of it.

The first to do so, as far as the record shows, was the architect and engineer William Strickland. In the United States Bank at Philadelphia (1818–24) Strickland introduced iron rods as reinforcing members into the arched openings at the ends of the transverse barrel vault over the main banking room.[3] Two years later he took the decisive step when he employed cast iron for the interior columns of the "Chesnut" Street Theatre in Philadelphia (1820–22; the name on the sign at the top of the building followed the old spelling). The theater was demolished in 1856, and there is little detailed information about its interior construction. The seats were arranged in three superimposed rows of boxes describing a semicircle 46 feet in diameter. Each semicircle above the main floor was supported by cast iron columns, the lowest tier of which was secured in iron sockets resting on stone footings. The columns rose one above the other through the entire height of the building, from the foundation to the domed ceiling. In the United States Naval Asylum, or Naval Home, at Philadelphia (1826–33), Strickland went even further. The exterior galleries along the wings and the sheltering roof are supported by 88 slender, hollow cast iron columns about 8 inches in diameter and spaced about 14 feet on centers. Wrought iron railings in a lattice pattern stand at the outer edge of the galleries. The ironwork is restrained in its decorative character and nicely integrated with the masonry construction. Many years passed before iron was again handled with the structural and architectural skill that Strickland revealed in this building, which still stands unchanged since its completion.

At the same time that the iron column was being introduced for structural purposes, another eastern Pennsylvanian took the next step, which was the construction of an entire wall of cast iron. John Haviland, a carpenter-builder of the Philadelphia area, built the Miners' Bank at Pottsville, Pennsylvania (1829–30), with a two-story façade made up of separate pieces of iron cast at the foundry and assembled on the site. Whether this iron façade was an actual bearing wall or merely a cover for masonry or an interior framework cannot now be determined. Haviland originally intended to finish the façade in stone, but finding no suitable variety in the local quarries, he turned to iron plates and painted and sanded them to produce what he called "the very beautiful and uniform texture of stone." [4] It was an ingenious stunt and stood as a credit to the skill of the local iron founders. Within a generation it was to multiply in the major cities of the East, and the glories of Renaissance masonry were to be reborn in painted iron.

New England, with its older iron industry, was not far behind Pennsylvania in adopting the new material, but the first uses of it are obscure. The Bond Building, on Merchants' Row in Boston (*c.* 1830), was one of the first with iron structural elements. Cast iron was used for interior columns and possibly for those on the exterior. In 1830 Cyrus Alger, owner of the South Boston Iron Works, offered a project for a cast iron dwelling. Nothing seems to have come of it except that the idea influenced Daniel Badger, who knew Alger and who was shortly to become the leading manufacturer of iron structural members in the United States. The most important iron structure for which the South Boston company rolled and fabricated the frame was the Black Rock Lighthouse on Block Island in Long Island Sound (1843). The 34-foot tower had an internal wrought iron frame similar to that of a number of iron-framed lighthouses built in England in the early years of the century. [5]

The first iron construction in New York City appeared in the mid-thirties. Here the major stimulus came in the form of two disastrous fires within a single decade. The first, or Great Fire, occurred on December 16–17, 1835, and destroyed 700 buildings in the 17 blocks bounded by Wall and Broad streets and the East River. The second, on July 19, 1845, burned 300 buildings in roughly the same area. In the face of these catastrophes iron became a matter of desperate necessity. Within a generation the city was to lead the country in the number, size, and variety of its cast iron buildings. Here enterprising manufacturers established the first foundries for casting columns and other structural and ornamental details. In 1835 Jordan L. Mott built a foundry on Water Street specifically for the manufacture of store fronts. In 1836 he was granted a patent for casting hollow iron columns and thus appears to have been the first recipient of an American patent for the new system of construction. [6]

One of the earliest buildings in New York with iron members was the Lyceum of Natural History, on Broadway between Prince and Spring streets, designed by Alexander Jackson Davis (1835). Davis used iron columns in the façade at the first story to reduce the size of masonry piers in order to obtain larger display windows. Probably the oldest building in the city still surviving from the initial period of iron construction is the Lorillard Building, on Gold Street, 1837 (fig. 3). It is a narrow structure, two bays wide and five stories high, with an attic under its gable roof. The brick wall from the top of the

3   Lorillard Building, Gold Street, New York City, 1837.

second story to the roof is carried on three stout iron columns of square section which extend through the first two stories. The lintels at the first and second stories are iron beams. The entire bay between columns is opened to window area.

The John Travers Library in Paterson, New Jersey (1846), seems to have been the first building in the United States in which interior cast iron beams resting on brick walls carried the floor and roof loads. The cross-sectional shapes of these beams showed how little scientific knowledge in such matters builders had and how much they relied on guesswork and rule-of-thumb experimenting. All the beams spanned 16 feet clear. Those under the floor had the shape of an equal-armed cross in section and a total depth of 9 inches, while those under the roof alternated between the cruciform and the T-section, the latter having a total depth of 5 inches.[7] Except for the wood flooring, the Travers Library was completely fireproof.

## 2. THE IRON BUILDINGS OF DANIEL BADGER AND JAMES BOGARDUS

The two men most responsible for making the construction of cast iron buildings into a major industry were Daniel Badger and James Bogardus. They both established foundries close together on the lower West Side of Manhattan in the 1840's and remained lively competitors for the next thirty years. Badger, born in Portsmouth, New Hampshire, in 1806, began his career in Boston in 1829. He constructed a store building on Washington Street in 1842 with cast iron columns and lintels at the first story. What building it was he did not say, but he admitted that he got the idea from Cyrus Alger. In 1843 Badger bought the patent of Arthur L. Johnson of Baltimore for a rolling iron shutter and began to manufacture it for use with his iron fronts. The shutter afforded protection to the wide show windows which the new structural material made possible. Badger's business in Boston of constructing iron fronts on a small scale prospered and he soon aimed at larger operations. In this respect a widely read English work on iron construction, William Vose Pickett's *A New System of Architecture,* had a profound influence on him.[1] He moved to New York City in 1846 and during the following year built a foundry on Duane Street between 13th and 14th. This was the famous Architectural Iron Works, which was within two years to begin the production of iron fronts and interior members for use throughout the East and Midwest.

Badger claimed every advantage for iron, with some exaggeration of its virtues. He urged its use above all other materials because of its strength, lightness and openness of structure, facility of construction, architectural beauty, economy, durability, incombustibility, and ease of renovation and restoration. He hesitated to recommend it for monumental buildings but felt that it had no competitor for a wide range of utilitarian structures, such as stores, office buildings, factories, warehouses, arsenals, ferry houses, oil tanks, grain elevators, and for a large number of functional and ornamental details.

Badger was diligent in advertising his product and in publishing his iron buildings by means of folio volumes whose colored illustrations are triumphs of the lithographer's art. Yet he seldom gave precise information about dimensions, dates of construction, and structural details. Since there was little variation in formal and structural characteristics, however, it is possible to provide a general description applicable to most of his commercial buildings. The bulk of them were from two to six stories high, with individual stories varying in height from 9 to 14 feet; spandrel depth was about 2 feet; column spacing in the façade was generally 6 feet, though in a few cases it ran less than 5; the hollow columns were seldom less than 12 inches in diameter. Interior framing generally consisted of iron columns and timber floor beams. Badger relied almost exclusively on Venetian Renaissance for the basis of form and ornament, since it provided the most suitable architectural expression for the basic functional pattern of columns, spandrels, and windows. The façades presented a uniform appearance of narrow iron columns and spandrels framing the large windows that nearly filled each bay, a series of rectangles set in successive rows, one above the other. All joints were made by bolting one member to another through flanges. Seldom has an extensive body of architectural work shown such remarkable homogeneity. It was a case of developing a standard form nicely adapted to certain urban building requirements and repeating it with no essential change in one structure after another. Along with the work of Bogardus, Badger's iron fronts pointed clearly to the iron- and steel-framed skyscrapers of New York and Chicago and to modern structural systems in steel.

Business at Badger's Architectural Iron Works flourished prodigiously during the two decades from 1850 to 1870. In New York City the best known of his buildings is the five-story block at Broadway and Broome Street, originally constructed as the department store of E. V. Haughwout and Company, 1857 (fig. 4). John P. Gaynor was the architect. It was in the Haughwout store that Elisha Graves Otis installed the first passenger elevator in the United States. Among buildings and other structures erected during the 1860's, two were of particular significance. One was a sugar storage shed in Havana, Cuba, which, in addition to the usual cast iron columns and wrought iron beams, had a roof in the form of a shallow barrel vault made up of cast iron plates bolted together. The other was the grain storage warehouse of the United States

4   Haughwout Building, Broadway and Broome Street, New York City, 1857. John P. Gaynor, architect.

Warehousing Company in Brooklyn, New York (*c.* 1865). Badger claimed that it was the first iron structure ever built for the storage of grain. The building, which had six stories and an attic, revealed the usual pattern of closely ranked columns and shallow arched lintels in its elevations. The interior was filled with rows of cylindrical bins of cast iron plate, each of which rested on four columns, to which the plates of the bin were bolted. The columns, arranged in a square in plan, were braced and tied by wrought iron rods set on the diagonals across the corners of the square. Because of the heavy load the columns were set on massive stone footings in the form of high, narrow, stepped pyramids.

    There can be no question that Daniel Badger left a large and important mark on the building arts of his century, and the record shows that he anticipated by several years his more famous contemporary James Bogardus in the manufacture of iron buildings. Yet it is equally certain that Bogardus was the more fertile inventor and that he developed systems of construction of far more decisive influence on the growth of modern structural techniques. Bogardus had the exuberant mechanical ingenuity that was a distinguishing characteristic of American culture in the nineteenth century. Born in Catskill, New York, in 1800, irregularly educated, apprenticed to a watchmaker at the age of fourteen, he early embarked on a career of invention. He won a prize at the New York Fair of 1828 for a clock. From then until 1845, and off and on during his career as a builder, he produced a steady outpouring of mechanical contrivances—clocks, parts for cotton-spinning and engraving machines, an eccentric sugar mill, printing dies, an eversharp pencil, a pigment grinder, a dynamometer, a rubber-thread cutter, a glass pressing machine, a pyrometer, and, of course, the technique of constructing completely iron-framed buildings. In addition, he found time to give many popular lectures on scientific and technical subjects and to make an extended European tour from 1836 to 1840. After his return he established a machine shop in New York City primarily to manufacture his eccentric sugar mill.

By 1847 the growth of his business necessitated a major expansion of his shop facilities. He made a cast iron model of the new building, which was itself to be wholly constructed of iron—columns, beams, spandrels, mullions, sash, inside and out. He began construction in 1848 at the corner of Centre and Duane streets, New York, and after one brief interruption, completed it in 1849 (fig. 5). His aim was both functional and aesthetic, to create an economical, fireproof structure, and to find a low-cost method of imitating the architectural beauties of past ages. In this latter respect he frankly admitted the derivative character of the style. "It was whilst in Italy, contemplating there the rich architectural designs of antiquity, that Mr. Bogardus first conceived the idea of emulating them in modern times, by the aid of cast iron." [2] With respect to structure his shop was a logical integration of Haviland's cast iron front for the Pottsville bank and the advanced English work in iron column-and-beam framing, which Bogardus had studied during his visit of the 1830's. Construction of the factory was astonishingly simple, and once the pieces had been cast and machined, it was possible to erect the whole thing in a few weeks. On a stone foundation, continuous around the periphery of the building, rested solid horizontal cast iron beams, or sills, previously planed to a smooth surface and an equal thickness throughout. The columns, whose flanged ends were turned on the lathe to provide smooth and parallel bearing surfaces, were bolted to the sills at their joints. The girders in the wall plane (spandrel girders) were bolted to the columns through their end flanges. The first set of

5 Factory building of James Bogardus, Centre and Duane streets, New York City, 1848–49.

columns, at the first story, supported in turn another group of sills, columns, and spandrels, and so on through the fourth story. Bogardus felt that the process could be repeated for any number of stories.

The pioneer factory at Centre and Duane streets survived for only a decade. The widening of Duane Street in 1859 required the removal of the building, which was taken down piece by piece simply by loosening and drawing out the bolts. Thus Bogardus's statement that his buildings could be disassembled and reconstructed on another site found partial confirmation in this case. There is no record that the shop was ever re-erected at another location.

Bogardus's patent illustrations provided further details of his method of construction. The framing system was usually revealed in the elevations: spandrel girders were cast as entablatures in the shape of channels and supported by slender columns. Formal details in these structural elements were determined by the principles of classical ornamentation. The proportions of bays in the façade were often fixed by window size and aesthetic considerations, with the result that the cast iron front was divorced from the framing system behind it. For flooring and roofing he proposed rolled iron plates with tongue-and-groove joints. The floor girders were cast in the form of shallow segmental arches, with wrought iron tie-rods inserted in the ends to provide greater resistance to the tension produced by the outward thrust at the ends of the arched girder. The beams or joists which were framed into the girders were cast in the shape of modern I-beams.[3] Bogardus believed that there was no height limitation to his iron structures, which, he claimed, could be carried up to ten miles! His enthusiasm, however, blinded him to the serious shortcomings of a naked cast iron frame, especially its inadequate capacity for fire resistance and the lack of rigidity in a frame joined with bolts set up by hand. At the same time, there is something to be said for Bogardus's emphasis on the ornamental possibilities of cast iron. Since it could readily be cast into any shape, there was a temptation to borrow rashly and indiscriminately from past styles to provide a superficial clothing of elegance. Yet Bogardus and the architects of many of his buildings usually subordinated their classical ornament to the general lines and rhythms and seldom allowed it to reach the redundancy of other work.

He was aware of one major disadvantage of iron as opposed to masonry, namely, its deterioration as the result of oxidation. Since it oxidizes slowly, however, he felt that it could be left unpainted in regions of normal humidity. This conviction could not always be justified, especially in a densely built urban environment, where acids and other impurities in the air make protection of the metal mandatory. Corrosion, he argued, could easily be prevented even in a moist climate "by a proper coating of paint, and thus, at a very small expense, a cast iron building can be made to endure a thousand years, unaffected by the winds or the weather." [4] Some of his work, and other iron structures of the time, have endured at least for a century.

What seems to have impressed Bogardus's contemporaries more than anything else was the spaciousness of his buildings and the ease and rapidity with which they could be erected. A contemporary description in the *New York Evening Post* of a group of stores erected in 1849 expressed the enthusiasm which the new system generated:

> The buildings are constructed . . . to secure the greatest strength with the least material . . . , being cast and fitted so that each piece may be put up as fast as it is brought on the ground. They may be taken down, removed, and put up again in a short time. . . . Nearly three feet of room is gained over buildings put up with brick. They admit more light, for the iron columns will sustain the weight that would require a wide brick wall. They combine beauty with strength, for the panels can be filled with ornamental figures to any extent.[5]

Once Bogardus had established himself in the business of manufacturing iron buildings and had attracted attention to their potentialities by means of his own factory, the orders began to multiply. Some impetus appears to have come from the California Gold Rush of 1849. There was a great demand for iron parts of buildings which could be cheaply and quickly assembled on the site. The New York inventor outdistanced his English competitors with pre-cast elements that could be put together into durable structures in a few weeks. Meanwhile, in the East, he was soon involved in the construction of buildings of relatively large size. The best known of these was the building for Harper and Brothers Printing Company, on Franklin Square in New York City. The original building burned completely on December 10, 1853, when a workman accidentally ignited a container of inflammable fluid for removing ink from printing rollers. The total destruction of a $1,000,000 plant was the largest single commercial loss in the United States up to that time. For the new five-story building the company was understandably determined to have fireproof construction throughout. They commissioned the architect John B. Corlies for the design and contracted with Bogardus to cast the beams and columns. All interior partitions were brick, and the floors rested on brick arches spanning between wrought iron joists rolled by the Trenton Iron Works (founded by Peter Cooper and Abram Hewitt). These joists, the first of wrought iron to be used for structural purposes in the United States, constituted an innovation of major importance in American building art. Rolled as I-beams, they rested on the partitions and on cast iron girders whose lower profile was a succession of shallow arches tied with wrought iron rods to take some of the tensile stress in the under side. It was this type of beam that Bogardus showed in his patent illustration (fig. 6). A classic of the cast iron age, the Harper building survived until 1920, when it was demolished to make room for a newer structure.[6]

The most prophetic but least known of Bogardus's iron structures were the two shot towers that he built respectively for the McCullough Shot and Lead

6   Harper and Brothers Printing House, Franklin Square, New York City, 1854. John B. Corlies, architect. Sketch of an iron floor girder.

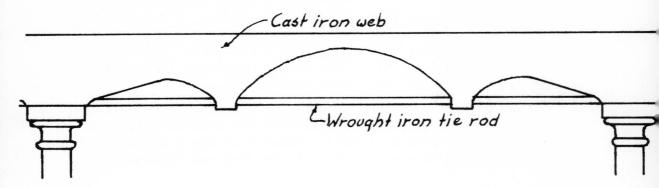

7  Shot tower, McCullough Shot and Lead Company, 63–65 Centre Street, New York City, 1855.

Company and Tatham and Brothers. The McCullough tower was erected in 1855 at 63–65 Centre Street, New York (fig. 7). Eight stories high, the tower was little more than a brick and iron shell free of interior obstruction. The method of manufacturing shot-gun ammunition required that the interior be open: molten lead, poured through a sieve, was allowed to drop the full height into a tank of water at the base. The traditional use of masonry bearing walls for high shot towers was abandoned for the McCullough tower, apparently because of the poor bearing quality of the soil. The octagonal iron frame of the structure was bolted to a foundation wall of brick. The framing consisted of eight cast iron corner posts, inclined slightly toward the central axis, tied together at eight interior platform levels by peripheral cast iron beams. There was no diagonal bracing, an omission which might have proved costly in a high wind, since the frame was not rigid. The whole framework was encased in brick panels which were entirely supported by the iron beams.[7] Thus the McCullough tower embodied, on a small scale, true skeletal construction, and may justly be regarded as an anticipation of Jenney's famous invention in Chicago thirty years later. The tower was demolished in 1908 to make way for the line of the Interborough subway.[8]

Bogardus continued to manufacture iron structural members up to his death in 1874. By the mid-century other builders were adding whole blocks of iron buildings to the downtown area of Manhattan, many of which stand to this day.

It would be difficult to overestimate the achievements of Badger and Bogardus. The influence of their structures was so profound and extensive as to constitute a revolution in American building art. They came at a time when the need and the means perfectly coincided, and whatever architectural horrors followed from cast, rolled, or stamped iron fronts, there is no question that sooner or later serious architects would have had to come to terms with the new techniques. As a matter of fact, both the pioneers pointed the way. Their work lent itself well to the requirements of urban building, both in a functional and in an aesthetic sense. They were able to combine a pleasing ornamental character with a simplicity, restraint, and directness that stood in marked contrast to the extravagant and heedlessly imitative façades of much of the surrounding work. Here was a major nineteenth century precedent for a new commercial architecture, exact in its uniform expression of utility and structure, anti-monumental, anti-picturesque, a nicely balanced and simple composition of horizontal and vertical lines. It should have led to something better; as matters turned out, it proved to be the forerunner of what one critic called "the endless architecture" of today.[9] The gridiron street plan, of course, had much to do with this state of affairs.

The long rows of iron façades, with their simple repetitive patterns, caught the eye of visitors from abroad. William Fogarty, an English architect, saw in them an emergent native style:

The warehouses and shops in . . . a commercial community assume colossal proportions. In them more particularly the use of cast iron is general, not alone for internal columns, as with us, but also for all external architectural features. Façades eight and ten stories high are executed in it, and with an excellence of finish and accuracy of detail that is seldom seen at this side. There are several large foundries called "Architectural Iron Works," in which the stock of models is very extensive, comprising all the best examples of the Greek and Roman orders to almost any diameter. The facility with which these can be put together to form fronts, has had a very decided influence on the street architecture, which exhibits a great tendency to run into columns, and the repetition of the same details through nine or ten stories is very common. Indeed, so prevalent have these characteristics become, that even where cast iron is not used, the influence of the cast iron school in this direction is felt. This is noticeable in some . . . buildings . . . which, although built of cut granite, exhibit one order with little variation used throughout the stories. This must be looked on as a decided element in what may be called the "American Renaissance" style.[10]

## 3. FROM IRON BUILDINGS TO THE NEW YORK SKYSCRAPER

The decade of the 1850's saw a great spurt of inventive activity in the whole field of construction, not only in buildings of every description, but in bridges and trainsheds as well. The period ushered in the most productive age of invention in the United States, which was to continue with undiminished vigor until the end of the century. A variety of new and ingenious ideas began to appear in the still immature technique of iron framing. The progress that culminated in the steel-framed New York skyscraper of the 'nineties was a fairly direct line: there were a few blind digressions and a number of fantastic structural curiosities, but for the most part it was a kind of orthogenesis, each structural innovation representing some progressive refinement of the system antecedent to it.

The main lines of evolution included both theoretical and practical developments: increasingly exact determination of the properties of materials and the stresses in members, followed by a general lightening of columns and beams and hence by greater openness of interior space; a constant expansion of the absolute size of members to carry ever-increasing loads; the invention of special forms of bracing against wind loads; and the growth of methods for framing wide-span enclosures. The solution to the last problem belonged chiefly to the province of the engineers of bridges and trainsheds, but the need for large open interiors in certain kinds of buildings required extensive changes in the common forms of column-and-beam framing. Theater roofs, skylights over inner courts, and the superposition of stories above a column-free main floor demanded special techniques. If the span was moderate, the load above was carried on deep built-up girders which were steadily refined into the simple riveted form familiar in the short-span railroad bridge. If the span was very wide, it was necessary to use truss framing to avoid girders of such depth and weight as to be unmanageable. Interior balconies around an open court and theater galleries required cantilever construction of various kinds, in the form of brackets, simple beams, or trusses. Domes and vaults posed special problems in which framing had to be developed as a system of arched ribs or trusses.

The most striking and most widely publicized structure of the 'fifties, and one which embodied the greatest variety of framing techniques, was the

Crystal Palace of the New York Exhibition of 1853, a derivative from the original Crystal Palace, Paxton's masterpiece for the London Exhibition of 1851. Two projects for the New York fair looked further ahead than the finished structure. Bogardus, in collaboration with Hamilton Hoppin, and Leopold Eidlitz submitted separate plans for a system of suspended construction in which the roof of the building was to be held in place by wrought iron chains radiating from an iron-framed central tower.[1] The Crystal Palace as built was designed by the architects Carstensen and Gildemeister. The site of the exposition was open land at Sixth Avenue and 42nd Street, a location well out in the rural edge of the city at that date. The main structure was a vast octagonal envelope of glass supported by an internal iron frame of remarkable lightness and delicacy. At the second or gallery level the plan was altered into the form of a cross, the four wings extending outward to the faces of the octagon. The dome rose above the central crossing. By all previous standards of iron-and-glass construction the Crystal Palace was an enormous structure—more than an acre of glass surrounded the entire enclosure. The glass was covered with a translucent enamel to introduce a glareless, diffused light into the interior, a provision which made the building in this respect superior to the London palace.[2]

The wall construction of the New York building consisted essentially of a series of cast iron columns carrying semicircular iron arch ribs. The curtain wall was prefabricated in 27-foot panels and erected on the site. The dome was supported on radiating, or meridional, trusses which sprang from a series of trusses disposed in a polygon to conform as closely as possible to the lower circumference of the dome. A complex arrangement of horizontal beams, arched girders, and arched ribs carried the vaults over the wings. All beams, girders, and columns were cast iron, while the trusses and ribs were wrought iron.[3] As a work of engineering, the Crystal Palace was a triumph of its time. Although it was architecturally inferior to Paxton's building, it stood in the front rank among iron structures.

Even bolder than its construction [wrote one historian] was the idea behind its ornament: "the plan of the decoration has been to bring out the beautiful construction of the building—to decorate construction rather than to construct decoration. . . . The result is surprisingly beautiful." The Crystal Palace heralded that reintegration of engineering and architecture which was to underlie the development of the modern style.[4]

The building might be regarded as a *tour de force,* but it was a powerful demonstration of the potentialities in the new system of construction. It was a national calamity when the wooden flooring and the combustible exhibits burned on October 5, 1858, and reduced the whole building to a mass of twisted metal and shattered glass.[5]

A more representative kind of construction for the time is the association of stone masonry and iron in the interior framework of The Cooper Union, on Astor Place (1854–59), the work of the architect Frederick A. Peterson. The Union was founded in 1854 by Peter Cooper as a free school of science and art for working young men and women. The most important structural feature in the building is the large number of wrought iron beams used to support the floor loads. Rolled in 1855, they were the third lot to be manufactured by Cooper's company, the Trenton Iron Works.[6] The Cooper Union has five stories and a basement, with considerable and inexplicable variation in story height. All columns throughout are cast iron. Floor loads outside the auditorium are transmitted to the columns by the wrought iron I-beams, all of which were rolled from a single mass, or pile, of the metal. In the auditorium, where bay spans are greater than in the rest of the building, the ceiling load was originally carried to the columns by a series of solid-spandrel brick arches springing from column to column. The main floor of the auditorium rested in turn on another series of brick arches set in line with those above. All columns at the basement rest on separate stone footings. Exterior walls are masonry construction with piers defining the bays.[7] There were two mechanical novelties in The Cooper Union, one the cylindrical Otis elevator and shaft, the other a 12-foot steam-driven exhaust fan to provide forced-draft ventilation. The fan, now electrically driven, is still in use; the elevator, of course, has been replaced, although the circular shaft has been retained.

In the 1880's failures began to appear in various structural elements of The Cooper Union. The original trouble seems to have occurred in the stone column footings as a result of excessive loading and improper distribution of loads.[8] An extensive renovation was undertaken in 1885. The footings were rebuilt and strengthened, and a number of columns and piers were replaced. The original brick arches of high rise were replaced by the present stone arch girders. Most striking, however, are the two diagonal wrought iron struts extending from basement to roof which were set into the building parallel to but some distance in from the east and west walls. There was no attempt to cover them, and they are clearly visible on the inside of the building. The strut consists of two wrought iron channels laced together with a latticework of iron straps to form a continuous box member. Although the original frame was bolted at the connections, the struts are of riveted construction.[9]

The building which marked the culmination of the iron-fronted, iron-framed structure in its heroic age was the Wanamaker Store, on Broadway between 9th and 10th streets, 1859–60 (fig. 8). This classic of the Bogardus era was originally built for Alex T. Stewart, a pioneer in the establishment of the modern department store. John Kellum designed the building and the Cornell Iron Works manufactured the castings. It was easily the largest iron building —indeed, one of the largest of any kind—to be erected up to that time: it em-

8  Alex T. Stewart (later Wanamaker) Department Store, Broadway at 9th Street, New York City, 1859–60. John Kellum, architect.

braced, within its five stories, a total floor area of 325,000 square feet. Except for variations required by the central light court, the Wanamaker Store followed the well-established structural system of iron columns and beams bolted together. The construction of this iron cage provided sufficient rigidity and continuity so that all floor, roof, and wall loads were transmitted in a vertical line directly to the stone footings.[10]

Although the building revealed the common practice of imitating stone through the shape and painted surfaces of iron, nevertheless, in its pleasing proportions, in the clear and incisive pattern of its repetitive column-and-beam elevations, and in the association of strength with lightness suggested by the narrow structural elements and the large windows in deep reveals, the Wanamaker Store was one of the architectural triumphs of the iron front. After A. T. Stewart's death the store passed to Hilton, Hughes and Company, who sold it in 1896 to John Wanamaker for about $3,000,000. The latter company closed the store, and the larger building between 8th and 9th streets, in

December 1954. On July 14–15, 1956, one of New York's most spectacular fires completely destroyed all interior flooring and joists. Yet the iron structural members suffered little damage. The entire frame, reduced to a vast open cage, stood free and upright. When the metal had cooled, the wrecking crews began the demolition that ended the history of this great structural landmark.

The end of the Civil War marked a turning point in New York building. Although the city had been expanding northward, so that 23rd Street no longer formed a frontier, the bulk of commercial building continued to be concentrated in the downtown area. The requirements of business and speculation in land drove real estate prices upward at an accelerating rate. The consequence was an intensity of land use that finally forced builders and municipal authorities to make a decisive break with the restrictive limitations of the past. The five-story height, rarely over 60 feet, and the narrow bay of the old iron front had to give way to a more radical approach to the urban business block. It was in such a context that the New York skyscraper was born. Defined in terms of height and the economic conditions which forced its constant increase, rather than in terms of novel structural features, the modern skyscraper may be regarded as a New York phenomenon, for it was in New York that conditions making it necessary existed.[11] Yet it was well into the last decade of the nineteenth century before the New York builders felt confident enough to use without qualification the new Chicago technique of complete internal framing, or skeletal construction. For the first twenty-five years of its upward growth, the New York skyscraper largely appeared in traditional form. Exterior walls were masonry, and, in spite of an early precedent, interior bearing members were seldom entirely of iron. If the columns were iron, the floors were often supported on masonry arches, and conversely, if iron beams carried floor loads, masonry bearing partitions took the place of iron columns. Thus, for all the exigencies that forced its sudden upsurge, the New York builders seldom trusted the iron frame that Bogardus saw rising to ten-mile heights.

If any one building may be said to mark the beginning of the New York skyscraper, it was the office building of the Equitable Life Assurance Company, at 120 Broadway (1868–70). Five stories high, it rose to 130 feet at the top of its Mansard roof. The original design was made by Arthur Gilman and Edward H. Kendall. Before construction began, however, the young engineer and architect George B. Post was called in as a consultant to determine whether any saving in cost could be effected in what was likely to be the most expensive building of its time. Post had studied civil engineering at New York University and had acquired his architectural training through practical experience in the office of Richard Morris Hunt. Post completely redesigned the internal system of construction. By using a combination of brick partitions, segmental brick floor arches, wrought iron I-beams, and granite piers, he was able to reduce the cost of the interior work by nearly half the low bid on the original design. The Equitable Building was demolished in 1912, following extensive damage by fire. Its construction, though by no means radical, was an impressive triumph and placed George B. Post in the front rank of his profession; yet there were few at first who were willing to follow him.

A number of factors operated immediately to push the New York skyscraper to even greater heights. The Equitable Building proved to be a highly profitable investment, and this, together with the saving in cost effected by the use of a partial iron frame, stimulated powerfully the new enthusiasm for greater height. Constant improvements in the elevator made the increase practical for tenants. The danger of collapse of iron members as a result of fire was much reduced by two inventions of the time: the earlier, patented by John B. Cornell in 1860, was a column consisting of two cast iron tubes, one inside the other, the space between filled with fire-resistant clay; the second, patented by Balthasar Kreischer in 1871, was a method of fireproofing floor beams by clothing them in refractory tile. Economic imperatives and mechanical refinements, rather than structural progress, gave the builders the confidence to double the height of the skyscraper within five years after the completion of the Equitable. Two towers completed in 1875 set new records: Post's Western Union Building, 230 feet high, and Richard M. Hunt's Tribune Building, 260 feet to the top of its penthouse roof. Neither building, however, was distinguished by any structural innovations.[12]

The most advanced system of interior framing prior to the advent of full skeletal construction appeared in George B. Post's New York Produce Exchange (1881–84). Located near the Battery, it was equivalent in height to about eight stories. The Exchange was carried on a complete frame of cast iron columns and wrought iron beams and joists, including wall columns and spandrel beams, but the peripheral columns were imbedded in brick buttresses 12 inches thick, which thus took much of the wall and outer floor loads (fig. 9). The remarkable feature of the Exchange was that the entire second floor was opened into a great trading room with a total area of nearly 32,000 square feet. Above its flat coffered ceiling of glass extended an iron-framed gable skylight. The framing of the ceiling and skylight consisted of a series of wrought iron arched trusses spanning between columns in both directions and of flat transverse trusses above the arches. A hollow rectangle of offices surrounded the skylight, the first office floor being at the level of the trading room ceiling. Because of its proximity to the river at the lower end of Manhattan, the building was located on unstable alluvial soil, and as a consequence, its wall and column footings had to be supported on wooden piles.[13]

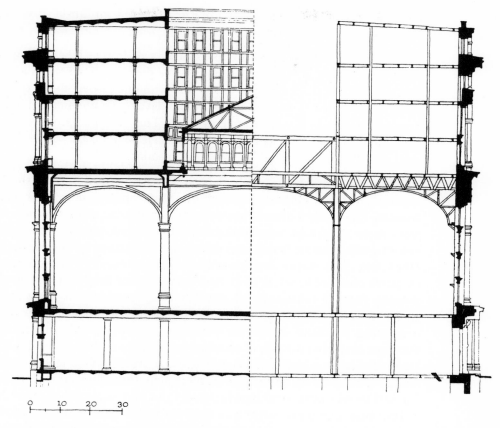

9 New York Produce Exchange, New York City, 1881–84. George B. Post, architect. Cross section showing the interior framing.

The Produce Exchange was demolished in 1957 to make way for another of New York's many post-war skyscrapers. Its framing very nearly anticipated Jenney's achievement in the Home Insurance Building at Chicago, under construction at the time the New York building was completed.

As the skyscraper climbed upward on its structural mixture of old and new techniques, the iron front of Bogardus and Badger was being exploited by builders with a much surer sense of its structural and architectural potentialities. It was ironic that while the elaborate masonry dress of the new office tower was setting the high fashion, the possibilities of iron buildings were beginning to be acknowledged by the architectural press. The author of an editorial in *Carpentry and Building* saw with unusual insight what the main promise was. After condemning the use of iron in imitation of stone or wood, he went on to its positive values:

But it is not necessary, therefore, to condemn cast iron as inherently inartistic and unsuitable for use in "true architecture." The problem presented to architects is to find new designs for the proper use of iron with due respect to the qualities of the material. They must abandon tradition and develop an architecture in iron, as the Grecian architects developed one in stone. This has been already done to some extent and the airy lightness of iron buildings is beginning to be as much appreciated as the massive strength of structures in stone.[14]

But the combination of airy lightness with great height in the New York skyscraper was a long time in coming. Meanwhile, a unique problem in iron framing gave the Eastern builders valuable lessons in the new technique. They were faced with what was essentially a structural task in assembling and erecting the interior frame and the copper sheathing of the Statue of Liberty (1883–86). The statue itself was the work of the French sculptor Frédéric Auguste Bartholdi, while its frame was designed and fabricated by the engineering firm of Gustav Eiffel (fig. 10). The sheer size of the statue—a little more than 151 feet high from the plinth to the top of the torch—posed a framing problem on a scale with that of the new Manhattan skyscraper. Further, the general form of the figure, its relatively small weight for its great bulk, and its exposed location brought the erectors face to face with the particular problem of bracing a framed structure comparable to a building against wind loads. And finally, it was the first structure in New York other than a bridge in which steel was used for major bearing members.[15]

The chief supporting element of the statue frame consists of an open horizontal square of heavy wrought iron girders at the top of the pedestal. Above this square, four inward-leaning steel posts rise to the neck of the figure and support the extremely elaborate trusswork which in turn carries the copper sheathing. The framework of the head is essentially a smaller variation of that of the main figure. Wind bracing is provided chiefly through the use of two diagonals in the panels formed by the posts and the horizontal struts. The iron and steelwork of the statue was erected on the site by the Keystone Bridge Company and the contracting firm of D. H. King, Jr.[16] The Statue of Liberty is easily America's most famous and most popular monument and is one of the foremost examples anywhere of building technology made wholly subservient to the plastic arts.

Before the end of the decade the so-called Chicago system of skyscraper construction—complete interior framing without bearing walls—appeared in

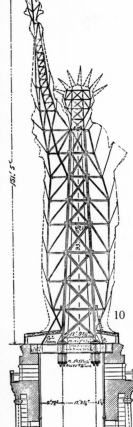

10 Statue of Liberty, 1883–86. Frédéric Bartholdi, sculptor; Gustav Eiffel and Keystone Bridge Company, designers and fabricators of the framework. Cross section of the figure and the pedestal showing the interior construction.

11  Tower Building, 50 Broadway, New York City, 1888–89. Bradford Gilbert, architect. View showing the columns of the iron frame.

New York. The first structure to embody the principle was the Tower Building, at 50 Broadway, designed by Bradford Gilbert and completed in little more than a year, between June 1888 and September 1889. The building had the ridiculous dimensions dictated by Manhattan's 25-foot lots: the width was 21 feet 6 inches, the depth 108 feet. Since the side walls had few openings, little natural light penetrated to the interior of the building. Structurally the 11-story Tower was an odd composite of skeleton construction and masonry wall, with the usual relationship reversed. There were no intermediate columns. The framing of the side walls consisted of cast iron columns irregularly spaced and resting on cast iron shoes on the top of the continuous footings at basement level (fig. 11). At each floor up to the seventh there were transverse wrought iron girders and spandrel beams spanning between the columns.

The beams carried the loads of the brick wall panels up to the next story above, while the girders carried the closely spaced wrought iron joists which supported the floors. This system of true wall framing terminated at the seventh floor. At this level a line of heavy wrought iron girders ran continuously around the periphery of the building. Above them on the sides and at the rear rose conventional brick bearing walls through the remaining four stories. Diagonal bracing, to give the frame rigidity under wind loads, was introduced into each panel.[17] As one might expect, Gilbert had great difficulty in getting a permit because of his novel system of construction and because of the prejudice of the Board of Examiners against iron construction in general. "So wary were New Yorkers of a building whose walls were supported by a metal frame, rather than vice versa, that Gilbert had to reassure them by occupying the topmost offices himself."[18]

The chief motive behind Gilbert's use of skeleton framing in the Tower Building was the need for space. If he had used masonry bearing walls on such a narrow lot, their thickness for an 11-story building would have left room for only a hallway at the first floor. Such a costly sacrifice of valuable land made the new system of construction imperative. Only the narrow Broadway elevation, the building's façade, was given an "architectural treatment," with sufficient window area to provide adequate natural light in the first row of offices. The blank brick side walls made continuous artificial illumination necesssary for the rest of the interior. This fact alone offers a graphic demonstration of the generally superior work of the Chicago school in commercial building at the end of the century. Yet Gilbert had taken the decisive step for the New York builders. Within a few years after the completion of the Tower Building, the high steel skeleton was to become a familiar sight to New Yorkers (fig. 12). By 1894 *Harper's Weekly* could say, "We are getting to be more accustomed to the lofty structures, and so conventional ideas, born of what we are accustomed to look at, are being gradually modified."[19]

But the builders were at first hesitant about adopting the new system of skyscraper construction, in spite of direct empirical evidence of its advantages. For five years the engineers tried various combinations of iron, steel, and masonry.[20] Complete freedom from the past came with Kimball and Thompson's Manhattan Life Insurance Company Building (1893–94), fully framed with a combination of iron and steel and set upon concrete caissons extending to bedrock. The Manhattan was 17 stories high; its main block rose 242 feet, the tower another 108, for a total of 350 feet. For this height, masonry bearing walls were out of the question, and the engineer, Charles O. Brown, was forced to employ skeletal framing throughout. In the next year Bruce Price's American Surety Building, at Broadway and Pine Street (1894–95), introduced the complete steel frame to carry its 20-story, 303-foot height.[21]

12 Empire Building, Broadway and Rector Street, New York City. Kimball and Thompson, architects. A portion of the steel frame during construction, 1897.

A system of construction adequate to the modern skyscraper had at last been developed in New York. Its subsequent evolution was characterized chiefly by ever-increasing height. In 1896 the St. Paul Building rose to 26 stories. In 1898 the height moved up again to 30 stories in the Park Row. It was the highest building in the world at the time, higher than anything Chicago was to see until the boom of the 1920's, and it was thought to be the upward limit to which a building could be carried. Yet the process continued, to reach its culmination at last in the 102 stories of the Empire State Building (1931). The engineers of the New York skyscraper knew their business well, but that is more than one can always say of the architects. Montgomery Schuyler felt that they had failed to develop an adequate, realistic, and native treatment of the tall office building. In all that new city of towers, he could find only one in which he thought that the problem had been faced and a valid solution attempted—Sullivan's Bayard Building, on Bleecker Street (1898). The full dramatic power of the steel-framed skyscraper in New York was not finally evoked until the completion of Cass Gilbert's Woolworth Tower in 1913.[22]

## 4. THE CHICAGO SCHOOL

The structural and formal inventiveness that flourished in Chicago during the three decades from 1880 to 1910 was at once a new movement in architecture and the culmination of technical and theoretical developments extending over a century of building art. Iron construction was fairly well advanced in New York before it was regarded as an acceptable alternative to masonry in Chicago. Once it was adopted, however, its structural potentialities were exploited to the full in one of the most concentrated bursts of creative energy in nineteenth-century technology. The two chief causes of this activity were, first, the explosive growth of industry and commerce which began in Chicago about 1860, and, second, the fire of 1871, a disaster that cut directly across the accelerating economic development of the city and hence raised economic pressures to an irresistible level. But, of course, there were other factors, intangibles associated with the life of the Middle West that attracted or encouraged a boldness of practical imagination and a forthrightness in dealing with the problem at hand. The work of the Chicago school represented a brilliant adaptation of new techniques to novel and often daring structural solutions. The same solutions appeared in New York, where builders had an older tradition to rely on and a greater proximity to Europe, the source of ideas, but in the Eastern city the decisive steps in the last decades of the century always came about five years behind the similar ones in Chicago.

The history of cast iron building in Chicago is in no way distinguished. First-story iron columns in the façade appear to have been used as early as 1848, but there can be little question that they were cast in New York by one of the early founders. The pioneer foundry in Chicago for casting structural members was the Union Iron Works, established by Bouton and Hurlburt in 1852. They must have confined themselves at first to the manufacture of fronts, since the interior column did not appear until 1855, and even then it was an importation. The first building with an entire cast iron front was the Lloyd Block, at Randolph and Wells streets (1855). Daniel Badger's company apparently cast the members, since he referred in one of his publications to a Lloyd and Jones Building at this address and approximate date. The Lloyd was quickly followed by a number of others, the fronts of which were manufactured by the Architectural Iron Works. Meanwhile, iron columns and beams appeared in John M. Van Osdel's Post Office and Custom House (1855).

By 1871—ironically enough—the Chicago builders were trying their hands at completely fireproof structures. The Nixon Building, at La Salle and Monroe streets, revealed the most thorough and costly work of fireproofing, and its fate during the fire justified the care lavished upon it. The iron front had by this time become less popular in Chicago, and Otto H. Matz, the Nixon's architect, followed the practice of using stone masonry piers in the façade. In the interior all columns and beams were cast iron and the joists wrought iron. The maximum beam span was 16 feet. The tops of the beams were covered with a 1-inch layer of concrete. Brick floor arches spanning between the joists carried marble floors, and a 1-inch coat of plaster on the ceilings provided additional fire protection. The Nixon was nearly complete when the fire struck on October 8, 1871. Except for wood moldings and trim, it survived intact and was opened for use a week after the fire burned itself out.

George H. Johnson's invention of a fireproof tile covering for iron structural members was first used in Chicago in Van Osdel's Kendall Building (1872). Johnson had developed his tile while working for Daniel Badger in New York, coming to Chicago to promote it in 1871, the year when it was likely to have its strongest appeal. The failure of iron members in many buildings during the fire led the Chicago builders to use combinations of stone and iron construction, with the iron generally confined to interiors.

Bogardus's technique of combining cast iron columns with wooden beams persisted until the 1880's in Chicago, where it was virtually standard for the less expensive and less showy buildings. The high point of this system of construction was reached in William Le Baron Jenney's first Leiter Building, now the Morris, at Monroe and Wells streets (1879). This curious mixture of boldness and vernacular naïveté came very close to true skeletal construction, which Jenney was to achieve a few years later in his famous Home Insurance

Building (1884–85). The construction of the five-story Leiter Building included three of the basic techniques in common use at the time: cast iron columns and girders, timber beams and joists, and brick piers.[1] If Jenney had placed the wall columns in the piers and had added three more columns, he would have built a fully framed structure.

It took Jenney four years to move from the tentative and awkward use of framed construction in the first Leiter Building to relatively mature iron and steel framing on the grand scale in the Home Insurance. No building in the United States has been investigated more thoroughly than it, for none has had a more decisive effect on the building techniques of our time. As we have seen, a century of exploration into the possibilities of iron construction lay behind Jenney's achievement, and when he was awarded the commission in 1883, he seems to have determined at the outset to take the ultimate step. A particular event in this development may have been the chief determinant in the architect's choice. One historian of iron construction has advanced the thesis that George H. Johnson, when he was employed by Badger in New York, had a first-hand knowledge of Bogardus's iron-framed shot towers, and that he carried news of these unusual structures to the Chicago builders on his two visits to the city (1871–74, 1877–79). If Johnson provided a reasonably accurate description of the towers, Jenney must certainly have understood the technique and seen its potentialities. At the same time, since he had studied at the École Centrale in Paris, he must have been familiar with the large-scale French examples of iron framing, especially the famous warehouse of the St. Ouen docks.[2]

Jenney's approach to the design of the Home Insurance Building, typical of so much building of the nineteenth century, was to an extent empirical and pragmatic; he changed it in detail several times as design and construction progressed. His grasp of the new structural techniques, however, and the systematic application of his knowledge revealed a scientific attitude toward the problem of building. After all, he was the product of a French technical school. His method was much more sophisticated than the "homely ingenuity" so often attributed to him.[3] To some extent, of course, Jenney relied on his engineering assistant, George B. Whitney.

The permit for the Home Insurance Building was issued in 1884, and construction, on the northeast corner of La Salle and Adams streets, was completed the following year. As originally built, the Home Insurance had nine stories, but two more were added in 1891. Test borings on the site revealed an extensive and homogeneous sheet of hard-pan clay at a depth of 12 to 13 feet below grade. Compression tests indicated that the clay would sustain a load of 4,000 pounds per square foot, and it was on this basis that Jenney calculated the dimensions of his footings. Each column footing was a built-up pyramid of cut stone surrounding a rubble core, the whole carried on a large raft of reinforced concrete 24 inches thick.[4] All columns extended from the footings to the roof except for those in the two street elevations, which rested on granite piers the tops of which stood just above the second-floor line. Of the wall framing Jenney himself provided a concise description:

Square cast iron columns are built into brick piers and connected at the top of each window by cast iron lintels. Each floor of beams and girders is tied together and also bolted to the columns, supplemented by heavy hoop iron, built into the brickwork in every place where increased bond or tie is desired, and also every stone is clamped or anchored so that settlement will produce as little displacement as possible.[5]

The building was set up 4 inches against future settlement, which was ¾ inch the first year.

The interior columns were hollow cast iron cylinders, and they would have carried the entire floor and roof load, as Jenney originally intended, had it not been required that some part of the load be shifted to the brick party walls. William B. Mundie, Jenney's future partner, explained the reason for the later decision:

The Building Commissioner ordered the wall columns could not be inserted up to the lot line in the party walls; thus the plan to build the complete unit as a cage with every column on its own isolated pier footing was defeated. Another ruling was, that interior vault tiers against the walls should be solid brick; this was demanded by the Insurance Underwriters. . . . The expansion and contraction of a column 150 feet high and the extreme variation in temperature . . . [was offset] by supporting the walls and floors of each story independently, story by story, on the columns.[6]

It was precisely this question that had given rise to the greatest controversy over the value of iron framing. The chief objection to skeletal construction was that the different rates of thermal expansion between iron and masonry would inevitably result in the twisting or buckling of the metal and the cracking of the masonry.

Another change in the original program for the Home Insurance Building was a major forward step in the progress of structural techniques. During construction Jenney sought and was given permission to substitute the first shipment of Bessemer steel beams for wrought iron above the sixth floor. The manufacturer was the Carnegie-Phipps Steel Company of Pittsburgh. Thus steel at last entered building construction in the United States, fifteen years after it was first adopted for an American bridge. The slowness with which its use spread was largely a matter of its relatively high cost, in spite of the fact that the Bessemer process had been developed in practical form in 1856.

The question whether the Home Insurance Building was the first to embody the modern system of complete internal framing was discussed off and on for thirty-five years prior to its demolition in 1931. On the evidence of Jenney himself, the early proponents had no doubt about his claim. The subject was first taken up in July 1896 in two articles in *Engineering Record,* published in reply to an inquiry initiated by F. T. Gates, president of the Bessemer Steamship Company. The editorial replies satisfied Gates that Jenney deserved the credit, and in a letter printed in the issue of February 13, 1897, Gates stated that his company planned to name their next vessel after the famous architect. The *W. Le B. Jenney* was constructed by the F. W. Wheeler and Company of West Bay City, Michigan, and launched in 1897. The issue was taken to be settled in the early years of the twentieth century. After Jenney's death in 1906 the work of the Chicago school was gradually forgotten, and with it the architect's great contribution.

In 1924, however, the controversy arose again over the question of the extent to which the load was supported by the framing members. The necessity for repair work made possible an investigation of a small part of the interior frame. An examination of one column-and-lintel connection appears to have satisfied the doubters that the brick piers carried none of the load delivered to the iron lintel. But to establish the full nature of construction and the materials used required a more extensive inquiry. Finally, when it was known that the Home Insurance Building was to be demolished, three investigating committees were established in 1931 to conduct a thorough examination. One was appointed by the Marshall Field Estate, with the Chicago architect and historian Thomas E. Tallmadge as chairman. A second represented jointly the Illinois Society of Architects and the Chicago Chapter of the American Institute of Architects, its chairman being Terrell J. Ferrenz. The third was appointed by the Western Society of Engineers and consisted of J. C. Sanderson, J. L. McConnell, and F. J. Thielbar. These committees substantially confirmed the claims that Jenney had made—skeletal construction in all essential respects, bolted connections, cast iron columns and lintels, wrought iron beams up to the sixth floor, and steel above. This last feature was determined by the Field Committee through chemical and photomicrographic analyses, physical tests, and a search of the records of the Carnegie-Phipps Company. The committee of the Western Society of Engineers made a critical appraisal that established precisely the place of Jenney's building in the evolution of the structural arts:

The Home Insurance Building was erected in the development period of the skeleton type of building and is a notable example of its type; while it does not fulfill all the requirements of a skeleton type, it was well along in this development and was principally lacking [in] not having curtain walls, no provision in the framing for wind loads, and not having made full provision for starting the masonry above the first floor.[7]

The Chicago builders, like those in New York, were slow to follow the new path. For four years they tried various combinations of iron and masonry construction, before they were willing to break once and for all with the past. Along the way, however, they produced two remarkable works of structural virtuosity, which represented the most thorough exploration of the techniques available to them before the Home Insurance Building was completed.

The first is The Rookery, at La Salle and Adams streets (1884–86), which still stands as Burnham and Root designed it, in an admirable state of repair and cleanliness. The building is a hybrid in construction, embracing both traditional masonry elements and advanced techniques of iron framing. In plan it is a hollow square surrounding an interior court. An unusual feature is the fact that all elevations face streets; the building is thus naturally lighted on four sides as well as the interior. The exterior walls up to the top, or eleventh, story are composed of a series of stout, widely spaced granite columns surmounted by brick piers. On the periphery of the court, however, the wall and floor loads are carried on a rigidly bolted system of cast iron columns and wrought iron spandrel beams in true skeletal construction. By extending the spandrel beams at the rear elevations a few inches beyond the outer edge of the columns, the architects were able to open the wall at the second story into a continuous window divided by narrow iron mullions. It is entirely possible, however, that Burnham and Root could have opened the wall in this way by using deep piers with the narrow face in or parallel to the wall plane.[8] The architectural treatment of the court walls is radically different from that of the outer elevations. The latter emphatically express masonry pier construction, while the former constitute a neutral screen of large rectangular openings clearly stating the cellular character of column-and-beam framing.

In every detail of The Rookery the subtlety of Root's creative imagination is apparent, but nowhere is his genius more obvious than in the glass-and-iron vault over the court (fig. 13). It is the finest example of its kind in the United States. Because of the square plan of The Rookery it was not possible to treat the skylight as a gable roof; as a consequence, Root turned it into a flattened glass dome, square in plan, of ribbed construction. The main structural ribs form a complicated pattern both in disposition and individual appearance. All have the familiar I-beam section, but some have straight parallel flanges, while others have slightly arched bottom flanges. All the ribs are perforated, either by large circular openings nearly filling the web, or by a great number of small holes. The perforations have some functional purpose in lightening the members, but the primary motive was decorative. On the system of primary and secondary ribs rests a roof of glass set into an intricate pattern of octagons

13  The Rookery, 209 South La Salle Street, Chicago, Illinois, 1884–86. Burnham and Root, architects. The glass and iron vault over the interior court.

and squares. The ornamental bands, stair rails, and lighting fixtures, added in 1905, were designed by Frank Lloyd Wright. The combination of delicate ironwork and gold and ivory decoration gives the court the quality of a rich and exuberant but thoroughly disciplined architectural fantasy. The ribbed dome forms an impressive structural symbol of the late nineteenth century's creative power in both art and technology.

The celebrated Auditorium Building, at Congress Parkway and Michigan Boulevard (1887–89), would have tested the best architectural and engineering abilities, and Adler and Sullivan rose with rare courage to meet the challenge. The functional problems and their structural solution went beyond anything that American builders had previously to deal with. The Auditorium, which extends the full block from Michigan to Wabash Avenue, embraces a ground area of 63,350 square feet and contains in its interior a huge theater surrounded by a block of offices on its west side and, originally, of hotel rooms on the east (fig. 14).[9] The combination of facilities, together with the great size of the theater, posed a host of structural problems, which Adler solved by using the traditional forms of masonry building along with every major invention of the age in iron construction. The office and hotel blocks could be dealt with readily enough by using exterior masonry piers and interior iron column-and-beam framing. The theater was another matter. To cover this immense volume with a minimum of interior supports required two entirely different approaches.

Over the orchestra floor, with nothing between the floor and the roof, he used an elliptical barrel vault which spans clear from wall to wall. Over the three balconies, however, the curving surface would have seriously restricted seating capacity, and as a consequence he had to turn to the conventional flat ceiling spanning without break half the width of the enclosure.

Adler called on a variety of structural means to deal with these changes of shape and dimensions. To support the roof over the orchestra floor between the proscenium and the forward edge of the balcony, there are six transverse trapezoidal trusses. Suspended from the roof trusses by hangers is a set of parallel elliptical arched trusses which carry the vaulted ceiling. At a point roughly half way between the stage and the rear wall the elliptical vault gives way to a flat ceiling which is hung from three transverse trapezoidal trusses.[10] At the forward edge of the upper gallery the roof steps up above the rehearsal hall. Its east end (toward the stage) rests on another trapezoidal truss set transversely, its west end on the bearing partition between the theater and the office

14  The Auditorium Building (now Roosevelt University), Michigan Avenue and Congress Parkway, Chicago, Illinois, 1887–89. Adler and Sullivan, architects. Longitudinal section through the building.

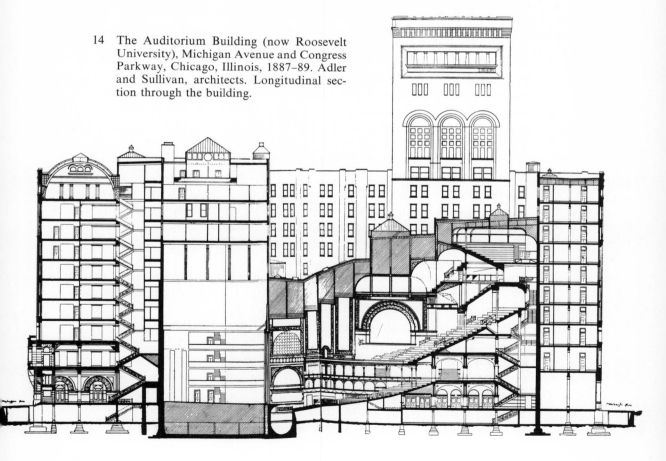

57

block. The roof above the rehearsal hall is supported by a series of modified Bollman deck trusses set in a longitudinal direction.[11] All trusses and hangers are wrought iron and the columns cast iron. The orchestra floor, balcony, and galleries rest on sloping wrought iron girders which form the major floor supports in a complete system of column-and-beam framing. The distinctive feature of the foundation work is the concrete raft which underlies the tower on the Congress Street side of the building. Five feet thick, it is reinforced with two layers of timbers, three of rails, and three of I-beams. The basement floor below the stage, lying 7 feet below mean water level in Lake Michigan, is composed of alternate layers of concrete, asphalt, and asphalt-saturated felt counterweighted with courses of rails to offset the upward-acting hydraulic pressure. The Auditorium Building thus sums up the structural art of its age. Under the rich ornament of the theater and the hotel none of this appears; yet Sullivan's architectural conception of surface, volume, and flat decorative detail, though purely formal in character, could have been possible only with the means of construction that Adler provided him.

There was one more tentative step in the Tacoma Building (1888–89) before the Chicago builders reached the goal of steel framing. Designed by Holabird and Roche and the engineer Carl Seiffert, the Tacoma was well in advance of the Home Insurance Building in some respects but behind it in others. The street elevations, along Madison and La Salle, were fully framed with cast iron columns, lintels, and mullions throughout. All connections were riveted, an innovation which provided much greater rigidity than was possible with bolting. In the interior, however, there were only five columns, the great bulk of the floor and roof loads having been carried by steel and wrought iron beams to the party wall on the north, the alley wall on the east, and two interior cross walls, all of brick, varying from 32 to 36 inches in thickness. Seiffert used the interior walls as wind bracing. Framing of the elevations was worked out so that brickwork, sash, and terra cotta could be started above the ground level, a novelty which excited much popular interest during construction. At the time of demolition (1929) there had been no substantial deterioration of ironwork and tile fireproofing, but there had been a considerable amount of unequal settlement. The building was 11¾ inches out of plumb to the east, a condition which plagued Chicago builders and eventually made piling or caissons mandatory.

Baumann and Huehl's Chamber of Commerce Building (1888–89), at La Salle and Washington streets, was the first building in Chicago in which the iron and steel frame was used without any masonry adjuncts. The columns of its bolted wrought iron and steel skeleton rested on the familiar spread footings of steel grillage imbedded in concrete. The total weight of metal in the 13-story structure was 32,000 tons. In form it was a relatively narrow slab, three bays by ten in plan. The narrow ends had a bay span of about 20 feet,

15  Chamber of Commerce Building, La Salle and Washington streets, Chicago, Illinois, 1888–89. Baumann and Huehl, architects. Interior light court.

while on the long sides it was contracted to about 15. In the interior nearly all of the central bay was opened to a light court that extended from ground floor to roof (fig. 15). The balconies, which ran continuously around the periphery of the court at each floor, were supported on columns at the four corners and on iron beams cantilevered from the columns in the two central rows. The whole court was another of those structural and architectural triumphs that transformed the sober utility of the commercial block into an object of visual delight. Richly ornamented railings and extensive marble sheathing on both the interior and exterior enhanced through their careful subordination the precision and clarity of the well-articulated elevations. The large proportion of glass in the Chamber of Commerce Building marked a long step toward the mature architecture of the Chicago school that was to come in the 1890's.

16  The Fair Store, State and Adams streets, Chicago, Illinois, 1892. William Le Baron Jenney, architect. The steel frame during construction.

It was mainly the use of glass in great bay-wide plates that became the dominant characteristic of the Chicago work. The structural evolution proceeded organically, step by step. By 1890 the steel frame had been mastered and its full potentialities were already being explored. The culmination of technical mastery and formal expression was Burnham and Root's Reliance Building, the first four stories of which were completed in 1890, the remaining ten in 1895. Credit for the design of this classic of the modern movement belongs to Charles B. Atwood, a member of Burnham's staff, and to E. C. Shankland, the structural engineer.[12] Steel beams and rails in concrete slabs formed the footings of the columns, which, along with all other structural members, were of steel. The relatively small area of plan, four by seven bays with a span of 12 feet, the height of 200 feet, and the astonishing proportion of glass in the total wall area made careful provision for wind bracing a necessity. To meet this requirement Shankland introduced columns of two-story length and plate and lattice-truss girders of 24-inch depth set between and bolted to all peripheral columns. The use of columns double the normal length was one factor in the record speed with which the steel of the upper ten stories was erected. The job required only 15 days, from July 16 to August 1, 1895.

An extraordinary number of large, steel-framed buildings were erected in Chicago between 1890 and the depression of 1893. All these buildings reveal a complete mastery of the new system of skyscraper, or "Chicago," construction—riveted steel frames, wind bracing, bedrock caissons under column footings, special framing for projecting windows. Jenney's huge Fair Store (1892), for all its architectural bad taste, is a sophisticated example of straightforward wind-braced framing (figs. 16, 17), while Clinton Warren's Unity Building, erected in the same year, is an example of the framing of oriels, or projecting bays, a treatment of the elevation especially dear to Chicago architects (fig. 18). Having mastered the frame on a large scale, the Chicago architects then adapted it to the construction of private residences. The architectural firm of Beers, Clay and Dutton made the W. H. Reid house (1894) a microcosm of

17  The Fair Store. Detail of a column-and-girder connection and the floor construction.

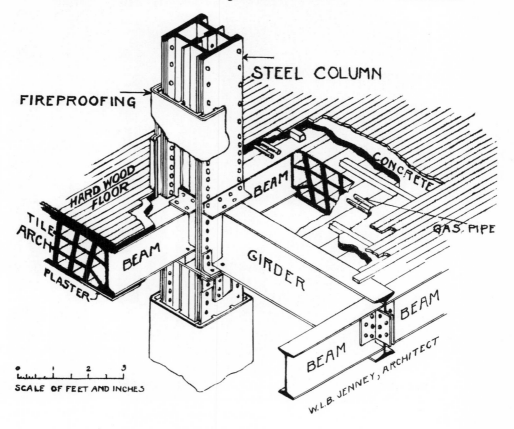

SCALE OF FEET AND INCHES

18 Unity Building, 127 North Dearborn Street, Chicago, Illinois, 1892. Clinton J. Warren, architect. The steel frame during construction.

the big steel-framed office block. Within the three-story house, a narrow rectangle in plan, floors, roof, stairways, and octagonal light court were supported on two rows of steel columns and a system of 15-inch steel girders which spanned the full width. Concrete floors rested on joists in the form of steel arches. The elaborate construction and the tile partitions indicate that the intention was complete fireproofing.

Among the most advanced structural creations in Chicago near the end of the century were the trainshed of Grand Central Station (1889–90) and the huge but temporary buildings of the World's Columbian Exposition (1893). Their distinguishing features, however, were the hinged arches of trusswork and the curved ribs of dome framing. Such elements owed more to the development of bridges and trainsheds than to iron framing for buildings, and are accordingly best treated in this connection.[13] The structural refinements of the World's Fair provided an engineering counterpart to the high level of civic art in Olmsted's brilliant site plan. Out of the latter came the City Beautiful movement, which had a profound and beneficial effect on American civic design and ultimately produced in Chicago the first comprehensive metropolitan plan, the famous Burnham Plan of 1909. Indeed, we might wonder now whether we could not do with more of the damage that the Fair was alleged to have wrought.

By the last decade of the century the pre-eminence of Chicago building with respect to structure and utility was taken for granted in the city itself and beginning to be acknowledged by builders in the East and abroad. A contemporary editorial in *Carpentry and Building*, a New York publication, paid the most enthusiastic tribute:

The character of the structures erected [in Chicago] demonstrates one notable fact —that is, that for the first time architects have risen to the plane of the highest constructive knowledge in structures. . . . In this respect Chicago is unique, and it is a common remark in Eastern and foreign cities among those actively engaged in building that Chicago today erects the best built structures ever known, and with the notable distinction that she does it with the closest economy in material and time. . . . It is a fact that in Chicago buildings the quality is better, the distribution of material is more skillful and the buildings are naturally more reliable.[14]

## 5. SPECIAL FORMS OF IRON FRAMING IN OTHER CITIES

The largest number and the greatest diversity of iron- and steel-framed buildings were erected in New York and Chicago, with the consequence that virtually the entire progress of the technique was concentrated in these two centers. At the same time, the cities cannot be regarded as the focal points from which iron construction radiated to the rest of the country. Up to the time of the Civil War, as we have seen, New York was far ahead of even the older cities of the eastern seaboard in the size and number of establishments for manufacturing iron structural members and in the inventive faculties of builders and manufacturers. Chicago's great development came with the decade of the war. But the new material and its appropriate structural techniques appeared in other cities at varying dates, depending on the local demand and the possibilities of satisfying it. The Pacific coast lagged far behind the rest of the country because of the prohibitive cost of transporting heavy iron members and the absence of a local iron industry. Most of the work outside the major centers paralleled the development in New York and Chicago but without the extreme demands that forced its rapid progress in those cities. In a number of places, however, innovations required or suggested by special conditions and unusual projects added their stimulus to the evolution of modern framed construction.

Domes and skylights always posed the most formidable problems and hence called forth the best inventive talents. The largest and most complex work of iron framing belonging to the early period supports the dome and present wings of the United States Capitol (1851–64). Moreover, it is a rare example of the new structural methods allied with traditional construction in one of the great works of nineteenth-century architecture. The original Capitol of Thornton, Latrobe, and Bulfinch had become badly overcrowded by 1840. In 1843 Strickland proposed the addition of fireproof wings with cast iron columns, roofs, and window frames. The proposal was not acted upon until 1851, when President Fillmore appointed Thomas U. Walter as official architect. Fire in the Library of Congress wing in December of that year decided Walter's wavering choice once and for all. He determined to use cast iron for all interior fittings and wrought iron roof trusses supported on masonry walls, in spite of the fact that he had had little previous experience with the material. On the basis of his familiarity with British, French, and American work he designed the Library of Congress room (1851–52) and the new wings (1852–54) as complete iron enclosures. The exterior bearing walls are masonry, but the roof trusses are wrought iron, and the ceilings, wall-paneling, window frames, moldings, and trim are cast iron. It marked the most extensive use of iron in any public building up to the time. Walter's chief engineer and superintendent of construction in this unprecedented undertaking was the hydraulic and bridge engineer Montgomery C. Meigs, later Quartermaster-general of the Union Armies during the Civil War.

By 1854 Walter realized that the old timber-framed dome of the Capitol was no longer appropriate to the new size of the building. Accordingly, with Wren's St. Paul's Church in London as a model, he drew plans in 1855 for an iron structure. The only example of an iron-framed dome in existence at the

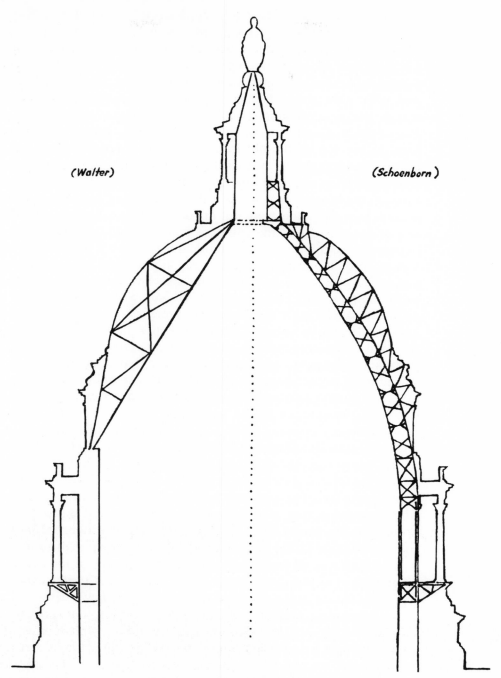

(Walter)　　(Schoenborn)

19　United States Capitol, 1856–64. Thomas U. Walter, architect; Montgomery C. Meigs and August Schoenborn, engineers. Cross section showing the framing of the dome.

time was that of the Cathedral of St. Isaac in St. Petersburg, Russia.[1] Walter and his engineering consultants, Meigs and August Schoenborn, studied it carefully, and it was largely Schoenborn's adaptations that were executed. Construction of the dome began in 1856 but was not completed until 1864 because of numerous delays occasioned by the war, inadequate appropriations, and other difficulties. The chief structural supports of the dome are iron trusses which approximately follow the inner curve of the ribs and spring from a circle of cast iron columns (fig. 19). The columns rest on iron brackets fixed to the top of the old foundation wall for the rotunda of Thornton's dome. The elliptical rib or meridional truss, uniform in depth, is a modification of the Howe truss in the disposition of web members: alternate panels contain double-diagonal braces, the posts being set on radial lines.[2] It is curious that diagonals were not introduced into all panels, as they would be in a bridge truss, since the unbraced panels would be weaker than the others. Superimposed upon the inner elliptical trusses are a series of crescent-shaped trusses, also elliptical in form, with radial posts and a single diagonal in each panel. The outer, or top, chord of the crescent trusses conforms to the profile of the dome itself.[3] The material of all trusswork is cast iron. In its general architectural character the celebrated dome is a masterpiece, the proudest example of the union between iron construction in its early phase and the great tradition of masonry building. It was the structural as well as the architectural precedent for nearly every statehouse dome that came after it.

The most extraordinary exception to this generalization was a curiosity of late-century iron construction in the New Orleans area which revealed still unexploited possibilities in the technique. William Freret's State Capitol at Baton Rouge, Louisiana (1880–82), was a remarkable example of structural and decorative iron framing for a dome in the style of the Gothic Revival. The dome, which rose above the central rotunda of the lobby, was an elaborate piece of iron-and-glass construction for which there seems to have been no native precedent. The rotunda was defined by a circle of six cast iron columns which carried a ring of iron beams on which rested the edge of a circular opening in the second floor. An iron spiral stairway mounted from the first to the second floor within the colonnade. At the center of the circle a solid cast iron column rose 80 feet from its footing to the apex of the ogival dome. The outer surface of this column was cast in the form of twelve cylindrical moldings in imitation of the clustered shafts of the medieval cathedral. At the top of the column the moldings spread without breaking outward and downward into the twelve ribs of the duodecagonal dome, whose base was held by a stout wrought iron tension ring set on twelve iron columns. Between the ribs lay a delicate tracery of wrought iron which supported the lights of the glass envelope. The whole structure was a *tour de force* in iron, an exuberant glorification, perhaps, of its endless ornamental possibilities, but at the same time a serious and consistent attempt to develop iron construction itself into a system of ornament. The metalwork of the Baton Rouge Capitol was manufactured by the Shakespeare Iron Works of New Orleans. It was a misfortune that the dome at least could not have been spared when the new capitol was built in 1932.

An equally remarkable but structurally more significant example of dome framing appeared in St. Louis near the end of the century, and it stood as a perfect antithesis to the Louisiana Capitol. The steel interior construction of Temple Shaare Emeth (1896), designed by the architects Link and Rosenheim and the engineer Julius Baier, was a work of sophisticated science in which structure was entirely hidden by visible form. The tabernacle of the synagogue was square in plan and was surmounted by an octagonal pyramid carrying an octagonal lantern at its apex. The basic members of the frame were eight steel ribs which rose vertically from stepped concrete footings to the height of the tabernacle walls, at the top of which they were inclined inward at the angle of the pyramid face. The distinctive feature was that the two parts of the rib formed a single unit, the knee of which was a rigid joint widened to take the greater stress at this point.[4] The main ribs through rigid connections supported the framing of the lantern, which was made up of eight ribs similar to but much smaller than those of the pyramidal roof. The lantern ribs were tied together and braced by light trusses. In this construction all vertical and diagonal members lying in one plane across the structure formed a continuous rigid system and thus constituted what later came to be called a rigid frame.[5] Baier appears to have been the first engineer in the United States to use this type of construction, which was originally developed in Germany. It was rare until about 1910, when it began to appear with growing frequency in girder bridges and wide-span enclosures. The first description of Temple Shaare Emeth referred to the ribs as "built beams."[6]

The skylighted interior court, or arcade, as it was frequently known, was extremely popular in the last two decades of the nineteenth century. Originating with the Arcade Building in Providence, adapted to iron construction in New York in the 1850's, it had spread by 1890 to every city large enough to support a multistory office block, hotel, or department store. The skylight was usually built in the form of a gable, which required the simplest kind of construction, but it also appeared as a flattened dome square in plan at its base. In spite of the prohibitive cost of iron on the Pacific coast, an early and elaborate example of domed skylighting formed the major structural feature of the Palace Hotel (1874–75) in San Francisco, the building which marked the transition from boom town to established city (fig. 20). Designed by John P. Gaynor, the hotel was an extravagant work of the bonanza era and em-

20   Palace Hotel, San Francisco, California, 1874–75. John P. Gaynor, architect.

braced three interior light courts rather than the usual one. Each was roofed by a flattened glass-and-iron dome, somewhat like that of The Rookery in Chicago, framed in cast iron ribs. An equally interesting feature of its construction was the iron reinforcing in the brick exterior walls: every 4 feet up the height of the wall there was a wrought iron strap between the projecting windows. The segments of the strap were bolted together, the gilded bolt heads exposed as decorative features in the outer surface of the wall. Although it had its own fire-protection system, the Palace Hotel burned to the ground during the earthquake of 1906.

The most remarkable example of the iron-framed interior court was that of the second John Shillito Store in Cincinnati, Ohio (1878), the largest department store in the Middle West at the time. The building was designed by James W. McLaughlin, the son of John Shillito's first partner, William McLaughlin. The architect had previously demonstrated his skill in the design of iron-framed courts with the original Cincinnati Opera House (1865), which for about eighty years after 1870 served as the city's public library. The octagonal court of the Shillito Store, which extended from the basement through six stories to the roof, was covered by a system of radiating iron-ribbed vaults supporting a glass-and-iron dome. The floors at the periphery of the court were carried on the familiar system of cast iron columns and wrought iron beams. The distinctive features of the court framing were its great size and the unusual length of the columns at the base, which extended from the basement to the second-floor level, a height of over 30 feet. The Shillito Store was in part demolished and in part altered beyond recognition during construction of the present store building (1936–37).

The architects John M. Eisenmann and George H. Smith produced in the Cleveland Arcade (1888–90) an unusually graceful example of iron truss framing to support the skylight. The interior court of the four-story building was surrounded by balconies and covered by an iron-and-glass roof in the form of a steep gable. The skylight was carried on a series of transverse trusses of a form that was then common in the gable trainshed. The two sloping members of the top chord made an angle conforming to the cross section of the gable, while the bottom chord was curved into the form of a graceful pointed arch. The web members were horizontal struts with single diagonals in each panel. A central light monitor along the ridge of the gable was supported by triangular trusses.

With the exception of the Chamber of Commerce Building in Chicago, the grandest interior court is that of the Guaranty Loan (now Metropolitan Life) Building in Minneapolis (1888–90). The exterior walls of the 12-story building are solid bearing masonry, while the floor loads are carried on cast iron columns and steel beams. The truss-framed skylight, of gable form, covers a court which has been aptly described as a fantasy in glass and iron. At the center of the court, which measures 53 × 84 feet in plan, one is surrounded by a series of open balconies, one above the other, punctuated by the grillwork of the elevator shafts. The hard parallels of the balconies are softened by the profuse, delicate, but well-subordinated iron tracery of the railings. The richness of this interior again reveals an exuberant delight in exploring the aesthetic possibilities of the new techniques; yet the forms and structural elements appropriate to iron were in no way sacrificed. A recent comment on the Guaranty Building in the architectural press reveals the acute nostalgia that such a building arouses and thus provides a melancholy comment on the current state of commercial architecture:

In 1890 people were not yet blasé about piling story on story and then whizzing up and down. This building shows their delighted excitement about these marvels; wherever you are, you know you are in a multi-storied hive. Essentially the building is 12 stories of galleries around a great skylighted court. The galleries are

21  Bradbury Building, Los Angeles, California, 1893. George H. Wyman, architect. Interior of the light court.

floored with translucent glass, one inch thick, through which the patterns of moving footprints show. . . . To make the most of the skylight, partitions between galleries and offices are all clear glass, gallery balustrades are open panels of ornamental iron, and open elevators ride in open shafts, letting everybody . . . enjoy the excitement of the light, glassy, lacy interior. When the building was opened, it was said, "the style is strictly modern and as original as may be in the nineteenth century." Today people describe the interior with surprised respect for qualities lost by the twentieth century.[7]

Iron construction, as we have seen, came late to the California cities, but because of its continued high cost only in that region was its supremacy challenged by reinforced concrete. Enthusiasm over its structural and ornamental possibilities led to another *tour de force* in glass and iron, in this case the Bradbury Building in Los Angeles (1893), designed by George Herbert Wyman (fig. 21). The characteristic features are all present—iron columns, beams, and brackets, glass-and-iron skylight on trusses, open elevator shafts and stairways, delicate strapwork of iron rails and balustrades—but here they are carried to their ultimate structural expression. In no other building is there a more extensive exposure of structural and utilitarian elements as a means—highly questionable—to aesthetic statement. The final effect is that of a harsh and restless pattern of hard lines and planes in brightly lighted space.

The iron roof truss of mills, trainsheds, and factories was developed in great measure out of iron bridge trusses, especially those invented by Fink and Pratt, and was modified in many details to suit particular conditions.[8] The remainder of the framing followed the standard column-and-beam system of the early mills and the commercial blocks. At least sixty types of roof trusses were in use by the end of the nineteenth century (fig. 22); yet full iron and steel construction in factory buildings came rather late, first appearing, as one might expect, in the mills of the iron industry itself. Steel was rare in factories before 1890, as it was in commercial buildings.

Increase in the height and internal loads of buildings and associations of compressive and lateral forces arising from wide-span truss framing and other special varieties led to dissatisfaction with the familiar cylindrical column of cast iron. Disasters such as the collapse of Pemberton Mill heightened the demand for more trustworthy forms.[9] Because of the relatively low tensile strength of cast iron, the builders around 1860 began to think of substituting wrought iron for the older metal in columns.[10] David Reeves of the Phoenix Iron Company, at Phoenixville, Pennsylvania, developed the first wrought iron column in the United States when he patented in 1864 a built-up column composed of four flanged wrought iron segments bolted together through their longitudinal flanges. The column was thus a cylinder with four stiffening flanges running up the length of the member. By 1870 the column came to be widely used for buildings and bridges.

In 1874 Clarke and Reeves, owners of the Phoenix company, incorporated the column in a project for the Centennial Exposition at Philadelphia (1876), which, if executed, would have resulted in the grandest monument of the age to iron construction. The two engineers proposed, with a combination of recklessness and technical sobriety, a Centennial Tower 1,000 feet in over-all height. Designed as a framed structure of wrought iron, it was to be an elongated truncated cone of 20 Phoenix columns tied by horizontal beams and braced with double diagonals in each panel. Clarke and Reeves substituted wrought for cast iron in the columns because the wind load on the great height of the structure would have produced high bending stresses in the members. The whole frame was designed to sustain a wind load from the side of 50 pounds per square foot, which would have produced a calculated tensile stress in the base of the column of 5,000 pounds per square inch. The open ironwork was to be left exposed except for a covered observation gallery at the top. Centennial Tower was regarded as a fantasy at the time; yet 15 years later Gustav Eiffel in Paris was to transform this idea into a structural reality.

Shortly after the Centennial project the engineer Alexander E. Brown patented a wrought iron column which marked another step in the direction of contemporary forms. The column consisted of four members of T-section bolted together in a box-like shape, the stems forming internal stiffening flanges. The column was first used in the mill building of the Youngstown Rolling Mill Company, Youngstown, Ohio (1877), where two rows of them carried the triangular trusses that supported the gable roof. Flanged box columns of steel were first used in several framed buildings in Chicago around 1890 (fig. 17). Built-up columns of steel that come close to the modern rolled H-section form the main structural members of the Carter (now Winthrop) Building in Boston (1893–94), the first structure of complete steel framing in that city. The Winthrop has an odd shape in plan because of its irregular lot, a long, narrow rectangle bent near the middle to form a widespread V. The column is made up of four Z-bars riveted to a central plate which thus acts as the web. The resulting section is essentially an H with four projections extending out at right angles from the ends. The most unusual feature of the Winthrop's framing is the elaborate provision for wind bracing, a possible consequence of the building's shape. Horizontal trusses were set into the framing of the floors, vertical trusses into the inner partitions, and single diagonals were placed in the bays of the main frame at the corners. It was the very end of the century before the rolled H-column, familiar today in buildings and bridges, began to appear, but the growth of its size was directly dependent on the capacity of the rolling mills rather than on its functional characteristics.

22  Iron roof trusses in common use for industrial and commercial buildings at the end of the nineteenth century.

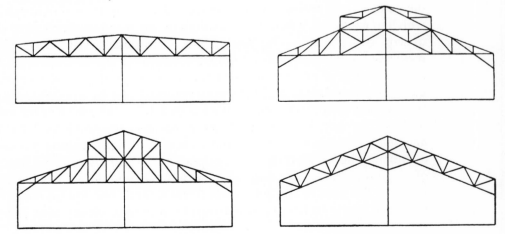

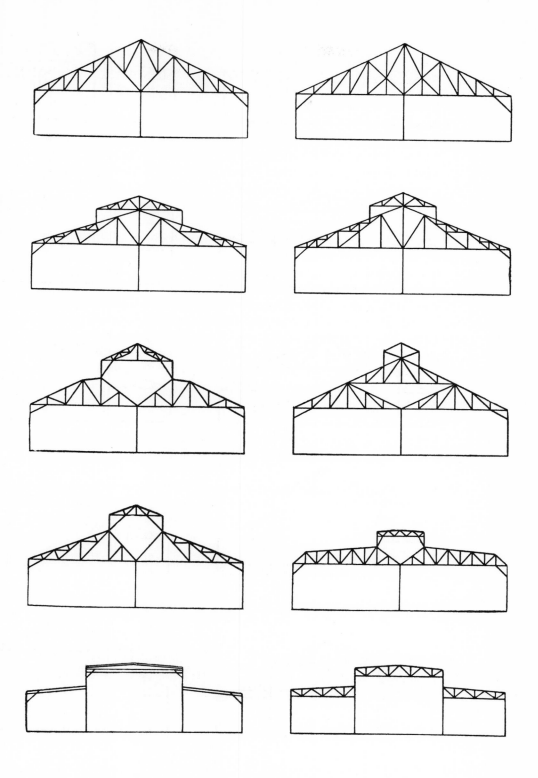

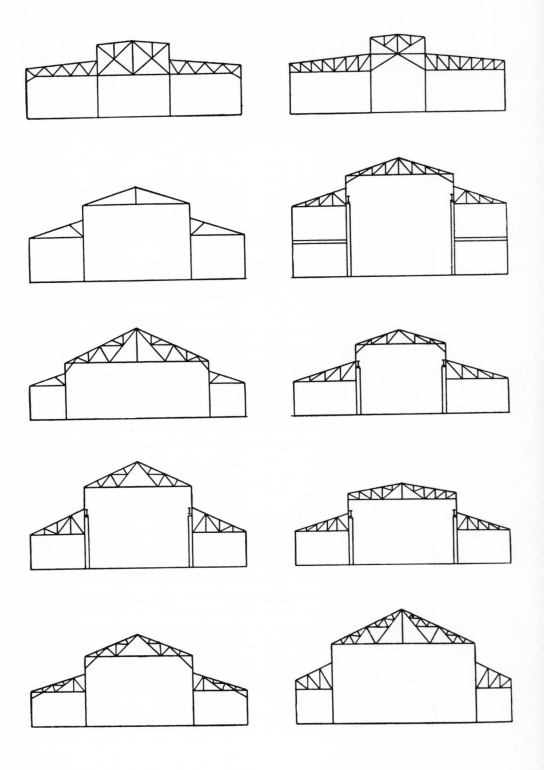

# THE WOODEN BRIDGE TRUSS

## 1. WOODEN BRIDGE CONSTRUCTION IN THE COLONIES

Like most elemental structural forms, the truss has a long history extending back to classical antiquity. Its beginning may very well have been the diagonal bracing introduced at the ends of long beams. An early example was the framing in the west half of the main cella of the Erechtheion (421–405 B.C.), where a transverse wooden girder, spanning 32 feet 3 inches and supporting wooden ceiling beams, was braced by diagonal struts, the lower ends of which were set into the masonry walls. Not much later the Greek geometers must have realized that the triangle is the only rigid figure. Some such combination of practical intuition and abstract speculation lay behind the invention of the truss by Hellenistic builders in the third century B.C.

The earliest extant description, of course, is in Vitruvius. The Romans were not technical inventors, a defect of character which paralleled their lack of interest in science and mathematics. For much of their structural art they depended initially on Hellenistic architects and engineers, who most certainly provided them with truss construction. Trajan's Bridge over the Danube River (A.D. 104), the longest Roman bridge, was a wooden structure built by Apollodorus of Damascus, the architect of the emperor's Forum. The representation of this bridge on Trajan's Column suggests the presence of truss-like elements. The long deck—3,720 feet between abutments—was carried on a framework of radial and diagonal members in turn supported by a succession of arch ribs spanning between masonry piers. The massive rail, with two diagonals in each panel, seems to have functioned in part as a supporting or stiffening truss, but this is by no means clear. The Pantheon (c. 125) included a bronze truss in the pediment over the portico. The truss was apparently removed in the seventeenth century, but—most important for the history of this valuable structural device—Palladio had made a drawing of it before 1570.

Whether the truss had a continuous life throughout the Middle Ages is a matter of speculation. Most of the early bridges, other than masonry, were pile-and-beam structures of such vulnerability to fire and flood that none survived. The larger of them, like the structure that preceded Peter Cole-church's Old London Bridge (1176–1209), undoubtedly had diagonal bracing at the piers. Two bridges at Lucerne, Switzerland, dating from the fourteenth century, the *Todtentanzbrücke* and the *Kappelbrücke,* were covered timber trusses, as near as one can make out from old representations of them. Truss framing of many varieties was common in the cathedrals after the twelfth century. Leonardo da Vinci made a sketch in one of his notebooks of a bridge truss with double diagonals, but none of this kind was built before the nineteenth century. Andrea Palladio has always been credited with the invention of trusses specifically designed for bridges, and his drawings indicate that he went far beyond his Roman and medieval predecessors, from whom, on his own admission, he derived his ideas. Of the four types of Palladian trusses, one was an arched truss which was later to play an important role in the early development of American truss bridges.[1] In spite of the great architect's authority, few truss bridges were built prior to the latter half of the eighteenth century. The best known and most influential of the early timber truss bridges on the Continent were those of the Swiss builders Johann (or Jean) and Hans Grubenmann, but most of them were destroyed during the Napoleonic Wars.

There is no doubt that the truss bridge was known to the American colonists, but the medieval village background of the carpenters provided them with little experience in its design and construction. Until the Revolution they seem to have relied exclusively on the simple pile-and-beam form, like those built in large numbers by the Roman military engineers, from whom the Anglo-Saxon peoples may have learned the art. The first bridge to span a major stream in the colonies was The Great Bridge over the Charles River at Cambridge, Massachusetts (1662). The piles, hand-driven directly into the river bed, supported the heavy timber girders, which in turn carried the transverse beams underlying the plank deck. The girder span was 15 to 20 feet. The type served well enough throughout the colonial period, the only deviations being floating structures of various kinds.[2]

Combinations of pontoon or floating spans with piling were sometimes used in the eighteenth century and continued throughout the nineteenth. The bridge of this kind with the longest and oddest history was laid over Glenmere Pond, near Lynn, Massachusetts, about 1800. Originally 511 feet long, the bridge consisted of a solid timber floating bed 5 feet thick made by spiking planks together and fixing them between piles. As the wood became waterlogged it gradually sank. To correct this defect further layers of planking were added over the years. By 1916 the bridge was a solid mass of waterlogged timber 28 feet thick resting on the bottom of the pond. It was still usable, even by fairly heavy vehicles, but the highway engineers decided to give up the struggle and replace it with a modern span. Such primitive structures, however, could no longer serve the needs of the young Republic; more sophisticated building techniques had to be called on.

To erect adequate timber bridges two structural techniques had to be mastered: one was the method of building substantial masonry piers up from a firm bed in watertight cofferdams; the other was the construction of truss framing. Both had been developed to a sufficient degree in Europe by the mid-eighteenth century, and by the end of the century the American carpenters were ready to try their hands. The bridge generally declared to be the first framed timber span in the United States was built by Colonel Enoch Hale over the Connecticut River at Bellows Falls, Vermont (1785). The deck crossed the river 50 feet above the water in two spans totaling 368 feet in length (fig. 23). The planking of the floor rested on four sets of parallel braced stringers, which in turn were carried by the abutment walls at the ends and by a framed center pier in the form of a trussed bent. The vertical piles and stringers were reinforced by heavy diagonal braces springing from the base of the pier. There was no attempt to found the piles in the river bed. Hale took advantage of an exposed reef in mid-river to provide support for the center bent. The railings along the deck acted as longitudinal stiffeners, but they were not rigid elements, since they consisted only of vertical posts

23   Bridge over the Connecticut River, Bellows Falls, Vermont, 1785. Enoch Hale, builder.

and two horizontal rails. Hale's bridge was replaced sometime between 1797 and 1803 by what the Reverend Timothy Dwight of Yale University called an "obtuse arch" of wood. This was again replaced by a Town lattice truss in 1840, which survived until 1930.

Like many pioneers, Hale was poorly rewarded for his achievement. In 1783 he obtained an initial grant from the legislatures of New Hampshire and Vermont to build a toll bridge over the Connecticut River between the towns then known as Walpole, New Hampshire, and Rockingham, Vermont. He was able to open the bridge in 1785 by borrowing the balance of the cost from a Mr. Geyer, a Boston merchant who in turn secured a mortgage on the bridge. The span was a profitable investment and Geyer was anxious to get hold of it. As the expiration date of the mortgage approached, Hale borrowed money from friends to liquidate it. He sent the cash to Boston by a messenger who took a holiday at Lowell along the way and arrived a day late. Geyer told the messenger that the mortgage had expired and assumed title to the bridge. Hale died indigent, while Geyer passed himself off as a public benefactor. It was apparently he who added the arch to the bridge around 1800, although it was thought that this was done more for purposes of advertisement than for structural improvement. The point of this melancholy tale is that the primitive methods of financing and the seventeenth-century foreclosure law had to be replaced by more modern economic and legal institutions if bridges were to be built in the number, size, and quality that the nation needed. The problem was partly solved by the greater financial resources of the railroad and turnpike companies. But eventually the public bridge had to be built by public agencies backed by the power of taxation.

## 2. EARLY FORMS OF THE WOODEN TRUSS: THE WORK OF PALMER, BURR, AND WERNWAG

Timothy Palmer of Newburyport, Massachusetts, a Yankee of unusual energy and skill, was the first of the great bridge builders who made the covered timber truss in America a work of structural art. A self-taught architect and carpenter, he was the first in his native land to recognize the need for heavy bridges of a span sufficient for large waterways, to use the arched truss on a scale adequate for such spans, and to urge the covering, or weatherboarding, of structural members. Palmer began the construction of bridges about 1780, and within a decade he had mastered the art sufficiently to take on an ambitious project. In 1792 he completed the long Essex-Merrimac Bridge over the Merrimack River near his native town of Newburyport (fig. 24). Actually the structure consisted of two bridges separated by Deer Island, which divides the

24  Essex-Merrimac Bridge, Merrimack River, above Newburyport, Massachusetts, 1792. Timothy Palmer, builder.

stream at this point. Throughout most of its length it was made up of a series of traditional pile-and-beam spans of short length. At the locations of maximum depth, however, where the driving of piles would have been hazardous if not impossible, Palmer introduced two trussed spans, one 160 feet in length, the other 113 feet. They were Palladian arched trusses, which Palmer must have known only from drawings, since there were no constructed examples available to him. Although his method of design was necessarily empirical and intuitive, he was not wholly in the dark with respect to predicting how his bridge might act under load. A framed timber bridge built by Jean Ulrich Grubenmann over the Rhine at Schaffhausen, Switzerland (1757), had been tested under loaded wagons weighing 25 tons. It was something of a sensation, and news of it undoubtedly crossed the Atlantic. With reason for confidence in a framed structure, Palmer then made doubly sure by arching the truss to make use of the compressive strength of the heavy longitudinal timbers under the deck.

The truss of the Essex-Merrimac Bridge consisted of a series of posts set radially above the flattened arch of the deck and a single diagonal brace set in each panel formed by a pair of posts. He further strengthened the truss against lateral forces by adding diagonal bracing under each end of the deck in a plane parallel to it. The ribs, or longitudinal timbers, under the deck were fixed in the masonry of the abutment wall so that the stonework could take both the horizontal and vertical components of the end thrust of the arch. The greater part of Palmer's bridge survived, with repairs, for more than a century. In 1810 the portion containing the 160-foot span was replaced by a chain suspension bridge built by James Finley.[1] The entire structure was replaced in 1909.

Two years after the opening of the Merrimack span Palmer completed the largest of all his bridges and very likely the largest ever built in America up to that time—the Piscataqua River bridge at Portsmouth, New Hampshire (1794). Not only was it the size of the structure that tested Palmer's courage, but also the fact that it was built over a tidal stream with swift and turbulent currents. The bridge was nearly a half-mile long overall, with about nine-tenths of its length made up of pile-and-beam spans. At the main shipping channel Palmer introduced another of his Palladian arched trusses set between masonry piers laid up in timber cofferdams. The deck of the truss rested on a series of stout arched ribs.[2] A contemporary description of the carpentry work of these members has survived:

There are three concentric ribs, the middle one carrying the floor of the bridge; they were selected from crooked timbers, so that the fiber might run nearly in the direction of the curves, and are connected together by pieces of hard and incompressible wood, with wedges driven between, the ribs being mortised to receive them; thus the ribs are kept at a regular and parallel distance from each other. Each rib is formed of two pieces laid side by side about 15 feet in length; they are all disposed in such a manner as to break joints, the end of one timber coming in the middle of the length of the other which is near it; their ends all abut with a square joint against each other and are neither scarfed nor mortised, the two pieces of timber being held together by transverse dovetail keys and joints; all the timbers are admirably jointed and freely exposed to the action of the air; any piece may also be removed in case of its requiring separation without injury to the rest of the structure.[3]

The best and most famous of Palmer's bridges was the Permanent Bridge over the Schuylkill River at Philadelphia (1806), built to replace a pontoon structure dating from the days of the Revolution (fig. 25). This was the first bridge in which Palmer used more than one truss span in a contiguous series, thus making it possible for the horizontal thrusts of adjacent arches to balance each other. The deck, which was slightly arched from end to end, was divided into three spans and was carried on three separate sets of arch ribs, but the truss was a single continuous structure whose top chord followed the curve of the deck. Palmer used the details of his earlier bridges: posts were set along the radial lines of the ribs, and each panel contained a single diagonal.[4] An important feature of the Permanent Bridge was, for that time, the great height of the west pier, which extended 41 feet 9 inches below common high water. The pier was of stone masonry laid up in mortar inside a watertight cofferdam of the kind built in England by William Weston. Palmer was not a man to be modest about his virtues. He described the framing of his bridge as "a masterly piece of workmanship, combining in its principles that of king post and braces or trusses, with those of a stone arch."[5]

The structural framework of the Permanent Bridge was covered against the weather at both sides and top. This was the first time that Palmer used covering, and its rarity at that date constrained him to defend the practice to the owners:

I am an advocate for weather boarding and roofing, although there are some who say it argues much against my own interests; notwithstanding I am determined to give my opinion as appears to be right. It is sincerely my opinion that the Schuylkill Bridge will last thirty and perhaps forty years if well covered. You will excuse me in saying, that I think it would be sporting with property, to suffer this beautiful piece of architecture (as you are sometimes pleased to call it), which has been built at so great expense and danger, to fall into ruin in ten or twelve years.[6]

Palmer was indeed cautious in estimating the life-expectancy of his work in the face of the weather, but he failed to reckon with another enemy. The

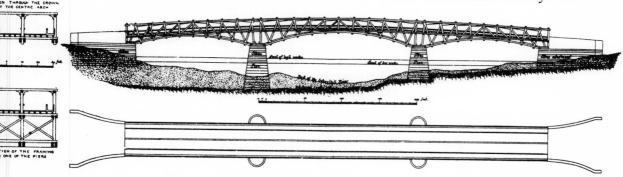

25  Top: Permanent Bridge, Schuylkill River, Philadelphia, Pennsylvania, 1806. Bottom: Bridge over the Delaware River, Easton, Pennsylvania, 1807. Timothy Palmer, builder.

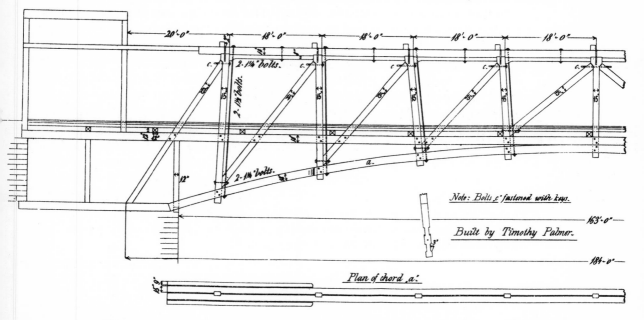

Permanent Bridge lasted about 55 years before it was destroyed by fire around 1860, while the one that followed, at Easton, Pennsylvania (1807), lasted nearly ninety years (fig. 25). There have been many covered timber bridges that stood for more than a century.[7]

By 1800 Timothy Palmer was easily the leading builder of timber bridges in the country; yet before he died in 1821, at the age of seventy, his position was being challenged by other equally inventive men. First among them was Theodore Burr, a relative of the more celebrated Aaron Burr. Although he was born in New England, he lived most of his life in Harrisburg, Pennsylvania. He began to build bridges shortly after 1800 in the form of a combination of arch and truss which he patented in 1817. The idea of combining the two structures had previously been given practical demonstration by Karl Friedrich von Wiebeking in Bavaria and Emiland Gauthey in France. It does not seem likely that the simpler Palladian truss of Palmer's bridges could have suggested the more elaborate technique. The Burr bridge consisted of two separate parts: the main member was a flat truss with parallel top and bottom chords and either single or double diagonals; distinct from it were two timber arch ribs, one on each side of the roadway, either outside or inside the truss plane. Thus the total load was distributed between the truss and the arches. Burr's chief motive was to increase the weight and strength of the Palmer bridge to meet the growing demands of commerce in the new Republic. He handled the forms with a skill that revealed a mature grasp of their structural character. But from a later standpoint his bridges were, like Palmer's, defective in one important respect, that is, the great difficulty—insuperable at the time—of making an accurate analysis of stresses in the individual members.[8]

Burr's first major bridge was built across the Hudson River at Waterford, New York (1803–4). It had four spans varying in length from a maximum of 180 feet to a minimum of 154 (fig. 26). The structural members were hand-

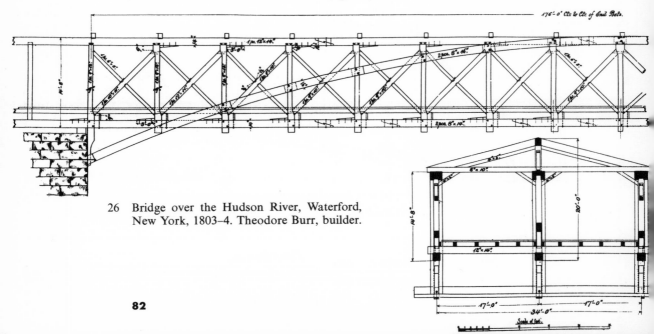

26   Bridge over the Hudson River, Waterford, New York, 1803–4. Theodore Burr, builder.

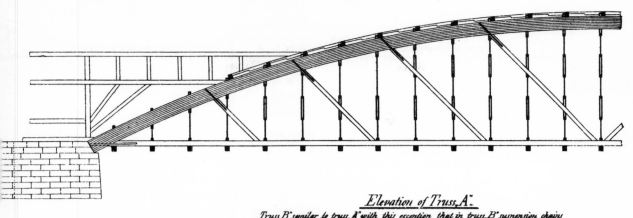

*Elevation of Truss, A.*

*Truss B similar to truss A with this exception that in truss B suspension chains occur every 16 ft. while in truss A they occur every 8 ft.*

27  Bridge over the Delaware River, Trenton, New Jersey, 1804–6. Theodore Burr, builder.

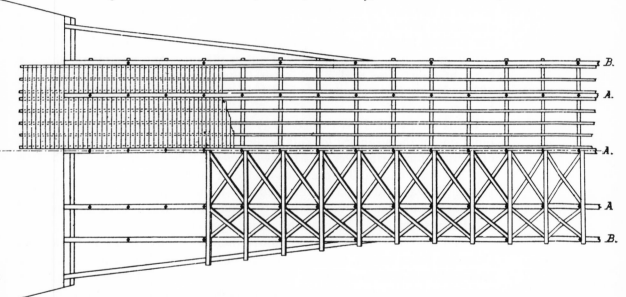

hewn white and red pine, the pins white oak, and the fasteners hand-forged wrought iron. The whole bridge was enclosed in white pine sheathing and covered by a shingle roof. The Waterford bridge stood in sound condition for over a century; it was finally cut down by fire on July 10, 1909. Before it was completed, Burr began a much more ambitious project, a five-span bridge over the Delaware River at Trenton, New Jersey, 1804–6 (fig. 27). The various spans differed considerably in length, the maximum being 203 feet. There were three parallel sets of arches and trusses, the center group dividing the deck into separate roadways. In addition to the diagonals of the truss there was a system

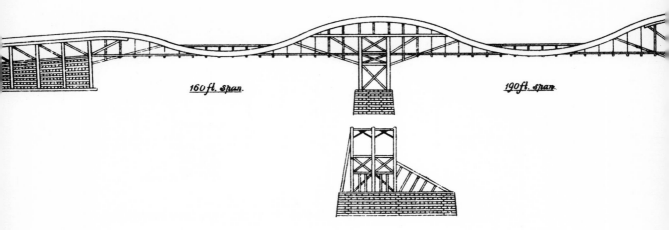

160 ft. span.    190 ft. span.

of counter-bracing whose members connected the lower chord of the truss to the arch. The lower ends of the braces were spiked to the truss chord, the upper joined to the arch by iron straps. The double roadway and two sidewalks were suspended from the arch ribs by vertical chains. The most curious feature of the Trenton bridge was the presence of wing arches set outside the main arch ribs near the pier ends and splayed out at the piers and abutments to act as wind bracing.[9] The bridge was several times repaired and strengthened, in 1832, 1848 (to carry a railroad), and 1869, before it was finally replaced by an iron truss in 1875.

In his next work Burr turned away from the combined arch-and-truss to build one of the strangest looking bridges of his or any other time, a continuous series of arch ribs over the Mohawk River at Schenectady, New York, 1808 (fig. 28). Burr had built a previous bridge at this site about which nothing is known. It was said to have collapsed and been swept away by a flood. The striking and unique characteristic of the 1808 bridge was a set of three parallel continuous ribs which formed the main supporting elements, dipping down between the piers and bowing up above them to act as arches. In his second Delaware River bridge, at Stockton, New Jersey (1812–13), he returned to the arch-and-truss combination but varied the form by using lattice trusses rather than the common variety with single or double diagonals in each panel.[10]

All of these structures may be said to have been preparation for Burr's most daring undertaking, the ill-fated McCall's Ferry Bridge over the Susquehanna River near Lancaster, Pennsylvania (1814–15). Here his courage became reckless, at the cost of his good sense. He determined to cross the 100-foot deep main channel with a single clear span 360 feet in length and to erect it from the ice when the river froze in the winter of 1814–15. It was a dangerous business, and sheer luck saw him through the construction. Burr wrote a detailed account of the project, which has been condensed into a lively description by the authors of *Engineering in History:*

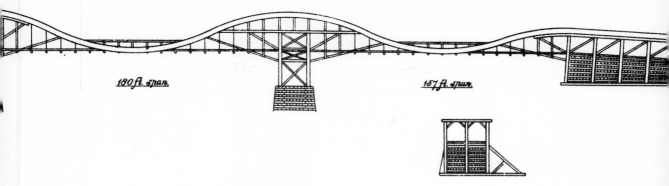

180 ft. span.    157 ft. span.

28  Bridge over the Mohawk River, Schenectady, New York, 1808. Theodore Burr, builder.

The ice was not solid; it was floating chunks from ¼ inch to 2 inches thick which had formed upstream, broken upon the rocks, packed into the narrows at the bridge site, and then plunged beneath the surface until the mass of icy particles was from 60 to 80 feet deep. By digging into it 3 feet, Burr could thrust a pole down 60 feet into the mush ice below by the mere strength of his hands. Upon this uncertain floor, rising and falling a couple of feet in a day and moving imperceptibly but steadily downstream, Burr slid his arch in halves with capstans, set them upon the abutment and the pier, drove in the keys, and cut away the scaffolding on February 1, 1815. Standing back to view his work by the light of great fires, he enjoyed the "grandest spectacle" he had ever seen—his arch "rising from the abutment and extending itself west out of sight." Although liquor was "handed round in great abundance," only one man was hurt. . . . Burr was very pleased with the quality of the workingmen from Lancaster and York Counties, and he might have added, with their good luck. Two years later the ice destroyed . . . the bridge. . . . It was never replaced.[11]

The disaster at McCall's Ferry was common enough at the time but had no adverse effect on the popularity of the Burr bridges. He continued to build them in close succession, but it was never possible to protect them against sudden destruction by ice, flood, or fire. At least two more were struck down before their useful life was ended by old age or new requirements.[12] After Burr's death bridge builders from the East coast to the Great Lakes region, having seen the merits of his massive and stable structures, continued to use his arch-and-truss form almost to the end of the century. The Virginias remained the major home of the type at least until 1880, but the last of them seem to have been built in Indiana. For all its virtues, however, the Burr bridge belonged to a vernacular building tradition that could no longer serve the needs of an industrial society. Like the contemporary structures of Town, Wernwag, and Howe, it could hardly survive in an age of steel and eventually had to go.[13]

Although the practical empiricism of the vernacular tradition was dominant until 1850, there was one early attempt to replace it with a more scientific technique. A New York architect and landscape gardener named Thomas Pope in 1811 published his *Treatise on Bridge Architecture,* the first systematic and analytical work on bridge construction to appear in the United States. Pope was a man of the eighteenth century, and he had great confidence in the possibilities of improving society by the methods of the new philosophy, as his poetic epigraph indicates:

> Exulting science now disdains
> The ties of custom's proud control,
> And breaks the rude and barbarous chains
> That fettered down the free-born soul.[14]

After this exuberant introduction Pope plunged into the main business of this naive but prophetic book. His preface contains a brief history of mechanics from Archimedes to his own day and concludes with an indictment of most contemporary work for violating "the fundamental laws of Architecture, . . . STRENGTH, SYMMETRY, and true ELEGANCE."[15] The reasons for this state of affairs, he holds, are the separation of theory and practice and the pretensions of the academicians. The text of his book is divided into four parts. The first is a historical account of different types of bridges, with an extraordinary number of examples drawn from pre-classical and classical antiquity, from primitive work in Asia and Africa, and from contemporary achievements in Europe and America. The second part is a mathematical analysis of Pope's own invention, a cantilever span which he called a "flying pendent lever bridge." This analysis is organized as an axiomatic and deductive system, after the classical manner of Archimedes, Galileo, and Newton, The third part moves into the broader field of the nature, strength, and structural possibilities of timber, stone, brick, and iron. The last part consists essentially of testimonials from the New York shipwrights on the soundness of his flying lever bridge, but he does not defend his view that they were competent to judge in the matter. The book concludes with another of his poetic flights, 210 lines of heroic couplets in lavish praise of his bridge and his country:

> Let the broad arc the spacious HUDSON stride,
> And span COLUMBIA's rivers far more wide;
> Convince the world AMERICA begins
> To foster Arts, the ancient work of Kings.[16]

Whatever one may think of Thomas Pope as a poet, there is no question about the fact that as an architect he was a rare combination of artist, engineer, and builder, a union that was to disappear as his century wore on. His own invention had real merit, although he proposed it for the fantastic project of crossing the Hudson River at New York in a single span of 3,000 feet. The main structural members of the "flying pendent lever bridge" were longitudinal ribs built up into a solid girder in the form of an extremely flat arch made up of a pair of cantilevers stiffened with diagonal bracing. The entire structure was then to be covered with diagonal sheathing. Pope made a model of his bridge on the scale of ⅜ inch to the foot, giving it a total length of 93 feet 9 inches. According to witnesses, one unsupported beam of this model was able to carry a load of 10 tons without yielding. Convinced of the soundness of his bridge, he proposed a second span to cross the East River. It is unfortunate that Pope had no opportunity to build any of his arch-cantilever bridges. They would have spanned neither the Hudson nor the East River, but the form was perfectly sound for shorter lengths and became the basis of the later cantilever bridge.[17]

While Pope experimented, a German-born carpenter and mechanic of the Philadelphia region, Lewis Wernwag, began the busiest bridge-building career of his time. Born in Riedlinger, Württemberg, Wernwag came to the United States in 1786. For twenty years, before turning to the work that made him famous, he was associated with various inventions and industrial enterprises, becoming in 1813 part owner of the Phoenix Nail Works, at Phoenixville, Pennsylvania. During the 27 years of his active life as a bridge builder, he erected 29 bridges scattered through Pennsylvania, Delaware, Maryland, Virginia, Kentucky, and Ohio. His first bridge was a 100-foot arched truss, derived with few essential changes from the Palladian trusses of Palmer's work, built to carry the New York-Philadelphia Road over the Neshaminy River in eastern Pennsylvania (1810). His intention was to build a more economical and more homogeneous structure than the Burr bridge. He advertised it as his "Economy Bridge" and claimed, most modestly it soon turned out, that it was useful for spans up to 160 feet.[18] The following year he began construction of the bridge that secured his reputation, the famous Colossus over the Schuylkill River at Fairmount Park, Philadelphia, 1812 (fig. 29). A single-span covered arched truss 340 feet in length, it was by far the longest timber span built in the United States up to its time. The main structural elements were five parallel laminated arch ribs, each 3 feet 6 inches deep, beneath the plank roadway and the two double-diagonal trusses, one on each side of the deck. The arch carried the entire dead and uniform live load in compression, the truss apparently being stressed only under eccentric loading. It was a tragedy of the building art that the graceful Fairmount bridge burned in 1838 and was never duplicated along similar lines.

Wernwag's next important bridge was built over the Delaware River at New Hope, Pennsylvania, 1813–14 (fig. 29). Here he used wrought iron diagonals in the truss panels and thus took the first step in America in the long series of experiments that eventually led to the all-iron truss.[19] His many bridges of

29 Top: The Colossus, Schuylkill River, Philadelphia, Pennsylvania, 1812. Bottom: Bridge over the Delaware River, New Hope, Pennsylvania, 1813–14. Lewis Wernwag, builder.

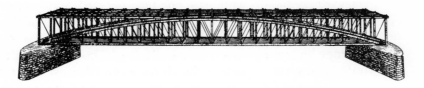

the 1820's made him the logical choice to build the first timber railway bridge. The Baltimore and Ohio Railroad in 1830 commissioned him to build the short span over a stream at Monoquay, Maryland. There is apparently no information on the structural details of this extremely important little bridge, which inaugurated framed construction for the American railway span. For railroad use, of course, Wernwag had to substitute a level for an arched deck. Whether he kept any characteristics of the arch is now impossible to tell.[20]

One of the last bridges Wernwag built became the most thoroughly investigated span dating from the heroic age of timber construction. The Kentucky River bridge at Camp Nelson, Kentucky (1838), was a 240-foot single span which differed from its progenitors in that it had three parallel trusses supporting two separate 12-foot roadways. In 1927 the Camp Nelson bridge was subjected to a complete stress analysis, which provided a thorough insight into the action of a timber span of the vernacular period.[21] The design revealed great statical exactitude; yet Wernwag had no accurate method of computing stresses in individual members. It represented a nice adaptation of form to the materials and skills available at the time and the locality. Age and heavier loads required that the bridge be strengthened in 1928, after which it continued to carry automobile traffic for several more years, thus sustaining a load far beyond the expectation of its builder. Actually the impact of heavy motor traffic was a negligible factor because of the large dead weight—260 tons—of the arched trusses. In spite of the solid strength of Wernwag's bridges, the railroad

30 Bridge over the Scioto River, Chillicothe, Ohio, 1817. Left to right, the center and north spans of a three-span bridge.

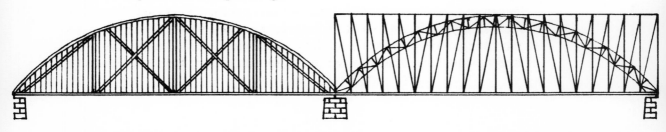

and highway builders felt safer with arch-reinforced trusses, or simple trusses composed of massive timbers. In addition, the arched deck was useless for railroad purposes and required more complex construction at the abutments to absorb the horizontal thrust of the arch. As a consequence of these factors, bridges like those of Palmer and Wernwag lost favor before the mid-century and were superseded by other types.

Although the major inventors erected a considerable proportion of the early timber bridges, there were individual carpenters throughout the East and the Great Lakes region ready to try their hands at the bridge-building art. Some of them had their own ideas on the subject and were willing to try any combination of forms that might fit the purpose. One of these in the tradition of the arched truss proved to be most prophetic of future designs, however fantastic it was in its extreme redundancy: a highway bridge over the Scioto River near Chillicothe, Ohio, 1817 (fig. 30). The three 150-foot spans represented two radically different types. The center and south spans were bowstring trusses of timber and hence anticipations of Squire Whipple's invention of 1841.[22] Not satisfied with the strength of his wooden structure, however, the builder of the Chillicothe bridge added a closely ranked series of wrought iron hangers, or suspenders, between the top and bottom chords to carry part of the roadway load. The arched top chord and the bottom chord were built-up members, while the posts were solid timbers.[23] The north span of the bridge was a combination of two distinct types with no connection between them, one a shallow arched truss, the other a rectangular structure somewhat like the iron Pratt truss with single diagonals. The arched form bore a close resemblance to the arched Howe truss which was used in railroad trainsheds after 1850. The vertical members of the north span were apparently wrought iron suspenders, all others having been built up of oak boards. The ironwork of the Chillicothe bridge was manufactured by the Juniata Iron Works of Pittsburgh and was transported to the site by pack horses and wagons. The timber was cut in the local area. The strange bridge survived until 1887, late enough to be regarded as a piece of vernacular primitivism.

## 3. TOWARD MATURE FORMS OF THE WOODEN TRUSS: THE WORK OF TOWN AND HOWE

For all the skill of Palmer and his immediate successors, their bridges possessed the complicating factor of functioning both as an arch and a truss, or more specifically, exerting both horizontal and vertical thrusts at their ends. The first to free the truss from this unnecessary dependence on the arch was the architect Ithiel Town, a most influential figure in the history of American building art. Town was born in Thompson, Connecticut, in 1784 and trained for his profession at an architectural school in Boston run by Asher Benjamin. He began his independent career in New Haven about 1810 and in 1829 formed a partnership with Alexander Jackson Davis, an association which left a deep mark on American architecture. Yet his busy career as a designer hardly exhausted Town's wide-ranging abilities. He turned his first-hand knowledge of carpentry to brilliant account in the invention of his bridge truss, wrote treatises on mathematics and steamship navigation, made himself at home in all the arts, read and traveled extensively, became one of the most cosmopolitan New Yorkers of his time and a principal figure in the city's liveliest conversational groups.

The truss which he patented in 1820, for all the multiplicity of its individual members, was actually simpler than any of its predecessors (fig. 31). It was a lattice truss, the chief feature of which was the closely spaced array of intersecting diagonals that formed the web. Without posts, it was thus not divided into panels and was used in both simple and continuous structures. It was frequently roofed and sometimes covered at the sides. The Town truss had two virtues that placed it ahead of earlier forms: although an indeterminate structure, it was a true truss, exerting only a vertical thrust, and it was easy to erect, being made up entirely of simple and common sizes of lumber requiring few bolts and metal rods. The horizontal members of the Town truss were each composed of two or more parallel timbers spaced so that the web members could be inserted tightly between them and fastened originally with wooden tree-nails. The top and bottom chords were usually built up of planks 2 to 4 inches thick and 10 to 12 inches wide. The diagonals of the web were fastened to each other, wherever they intersected, with nails. Uniformity of timber size and nailed connections meant that any carpenter could erect the truss in a short time and at a minimum of expense. In this respect it was the bridge-builder's equivalent of the balloon frame. Its popularity was thus assured. But it had one defect which could become serious in long spans: because of the thin web section and the absence of posts the truss had a tendency to warp, and as it aged it became excessively flexible through the insufficient rigidity of the nailed connections.

In the first publication on his truss (1821), Town discussed rigid iron bridges, fifteen years before the first one was built in the United States, and in his second pamphlet (1831), he explained how his own truss could be adapted to cast and wrought iron. It was not until 1859, however, that the iron form appeared.

In spite of the popularity of the Town truss, records of its construction are much scantier than those of the earlier types. One reason for this is that the bridge was widely adopted by the early railroad builders, particularly in New England, and hence had to be replaced in a short time by heavier structures because of the rapid increase in the weight of locomotives and cars. Many

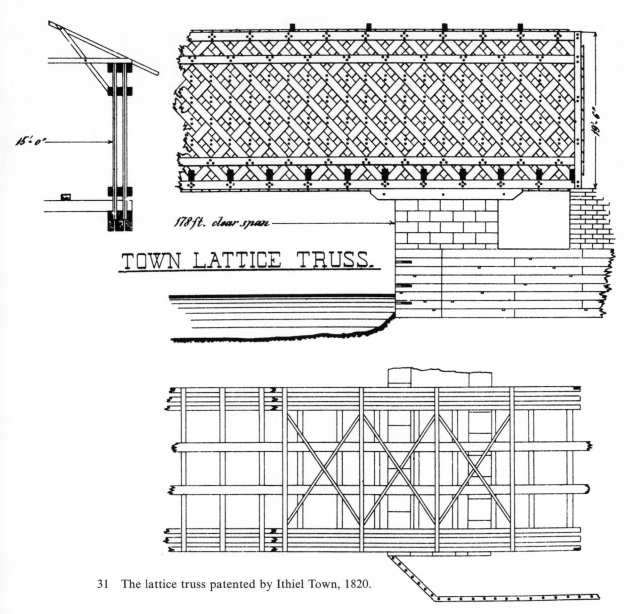

15'-0"

19'-6"

178 ft. clear span

TOWN LATTICE TRUSS.

31  The lattice truss patented by Ithiel Town, 1820.

Town trusses were built on the lines of the companies that were later merged to form the Boston and Maine system, and some survived on branch lines until well into the twentieth century. Early highway bridges, possibly dating from about 1830, were those over the Pemigewasset River, Grafton County, New Hampshire, and over the Connecticut River at Orford, New Hampshire. Both were roofed but uncovered at the sides. A completely covered bridge was built to carry the National Road over the Mad River near Springfield, Ohio, in 1837.

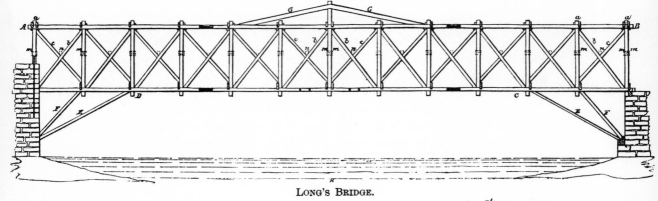

LONG'S BRIDGE.

DETAILS OF SPLICED CORD.

32  The "assisted truss" patented by Stephen H. Long, 1830.

It consisted of three 60-foot spans each carried by three parallel trusses. The center truss separated the deck into two 8-foot traffic lanes. Most of the timberwork in the structural parts of the bridge was made up of 4 by 12-inch yellow poplar boards fastened with hickory pins. The plank flooring rested on oak beams and stringers. The piers were of loose rubble masonry in cribs. When the bridge was replaced in 1933—after the National Road had become the heavily traveled U.S. Highway Number 40—all lumber was salvaged in usable condition except for the weatherboarding and the roof shingles.[1]

By 1840 it was clear that the railroad was going to place the greatest demands on the bridge builder and require an extensive reconsideration of structural forms then in use. Since wood was still the dominant material, the railroad's major need in truss construction was a form which would involve a relatively small number of members sufficiently massive to withstand the growing vertical and lateral impacts of moving locomotives. A reduction in the number of joints was necessary to reduce the number of points of maximum wear. The ideal aim was to find a form which could be erected most easily and which was a determinate structure, without any redundant members.[2] Of all the timber varieties it was the Howe truss that came closest to the ideal and as a consequence enjoyed the longest and most vigorous life in the nineteenth century. Yet in both its common forms, with either single or double diagonals between posts, it was far from novel, its precedents going back to the very beginnings of the modern truss. As in the case of Palmer's truss, it was derived directly from two of Palladio's inventions. In the United States there were several anticipations.

Stephen H. Long in 1830 patented an "assisted truss," as he called it, the main body of which consisted of a row of panels each containing two diagonals, a main and a counter, according to their later designation (fig. 32).[3] But Long, a cautious man, did not realize that he had a perfectly good truss in the primary element, and so he strengthened, or assisted, it with a king-post truss above the two center panels, the region of maximum bending moment where the truss would be most deeply deflected. He was granted two subsequent patents on the form, in 1836 and 1839, in which he dropped the redundant king-post truss. The precise form and proportioning of Long's 1839 truss suggest that he knew a valid method for calculating stresses in the members of a truss, although his description of what he called an "Improved Brace Bridge" in the patent specification does not give any details of such analysis. Of all the American builders Long most impressed the great German engineer and theorist Karl Culmann on his visit to America in 1849. Culmann tried to learn more about Long but without success. His remarks in this connection provide a penetrating description of the state of engineering in the United States at the time. "The American engineers," he wrote, "are too practical to be interested in thinking about their outstanding men. Each practical engineer considers himself the highest authority, looks down on the others and pays no attention to them."[4]

Meanwhile, as we have seen, local carpenters in various regions were carrying on their own experiments. It was in Ohio that the classic precedent of the Howe and many other bridges appeared, the so-called Y Bridge over the Muskingum and Licking rivers at Zanesville, 1831–32 (fig. 33). The bridge took its name from its Y-shaped plan: the stem crossed the Muskingum, and two

33  Y Bridge, Muskingum and Licking rivers, Zanesville, Ohio, 1831–32. Part of the trusses at a pier.

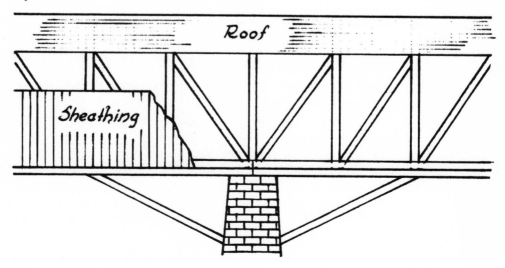

branches, spreading out at equal angles, crossed the Licking. The stem consisted of three spans of 150 feet each, and the branches of three at 115 feet each. The covered timber trusses had parallel top and bottom chords, and there was a single diagonal between the posts of each panel. The entire bridge was covered on top by a gable roof and at the sides with vertical sheathing that extended from the floor through about two-thirds the depth of the truss. This masterpiece of timber bridge construction was replaced in 1900 by a concrete structure.

It was William Howe, an uncle of Elias Howe, inventor of the sewing machine, whose truss designs were to have the greatest influence on timber bridge construction throughout the remainder of the century. Born in Spencer, Massachusetts, in 1803, he turned to bridge building about the time that Long secured his second patent.[5] His first bridge was completed in 1838 for the Boston and Albany Railroad at Warren, Massachusetts. The truss was of rectangular profile with single diagonals extending across two panels. All members were wood except for the vertical pieces, which were wrought iron rods, indicating that Howe designed them as tension members. In a later design Howe introduced a large number of diagonals which intersected each other at three points, and in 1840 he was granted two patents on this modification (fig. 34). During the following year Howe and Amasa Stone, his brother-in-law and a New England railroad builder, gave the new invention a practical demonstration on a large scale by building the bridge of the Western Railroad of Massachusetts across the Connecticut River at Springfield.[6] The seven spans were made up of deck trusses each 190 feet long and 20 feet deep. There is some confusion about the details of this bridge, but it seems to have been weatherboarded at the sides. There was no roof, of course, since the track was laid on

34   The truss patented by William Howe, July 10 and August 3, 1840.

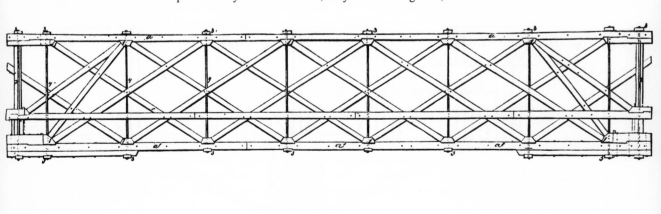

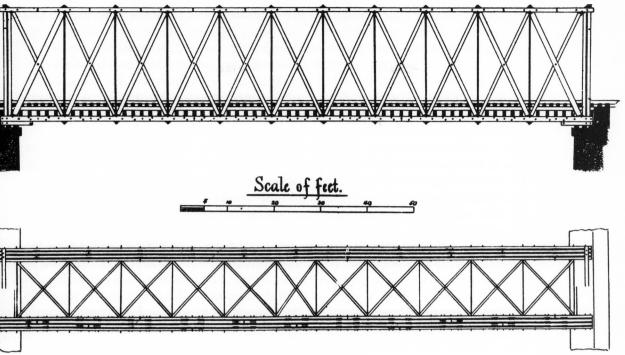

Scale of feet.

35    The Howe truss as modified by Amasa Stone, 1841.

top of the trusses. All members of the truss except for the wrought iron verticals, all transverse beams, and the decking were timber. As far as the record shows, it was the only Howe truss built in the form on which the second patent was secured.

Howe was granted his final patent in 1846 for a variation on the standard Howe-Stone truss in which a timber arch was introduced along the side of the truss between abutments to act as a reinforcing member to carry part of the load. The complete form was very much like Burr's combined arch and truss. Howe had already used it for the triangular trusses built to carry the trainshed roof of the Boston and Worcester Railroad station at Boston (1842).

In 1840 Stone and D. L. Harris founded a company at Springfield, Massachusetts, to construct bridges on the Howe patent. Either they incorporated Howe's own refinements in the direction of greater simplicity or introduced them themselves, and began to build bridges on this basis in both wood and iron (fig. 35). The form which was everywhere known as the Howe truss and which dominated the railroad timber bridge during the remainder of the century was thus first built by Stone and Harris. It was essentially the Long truss without the king-post. The rectangular profile was divided into a series of panels each of which contained two diagonals. The vertical end posts, top and bottom chords, and diagonals were heavy timbers; the vertical members between end posts were generally wrought iron rods but were sometimes also of wood. In the East the use of iron for rods and bearing blocks was nearly universal. In the West, where iron was costly and wood plentiful, the construction was entirely of timber. Some of the longer spans (180 feet or more) were strengthened with arch ribs in the manner of the 1846 patent. All connections throughout the truss were bolted.

Early in the history of the second, or common, Howe truss either Stone or an anonymous builder introduced the further refinement of reducing the number of diagonals to one in each panel, all diagonals sloping the same way in either half of the truss. Whoever accomplished this decisive improvement made the truss a determinate structure; yet the bridge builders were slow to take advantage of it. The first large bridge to be built in this manner was the immense structure that carried the tracks of the South Side Railroad over the valley of the Appomattox River at Farmville, Virginia (1851–53), the work of the railroad's chief engineer, W. O. Sanford.[7] The timber trusses of its 21 spans were carried on brick piers. The single diagonals and the deck trusses made the Farmville bridge essentially the equivalent in wood of the contemporary steel railroad bridge.[8]

From 1850 to the end of the century Howe trusses or minor variations thereon were so common that one can do little more than make a random selection of representative structures. The span length had grown to the maximum for any bridge at the time. The most spectacular of all timber railroad spans was built by Silas Seymour to carry the line of the Buffalo and New York City Railroad across the deep gorge of the Genesee River at Portage, New York, 1851–52 (fig. 36).[9] The individual Howe trusses were small, having a span of about 50 feet, but they stood at a maximum height of 234 feet above the river bed. The trusses, entirely of wood, had two diagonals in each panel, plus another pair, each of which extended from the end of the truss to the center point. The trusswork rested on a series of high timber bents which were joined by a set of horizontal ties, one above the other, that crossed from bent to bent, the whole forming a continuous system of trestlework. A system of diagonal bracing provided lateral stiffening. The bents rested on slender masonry footings. The Portage bridge was a big and daring project for its day. From a distance it must have looked like a collection of flimsy sticks, but it served the railroad satisfactorily until 1875, when it was completely destroyed by fire. It was rebuilt in iron by George S. Morison, one of the great bridge engineers of his age.[10]

The westward extension of the railroads from Chicago after 1848 soon brought the bridge builders face to face with the Mississippi River, whose shifting bed and turbulent floods posed a challenge beyond anything they previously

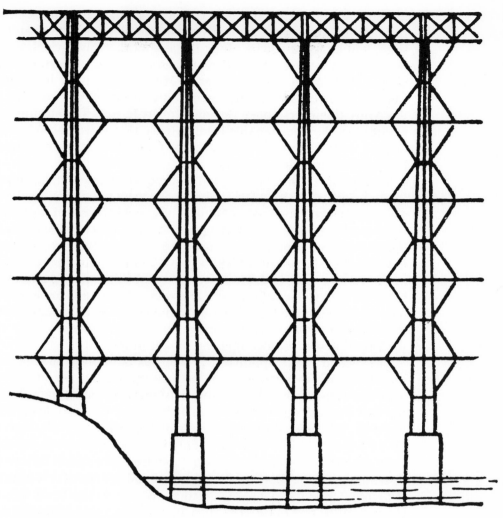

36  The timber bridge of the Buffalo and New York City Railroad, Genesee River, Portage, New York, 1851–52. Silas Seymour, engineer.

met. The first to cross it were the engineers of the Chicago and Rock Island Railroad, who built the initial span between the towns of Rock Island, Illinois, and Davenport, Iowa.[11] The history of its building is a tale of frontier techniques in business, when unscrupulousness was livelier and more colorful than it is now. Construction, which began in 1853, was hampered from the beginning by a shortage of skilled labor, even at wages of $1.25 per day. But this was a minor difficulty compared to the trouble that the steamboat lines were prepared to make. They fought the railroad with every legal weapon, then turned to the illegal. On the night of May 6, 1856, the steamer *Effie Alton* passed through the draw span, suddenly came completely about, headed for a fixed span, and struck it square along the side of the truss, which caught fire and burned away between piers. The railroad company, suspecting sabotage, hired a legal staff composed of George E. Hubbell, Norman Judd, and Abraham Lincoln. They based their arguments on a report of river currents prepared by the Army Engineers under General Robert E. Lee. The steamboat companies resorted to the questionable legal defense that it was blasphemous to build bridges over waterways provided by God. The Supreme Court, however, decided for the railroad in 1860.

Meanwhile, the huge bridge had reached its completion, having been opened in the summer of 1856. The timber spans were variations on the Howe truss, since they lacked posts, except at the ends, and had arched top chords. A closer form would be the double-diagonal Warren truss.[12] There were six spans divided into two separate and unequal groups by Rock Island, from which the town takes its name and which lies close to the Illinois shore. It is still the site of a government arsenal. There were longer bridges than the Rock Island span, but none with trusses of such size and with so many difficulties of construction, natural and contrived.[13] The steamboat companies must have felt temporarily vindicated in 1868, when the bridge was largely destroyed by a tornado, but the structure was soon completely rebuilt in iron.

The second Mississippi River bridge was built between Clinton, Iowa, and Fulton, Illinois, over two different periods separated by an interval of five years, a division made possible by another island near midstream. The crossing of the east channel was completed in 1859 by the Chicago, Iowa and Nebraska Railway. It consisted of seven spans of McCallum trusses, derived from the Howe truss and differing from it only in the arched top chord (fig. 37). They were about 200 feet long and were constructed entirely of wood except for fastenings and the diagonals in the third and fourth panels from each end of the truss.[14] For the remainder of the crossing to the Iowa side, trains were carried on car ferries. In 1862 the Chicago, Iowa and Nebraska was leased to the Galena and Chicago Union Railroad, which then began construction of the west channel crossing, completing it in 1864.[15] The later structure consisted of three fixed Howe trusses varying from 175 to 200 feet in length and one swing span 300 feet long which was a Howe truss reinforced with a double set of wrought iron diagonals radiating out from the upper corners of the truss.[16] The Clinton bridge was a sound work of the builder's art, but the railroad company, probably fearing a repetition of the Rock Island disaster, began a progressive replacement of the spans with iron Pratt trusses in 1869. The engineers did not feel a sense of urgency, however, because the reconstruction was not finally completed until 1898.

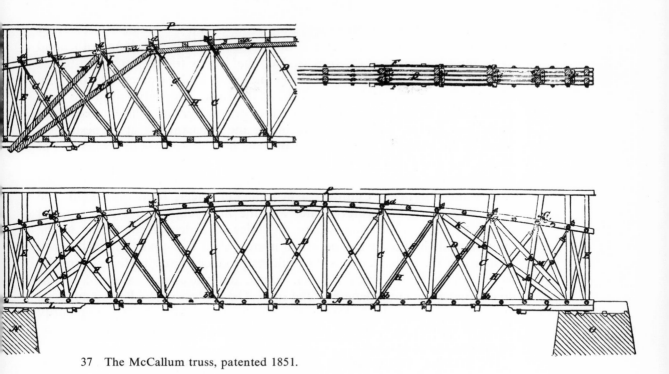

37   The McCallum truss, patented 1851.

The Howe truss reached its high point with the construction of the Susque-hanna River bridge of the Philadelphia, Wilmington and Baltimore Railroad at Havre de Grace, Maryland (1862–66).[17] This great structure, designed by the railroad's chief engineer, George A. Parker, had few competitors for size among the timber bridges of its time. The extreme width of the river near its mouth required a bridge nearly a mile in over-all length. The main portion of it embraced twelve spans, each about 300 feet long and 50 feet deep. The deck trusses were reinforced with huge arch ribs, two on each side of the truss. All members were wood except for the vertical rods of wrought iron. For all its size and strength, however, the bridge lasted only eleven years, hav-ing been replaced in 1877 by an iron structure.

The decade of the Havre de Grace bridge saw the construction of the largest number of Howe trusses and their initial appearance in the far West, where they continued to be used up to about 1910, well after their useful life was over in the more densely settled parts of the country. The first transcontinen-tal railroad line was being steadily pushed east and west from its two termi-nals, the Union Pacific working west from Omaha, Nebraska, and the Central Pacific east from Oakland, California. After seven years of construction the two tracks met at Promontory Point, Utah, in 1869.

Between the Missouri River and the Pacific Ocean the builders faced every physical obstacle in its extreme form. Armies of men, working with hand tools, built bridges over canyons so deep that flimsy timber bents had to rise 300 feet to support the track, or along mountain walls so steep that the base of every footing had to be carved out of the rock. They labored in the West under killing desert heat, in the East under prairie blizzards that buried whole trains and camps, and everywhere under the constant threat of pestilence. None of the scores of bridges was especially notable for size or refinement of design, but every one was the product of a bitter and often fatal struggle. The Sierras proved the most formidable challenge and tested to the ultimate the energy and skill of the Central Pacific's chief engineer, Theodore Judah. The most striking of his achievements was the arch-reinforced Howe truss at Lower Cascade, California, where the sides of a deeply cut ravine in the mountainside had to be carved into a narrow shelf to support the abutments. In many of the wider canyons the builders produced amazing feats of trestle-work, densely built frames of posts, beams, and braces that extended continuously under the entire length of the span. The bridges of the Pacific railroads marked a climax in the history of the wooden truss. After 1870 its popularity declined rapidly as iron and steel took the place of wood to carry the ever-increasing traffic loads.[18]

The eventual disappearance of the timber truss did not mean that wood gave way completely to iron and concrete as a structural material for bridges. Other forms, some of great antiquity, never died out. The simple pile-and-beam bridge was the predecessor of hundreds of railroad spans made up of timber girders resting on pile bents. Although usually confined to crossings over small streams, the type was sometimes employed for much longer structures. The record, never likely to be broken, was reached by the 13-mile trestle built by the Southern Pacific Railroad to carry its Lucin Cut-off over part of Great Salt Lake (1903). Fifteen miles of the lake crossing lie on an earth and rock fill, which the company began to extend in 1956 over the remaining distance. It marked the end of the famous bridge.

There were other experiments in timber bridge construction which laid the basis for important twentieth-century techniques. The arch rib, emancipated from association with the truss, appeared in the 1840's. One of the earliest was the Broadway bridge across the Pawtucket Canal at Lowell, Massachusetts (1846). Each of its pair of ribs was a segmental arch consisting of two braces springing from the abutments and supporting a horizontal girder between them. The deck was laid on transverse beams set on posts rising from the main ribs. The bridge was built on a skew spanning 62 feet on the upstream side, with an over-all width of 51 feet. It carried streetcars toward the end of its life, a load which required its replacement by a steel structure in 1920.

A true arch-rib span, revealing a fully developed mastery of the form, was the Cascade Bridge of the New York and Erie Railroad near Susquehanna, Pennsylvania (1847–48), the work of the Erie's chief engineer, John Fowler. The span of 250 feet was unusually long for the time. The chief structural elements were eight massive parallel arch ribs of white oak springing from masonry abutments. The ribs were interlaced and stiffened laterally by a system of wood and iron bracing. The deck rested on spandrel posts with diagonal braces.[19] The Cascade Bridge was an exact forerunner of the steel arch in its mature form, which it reached only at the end of the nineteenth century. Although the structure was perfectly sound, its strength was questioned, probably because no one had seen a bridge of such length carried exclusively on timber arches. It came to be regarded as a bad advertisement for the railroad and within a decade it was demolished. The line was relocated to avoid the deep ravine which the bridge had spanned. The timber arch was rare in the nineteenth century, but it enjoyed something of a revival in the twentieth. It found its major use, however, in the construction of wide-span vaults in buildings.

The movable bridge forms a special category whose distinguishing features were the work of the mechanic rather than the carpenter. It had medieval origins, and although it was first used for the purpose of protection, it was later built wherever spans provided insufficient clearance over waterway traffic. The spread of railroad lines after 1830, along with the presence of an extensive system of waterways, required a growing number of movable bridges capable of carrying heavy vehicular traffic. The medieval drawbridge, generally of plank-and-beam construction, was the chief precedent for the type. An early example of the traditional form for fairly wide streams was the first movable span in Chicago, the Dearborn Street bridge, built in 1834. It was a double-leaf structure, each half of which was raised separately by winch and chain. The mechanism of this bridge frequently jammed, sometimes holding up traffic for as much as two days. After six years of such delays the citizens of the town, their patience exhausted, forced the city council to replace it by the simple expedient of destroying it. It was the inauspicious beginning of a program of construction that eventually gave the level city, with its enormous network of streets, railroads, and canals, the greatest concentration of movable bridges in the world.

The hand-operated drawbridge of planks, however, proved unsatisfactory for railroad service. The problem was to find a sufficiently heavy form which would move easily and fit accurately between approaches without sacrifice of safety. It was first solved in 1835 by the builders of the Boston and Lowell Railroad, whose tracks had to cross the Charles River close to the Boston station. The bridge consisted of a plank-and-beam deck resting on several parallel wooden trusses tightly laced together, the whole structure hinged at the corner of one end. A system of cables radiating from the top of a tower to points along the length of the bridge made it possible to swing the span in a horizontal plane to a position along shore parallel to the river channel, thus providing a narrow opening for the passage of vessels. The operation was by hand power. This structure was the forerunner of the jackknife bridge, and crude as it was, it survived for nearly a century. The several companies which were later merged to form the Boston and Maine Railroad built their Boston terminals adjacent to that of the Lowell line. As a consequence, over the succeeding two decades four more bridges of similar construction were built side by side next to the original span.[20] These antiques of the bridge-building art carried one of the greatest volumes of passenger traffic in the United States until 1931, when they were replaced by four steel bascule bridges during construction of the present North Station.

The first true jackknife bridge, according to its inventor, was patented in 1849 by Joseph Ross, a Massachusetts contractor for earthwork, masonry, and timber construction. The first such bridge had been built in 1845 for the Eastern Railroad at Manchester, Massachusetts, by Joseph Ross and Samuel Ashburner, the latter a draftsman for the railroad company. It is difficult to determine, however, in what way the Manchester bridge differed from the Charles River span of 1835, since both swung in a horizontal plane by means of chains or cables. Ross built a number of movable bridges for the Boston and Maine, but they were progressively replaced by steel bascule spans beginning in 1890. The major defects of the horizontal jackknife were the difficulty of moving large spans and the fact that it seriously constricted the waterway passage in open position. The latter not only hampered the movement of vessels but exposed the bridge to damage from collision. The useful characteristic was swing in a horizontal plane, which made it unnecessary to lift the weight of the truss. To preserve the advantage and partially avoid the defect, the builders, about 1850, adapted the center-pivoted swing span to railroad use. These quickly proved their value in the Mississippi River bridges and were built in spans of great length. But the center pier and the open span also proved a hazard to navigation and left the truss exposed to damage.

For relatively narrow waterways there was no way of avoiding a return to the lift bridge, but two inventions were necessary for its satisfactory use. One was the balanced span, either bascule or vertical lift, the counterbalancing of which made it possible to raise the great weight with a minimum of power. The other was the electric motor. Both were available by 1890, when steel bascule and lift bridges began to be substituted for other types. For extremely heavy spans the straight lift bridge proved to be the best, although it is a costly form because of the high towers between which the span rises.[21]

# IV

# THE IRON BRIDGE TRUSS

## 1. THE FIRST IRON BRIDGES

The same demands that led to the substitution of iron for wood in buildings lay behind its use in bridges—strength, durability, and fire resistance. Its great advantages over stone masonry are its high tensile strength and elasticity, physical properties non-existent for practical purposes in unreinforced masonry, and the ease with which it can be worked. It was the railroad that made the nineteenth century the age of iron, and the rapid growth of the new system of transportation made the iron bridge a matter of necessity from the second decade of railroad construction. Since wood has certain physical properties comparable on a lower scale to those of iron, the bridge builders took over the techniques and forms of timber construction with little change. The chief difference was a saving of material made possible by the use of thin rods for members subjected only to tension. The approach of the American builder was again characterized by that forthright anti-traditional empiricism which always seemed to astonish the European. In the United States the criteria of adequate construction were always pragmatic, seldom either scientific or aesthetic: the minimum of material consistent with safety; the most rapid and efficient means of construction; design for expansion and relocation rather than permanence. It was a simple program, and if it seldom produced finished structural art, it could at least satisfy the demands of immediate mechanical utility. The great defect in it was that the science of ferrous metallurgy in the United States lagged far behind the requirements of construction. Carelessness and irresponsibility too often characterized the rapid expansion of wealth. The consequence was that the history of the iron bridge in the nineteenth century was to a melancholy extent a history of disaster. By 1875, however, the methods of science were applied to the techniques of construction, and the series of tragedies were eventually brought to an end.

The first man in the United States to see the need for and to appreciate the possibilities of the iron bridge was Tom Paine, who made several models of a 400-foot cast iron arch in 1786. The only iron bridge in existence at the time was the arch built by Abraham Darby and John Wilkinson over the River Severn at Coalbrookdale, in western England (1775–79). But half a century passed before Paine's project bore fruit. The first American bridge of iron was an arch span built to cross Dunlap's Creek at Brownsville, Pennsylvania, in 1836.[1] The initial proposal to use iron, however, had come three years earlier. In 1833 August Canfield of Paterson, New Jersey, was granted a patent for an iron bridge of such curious hybrid form as to be difficult to characterize (fig. 38). At first inspection it would appear to be a truss, but a consideration of the materials and the way Canfield used them suggests that he was guided in part by the principle of the suspension bridge, which was less of a novelty then than an iron truss. The top and bottom chords and the vertical tension members, or suspenders, were wrought iron. A single diagonal of cast iron was set between each pair of suspenders. Unmistakable evidence of the suspension principle is the fact that Canfield extended the top chord not between end posts, as would be the case in a truss, but between the side walls of the abutments, which were raised to a height sufficient to make this possible. Further, the top chord was anchored, through a hook-and-eye connection, to a long downward curving wrought iron rod imbedded in the abutment masonry. The Canfield bridge may thus be described as a flat suspension rod under tension from which a truss was hung.

The first iron truss to be constructed in the United States followed mainly from Canfield's patent and was again a combination of truss and suspension forms. In 1840 Earl Trumbull built a highway bridge of 77-foot span across the Erie Canal at Frankford, New York, the design for which he patented in the following year (fig. 39). The chief difference between this structure and Canfield's was that the suspension rod of the Frankford span was not anchored in masonry but attached to the end posts.[2] The significant detail of Trumbull's bridge was that the two main structural parts were securely connected throughout their length. To accomplish this successfully Trumbull must have made a very nice calculation of the shape of his parabola and have had great confidence in his prediction of the distribution of load between the two major elements. The structure was radically indeterminate, and it is difficult to decide what action he might have attributed to the truss.

38   The truss patented by August Canfield, 1833.

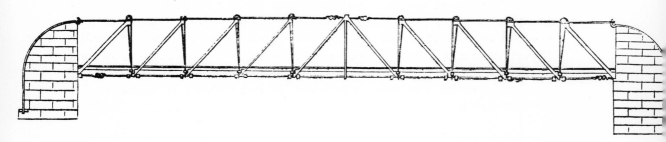

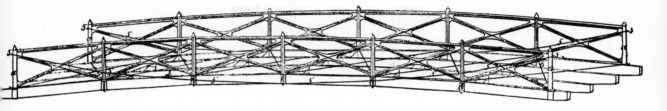

39  The truss patented by Earl Trumbull, 1841.

The designs of Canfield and Trumbull undoubtedly grew from two sources, the wrought iron chain suspension bridges of James Finley, and the growing number of wooden trusses which were being constructed at the time.[3] The deliberate choice to combine the two reveals a common error of the early nineteenth-century bridge builders; namely, the belief that one can add the total loads that two different bridges are capable of supporting by simply superimposing one bridge upon the other. The builders of the first iron railroad bridges, however, seem to have been skeptical of the validity of this notion, and certainly they had little enthusiasm for the costs involved. Their usual practice was to adopt a single form for a particular bridge, but that was often the only clear intention they had in mind. The early history of iron structures was frequently marked by trial and error methods, arbitrary adoptions and rejections, irresponsibility, and catastrophe.

The first man to build an iron railroad bridge in the United States was Richard Osborne of Philadelphia, who constructed a small one for the Philadelphia and Reading Railroad at Manayunk, Pennsylvania, in 1845. The bridge spanned 34 feet and consisted of three parallel Howe trusses, located at the sides and the center to carry a double-track line. The truss was of standard form, with two diagonals in each panel. Its over-all length was 38 feet, a good part of each end panel being carried by the paired bearings resting on the abutment wall. The depth of the outside trusses was only 3 feet 7 inches, the center one no more than 3 feet. The two diagonals, regarded as compression members, were cast iron, while top and bottom chords and vertical members were wrought iron. The presence of wrought iron in the top chord is puzzling, since it could only be subjected to compression. Osborne thus followed the wooden prototype with respect to the web members, but elsewhere it is not clear how he regarded the distinction between tensile and compressive elements. The arrangement was to be much improved in the Pratt truss. But whatever its defects, from Osborne's little span grew the vast proliferation of iron and steel railroad trusses, which became so familiar in the United States that they seemed like natural features, omnipresent and permanent.[4]

The iron truss was no sooner launched, however, than the builders began to look for other forms that might be more reliable in action under train loads and more easily erected. A major factor in this further search was again the realization that the tensile strength of cast iron has a comparatively low limit. As a consequence, there were early essays in the use of wrought iron for all members, or in forms much different from the truss. Of these the most important was the plate-girder span, the first of which was built by James Milholland for the Baltimore and Susquehanna Railroad at Bolton Station, Maryland, in 1846–47.[5] A single-track deck-girder bridge, it extended a total length of 54 feet with a clear span of 50 feet between abutments (fig. 40). The main structural members were two pairs of parallel built-up plate girders, of great depth for the short span, supporting a series of closely spaced transverse timber beams which in turn carried the track stringers.[6] The structure

40  Bridge of the Baltimore and Susquehanna Railway, Bolton Station, Maryland, 1846–47. James Milholland, engineer.

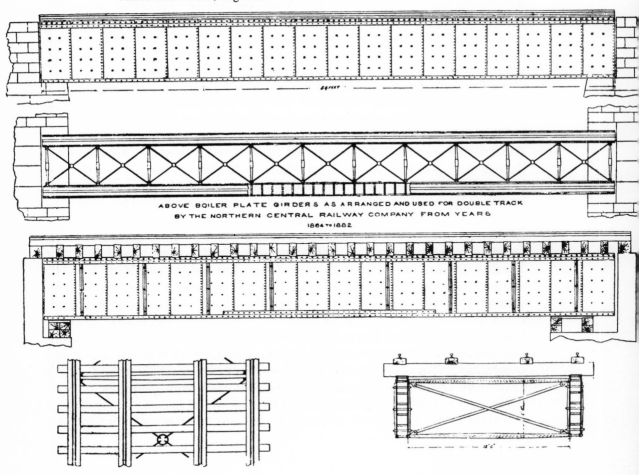

ABOVE BOILER PLATE GIRDERS AS ARRANGED AND USED FOR DOUBLE TRACK BY THE NORTHERN CENTRAL RAILWAY COMPANY FROM YEARS 1864 to 1882

was completely fabricated at some distance from the site, slung from a temporary wooden truss by chains, and lashed down to a pair of platforms on freight car trucks. This precarious load was then hauled 19 miles to the site, the existing timber bridge cut away, the plate-girder span lowered to position, and the rails spiked down. The whole operation at the site was accomplished in two hours. This method of transporting and installing fabricated sections of a new bridge has been used by the railroads ever since. Milholland thus established the girder bridge as a practical type for short spans, and in time it became the only serious competitor of the truss for railroad use.[7]

In spite of inadequate knowledge of the physical properties of iron and of the distribution of stresses in an iron or timber truss, there was growing enthusiasm among some of the railroad builders for making practical use of it. Because of its great success as a wooden structure, the Howe truss was the inevitable choice for early truss bridges on the railroads. In 1846 Frederick Harbach, of New England origin, patented a variation of the Howe truss based on a different estimate of the distribution of tensile and compressive stresses. The top chord and diagonals of the truss were cast iron, all except the counter-diagonals in the form of hollow cylinders, while the bottom chord and the vertical members were wrought iron. The bottom chord was a hollow tube built up of riveted iron plates. The first Harbach truss was built by the Western Railroad at Pittsfield, Massachusetts (1846–47).

Between 1847 and 1850 Nathaniel Rider, a New York builder, constructed several modified Harbach trusses for the New York and Harlem and the New York and Erie railroads.[8] Rider followed the original model closely but enjoyed a short-lived success. In 1849 and 1850 two of his bridges on the Erie failed—bad enough in themselves but made worse by the fact that the failures followed shortly after the collapse of an iron bridge over the River Dee in England. Karl Culmann saw the results of one of these catastrophes, and his criticism of Rider's methods as well as of his bridges suggests that the American engineer had a most inadequate sense of responsibility. Culmann made the charge that Rider was exclusively interested in making money from his invention and cared nothing about improving his design. He held that the truss was seriously defective in the insufficient rigidity of the compressed top chord, which resulted in lateral buckling of the chord and consequent failure of the structure. The Erie officials decided to take no further chances. On the belief that iron bridges of any kind were untrustworthy, they not only called a halt to all plans for future construction in the material, but ordered that all existing structures (which included Whipple as well as Harbach and Rider trusses) be replaced with wooden spans. The order apparently stood until 1865, when Post built the first of his trusses for the Erie.[9]

Amasa Stone was one of the pioneers in the substitution of wrought iron

41    Bridge of the Cleveland, Painesville and Ashtabula Railroad, Ashtabula, Ohio, 1865.

for cast in the Howe truss.[10] In 1865, as president of the Cleveland, Painesville and Ashtabula Railroad, he authorized the construction of a single-span
Howe deck truss over a stream at Ashtabula, Ohio, and undoubtedly had a
hand in the design of its prototypes (fig. 41).[11] All members of the truss were
wrought iron except for the cast iron bearing blocks. For a single span the
Ashtabula bridge was a sizable structure: the two parallel trusses, carrying a
double track line, were 154 feet long, 19 feet 9 inches deep, and spaced 16
feet 6 inches on centers. It was a bold design, prompted by the new enthusiasm for wrought iron, but it was destined for a terrible fate. At eight o'clock
on the night of December 29, 1876, after a prolonged Lake Erie blizzard, an
11-car train with two locomotives crossed the bridge westbound. When the
pilot truck of the first engine reached the west abutment, the leading engineer
felt the bridge sink under him. He opened the throttle wide and got his own
engine across. Behind him the whole structure went down, carrying the second
locomotive, two tenders, and several cars with it. It was the worst bridge disaster of the century in the United States. Smashed cars, wind, cold, snow, and
fire took 92 lives. Of the remaining passengers hardly one escaped uninjured.
The final victim was Stone himself. Broken in physical and mental health, in part
as a result of the charges laid against him, he took his own life in 1883. Yet
as bad as it was, the investigation that followed ushered in a new age, which
at last saw the possibility of ending such catastrophes. The precise point of
initial failure was quickly found: the top chord of one truss sheared through
at a point 23 feet from the west end. The iron itself was defective, but more

than this was involved. The bridge had been subjected to heavy snow and wind loads, hazards in themselves, even before the structure had to meet the impact of a long double-headed train. It took one more accident like that at Ashtabula—the collapse of the Firth of Tay bridge in Scotland (1879)—to make everything perfectly clear.

The program for adequate bridge design henceforth had to include a comprehensive scientific investigation of all the variables that enter into the problem. To begin with, mill and construction workers had to be carefully trained and supervised, and their work submitted to regular, thorough, and honest inspection. In the field the engineer's first responsibility was investigation of the geological and topographic characteristics of the site. He was next obligated to learn all that he could of meteorological conditions—snow and rainfall, ice formations in streams, the frequency and magnitude of floods, the maximum wind velocities, and the extremes of temperature. The manufacturer had the responsibility for making metallurgical analyses and testing sample pieces. With all these factors behind him, the engineer was then in a position to design his bridge, not on the basis of rule-of-thumb practice but according to the most advanced theories of stress analysis and strength of materials. Society itself had the final responsibility: to fix by law standards of safety and workmanship, to establish decent wages and working conditions, and to enforce such requirements by the appropriate legal techniques. By 1890, after fifty years of preparation, the technical part of iron bridge construction reached this level, but a good many more years had to pass before ethical demands were to some degree translated into laws backed by the authority of the state. This part of the problem, of course, is never finally solved.

## 2. PRATT AND WHIPPLE TRUSSES

The creator of what the modern engineer would call the first scientifically designed truss was Thomas Pratt of Boston, who was the most thoroughly educated American bridge builder at the beginning of the railroad age. He was, in fact, a completely trained engineer insofar as the educational institutions of his native land could make him one. He was born in 1812, the son of the Boston architect Caleb Pratt, who began the boy's education in early childhood. By the age of twelve Thomas was preparing plans in his father's office. Two years later he went to Rensselaer Polytechnic Institute in Troy, New York, where he studied architecture, building construction, mathematics, and natural science. Rensselaer offered him an instructorship before he was twenty, but he chose to join the United States Army Engineers on the construction of the dry docks of Charleston, South Carolina, and Norfolk, Virginia. He must have remained with the Engineers for no more than three

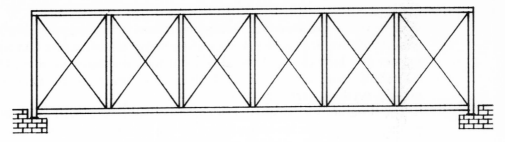

42    The first truss designed by Thomas Pratt, 1842.

years, for in 1833 he began the career that continued to his death in 1875, that of bridge and general structural engineer for a number of New England railroad companies which were later absorbed into the Boston and Maine and the New Haven systems. It was early in his railroad career that he invented the trusses since associated with his name.

Thomas Pratt's first truss, which he probably designed about 1842, was a modification of the Stone-Howe form. It was rectangular in over-all profile; the posts and top and bottom chords were timber, and the double diagonals were wrought iron (fig. 42). This form was distinguished from the Howe truss in the fact that Pratt treated the posts as compression and the diagonals as tension members. His chief purpose in placing the posts in compression was to shorten compression members as much as possible in order to reduce lateral buckling. In 1844 he and his father were granted a joint patent on a truss with either parallel chords or polygonal top chord, which they proposed for construction in a combination of wood and iron or iron alone (fig. 43). In the truss as ordinarily designed, the posts and top chord were in compression,

43    The trusses patented by Thomas and Caleb Pratt, 1844.

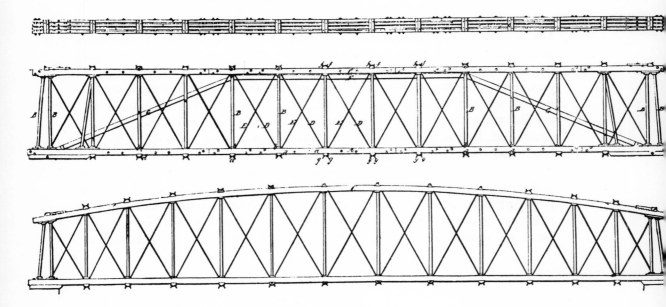

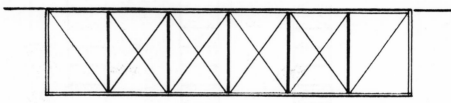

44 Simplifications of the Pratt truss developed in the latter part of the nineteenth century. Top: Deck truss. Bottom: Through truss.

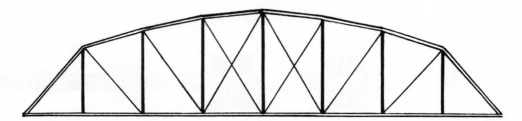

the bottom chord, diagonals, and end posts in tension, with the posts probably functioning only as supports for the top chord. In a through truss supported at the level of the bottom chord, however, the end posts would be in compression and all posts would be important bearing members. The design was superior to Howe's mainly in the more functional distribution of tensile and compressive stresses in the various members. Later simplifications of the Pratt truss, in which the diagonals were reduced to a single one in all but the center panel, came to be widely used for iron and steel bridges, but by this time it had a number of successful competitors (fig. 44).

The first group of iron Pratt trusses was built by the Pennsylvania Railroad, the earliest dating from 1850, when this rapidly expanding company adopted iron bridge construction for its lines in Pennsylvania. The engineers apparently distrusted it, however, for they not only chose wood for the largest structures but often fell back on the technique of strengthening iron bridges with separate arch ribs on either side of the truss span. In the construction of the iron truss they followed what soon came to be the customary distinction between cast and wrought iron members. By 1870, however, the standard Pratt truss, without special reinforcing, was becoming a common feature on the Pennsylvania Railroad and its numerous affiliates.[1]

The most spectacular bridge with Pratt trusses was the second, or iron, bridge of the Erie Railroad at Portage, New York, which took the place of the wooden structure destroyed by fire in 1875. It was one of the many triumphs of George S. Morison, who was at that time assistant to Octave Chanute, chief

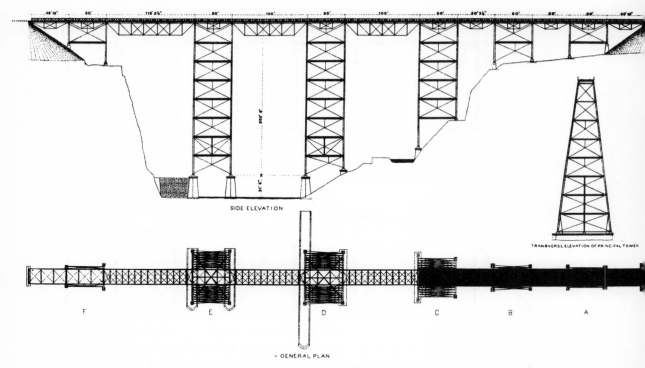

SIDE ELEVATION

TRANSVERSE ELEVATION OF PRINCIPAL TOWER

- GENERAL PLAN

F      E      D      C      B      A

45   Iron bridge of the Erie Railroad, Genesee River, Portage, New York, 1875. George S. Morison, engineer. Side elevation and plan.

engineer of the Erie. The bridge is still in use, its site now within the boundaries of Letchworth State Park (fig. 45). The thirteen cast and wrought iron spans are composed of Pratt deck trusses with double diagonals in the center panels. What is remarkable about the bridge is the extensive iron trestlework of high bents which take the place of the conventional piers. The ends of two adjacent spans rest on a single pair of wrought iron columns set side by side, the ends of two adjacent trusses thus falling on one column. Alternate groups of four such columns are laced together by horizontal wrought iron beams and by a double set of diagonal rods in each panel formed by the beams. In place of piers, then, the bridge is carried on a series of six four-post bents, or trestles, of extraordinary size. Their unusual width resulted from the fact that the structure was built for two tracks, although only one was laid.[2] Morison's design of the trusses and the bents was based on careful calculations of wind as well as traffic loads.[3] Perhaps the most impressive of the facts associated with the Portage bridge is that the whole structure was erected in 82 days, between May 10 and July 31, 1875. It was a powerful demonstration of what the bridge builder could do, and given the unusual height of the structure, it was as significant as great length of span for the advancement of the art.

By the time of the Portage bridge, the Pratt truss was being used in large bridges wherever the railroad had penetrated, although it was never as popular as the Whipple truss and was frequently confined to the shorter spans of the bridge approach. It had reached the Mississippi River before 1870. When the Galena and Chicago Union Railroad began the progressive replacement of the timber spans in its Mississippi bridge at Clinton, Iowa (1869), cast and wrought iron Pratt trusses took their place. The most important bridge in which the designer made use of Pratt's invention was the Chicago and Alton's Missouri River bridge at Glasgow, Missouri (1878–79), one approach of which was carried on steel and wrought iron Pratt deck trusses. The Whipple trusses of the river crossing were the first all-steel spans in the United States.[4] By 1900 the steel Pratt truss was firmly established, but during the nineteenth century it could hardly compete with the Whipple truss for long-span bridges.

By far the most widely known and respected of all American bridge engineers for both his practical and theoretical contributions is Squire Whipple. He was born in Hardwick, Massachusetts, in 1804 and moved to Otsego County, New York, in 1817, in the immediate area of which he lived most of his long life. Up to 1830 he engaged in a variety of activities that included study at Fairfield Academy and Union College, farming, and school teaching. He found his true bent in the early 1830's, when he became a surveyor for the Baltimore and Ohio Railroad. From here he went to the position of surveyor for the Erie Canal and thence to that of resident engineer for the New York and Erie Railroad. He had already made improvements in surveying instruments and had invented a lock for weighing canal boats (1840) by the time he turned to the design of bridges, the activity that occupied him until his death in 1888. He was granted his first bridge patent in 1841 for what later came to be called the bowstring truss, although he referred to it as an arch truss (fig. 46). Its distinguishing feature was a polygonal top chord which arched upward from the ends of the bottom chord at the abutments and was apparently designed to function as an arch as well as a truss member. The panels ordinarily contained two diagonals, but in a few cases they were limited to one. Top and bottom chords were of cast iron, with the top designed to be in compression; vertical and diagonal members were of wrought iron in tension. Whipple built the first bridge of this kind in central New York in 1841–42, but he does not indicate exactly where or for what purpose.

46   The bowstring truss patented by Squire Whipple, 1841.

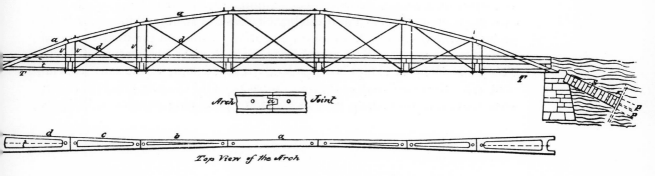

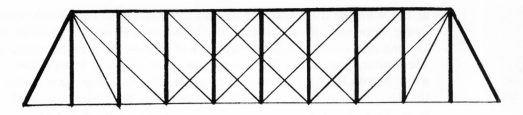

47  Top: The trapezoidal truss patented by Squire Whipple, 1847. Bottom: A modification designed by John W. Murphy, 1863.

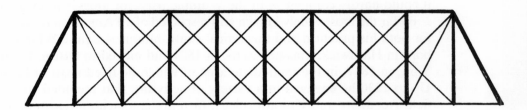

In 1846 he designed the truss which played an enormous part in railroad bridge construction and obtained a patent on it in the following year (fig. 47). Everywhere known as the Whipple truss, it appeared with many minor variations on the basic pattern of parallel chords, inclined end posts, closely spaced intermediate verticals, and diagonals each of which extended across two panels. Posts and top chord were cast, the other members wrought iron. In many bridges the diagonals were doubled at the center panels. In 1863 John W. Murphy, chief engineer of the Lehigh Valley Railroad, redesigned Whipple's original invention as an all-wrought iron pin-connected truss (fig. 47).[5] Karl Culmann found the Whipple truss superior in its rigidity to any other iron truss he investigated at the time of his American visit (1849). The German engineer felt that it was not only a sound truss under ordinary conditions of railroad loading but also that its compressed top chord was stable under lateral thrusts because of adequate bracing in the horizontal plane. Culmann's verdict, as well as Murphy's improvements, was one factor that led to the later widespread adoption of the Whipple truss for long-span railroad bridges.

Not only did Whipple invent functional trusses, but he was foremost among his American contemporaries in understanding the nature of truss action. This knowledge he set forth in a now celebrated classic of structural theory, *A Work on Bridge Building* (1847), a pioneer scientific treatise on the distribution of stresses in the members of a truss.[6] Four years after the publication of Whipple's book, Herman Haupt independently reached some of the same conclusions in his *General Theory of Bridge Construction* (1851)—proof that the earlier work had little immediate influence among practicing engineers. Whipple recognized that a bridge in the form of a truss or an arch is necessary wherever a simple beam is insufficient to sustain the required load and wherever the condition of the ground or the uses of a stream are such that intermediate supports cannot be built. In the case of the truss he understood that it is a rigid body made up of oblique and rectangular members and that the load must be distributed through the joints to the separate members without ambiguity.[7] What follows is a presentation of the mechanical and mathematical principles on which accurate stress analysis in a truss rests. They are, first, that the load on individual members must be axial, or transmitted through them in an axial direction; second, that the forces transmitted must lie in the same plane and meet at single points, joint by joint; and third, that for the purpose of analysis forces in oblique members must be resolved into horizontal and vertical components.[8] Whipple analyzed stresses in the individual members for a uniformly distributed dead load, then added to these the stresses resulting from moving loads, which he calculated by finding the most unfavorable position of the live load for the truss as a whole.

The remainder of the treatise forms a handbook of bridge construction. Whipple gives complete analyses of trusses of statically determinate designs common at the time for a varying number of panels, and makes an approximate analysis of arches. He investigates at length the form, strength, and construction of iron bridges, both arch and truss, and makes a comparison of the merits of different types of trusses. After discussing iron bridges, he takes up wooden bridges, both arch and truss. He concludes with tables of maximum tensile and compressive strength for wood and iron members. The limits which he gives for wrought iron are a tensile strength of 60,000 pounds per square inch and a compressive of 70,000 to 80,000 pounds. He warns, however, that the metal suffers permanent deformation before these limits are reached. "It can never be safely exposed in practice to more than a small proportion of these stresses, say from ⅙ to ¼."[9] For cast iron he gives a tensile strength of 15,000 to 30,000 pounds per square inch and a compressive of 80,000 to 140,000 pounds. "But it is seldom relied on to sustain [tension], especially in bridge work, wrought iron being much better adapted to the purpose. On rare occasions, it may perhaps safely be exposed to a strain of 3,000 to 4,000 pounds to the square inch. . . ."[10] Whipple gives good reason for this distrust. Iron at the time was far from uniform, and it was hence necessary to make direct tests of sample pieces, and even then to make generous allowance for the absence of uniformity.

The first of the Whipple trusses, the bowstring, eventually proved to be popular for short highway spans and for the support of trainsheds and other curved vaults. As a highway bridge for crossings over small streams it survived until well into the twentieth century, and a number still remain on rural roads. It was seldom chosen for long-span or multispan structures. Perhaps the longest of all was the Goat Island Bridge over the Niagara River immediately above the Falls (1855). It was built to offer access to the wooded island and took the place of a bridge of unknown form which was constructed in 1817 and destroyed by ice the following year. Both bridges extended only to the island and thus crossed that portion of the river which forms the American Falls. The bowstring trusses of the later span were of cast and wrought iron, the two materials distributed among the various members according to the usual division of tensile and compressive stresses. The bridge survived until 1901, when it was replaced by a series of concrete arches.

Builders of bowstring trusses sometimes adopted an arrangement of members for the web other than the simple system of posts and diagonals that Whipple used. In at least one case, Black's Bridge, near Jonestown, Pennsylvania (1878), the web was a lattice truss. Black's Bridge consisted of two spans of 119 feet each carrying an 18-foot roadway of planks. The top chord was a 15-inch wrought iron tube bent into an approximately elliptical shape, and the bottom chord was a cast iron plate $\frac{1}{2} \times 14$ inches in section. The lattice webbing was composed of thin cast iron members. It is difficult to detect any rational ground for the distribution of cast and wrought iron members, which seems to be very nearly the opposite of what it should be. The record does not show how long this bridge lasted.

48 Bridge of the Rensselaer and Saratoga Railroad, near Troy, New York, 1852–53. Squire Whipple, engineer. Side and end elevations, plan, details of joints.

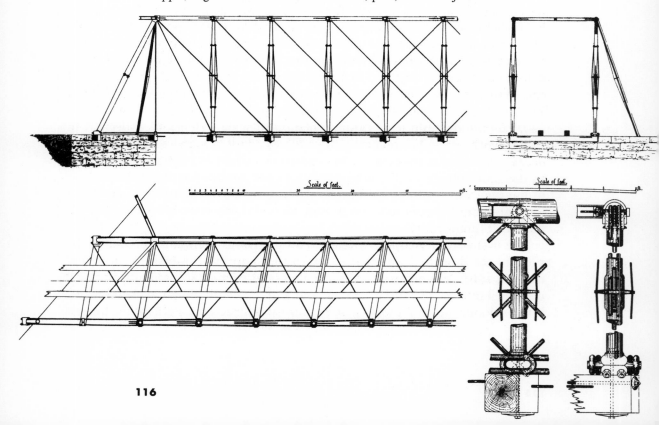

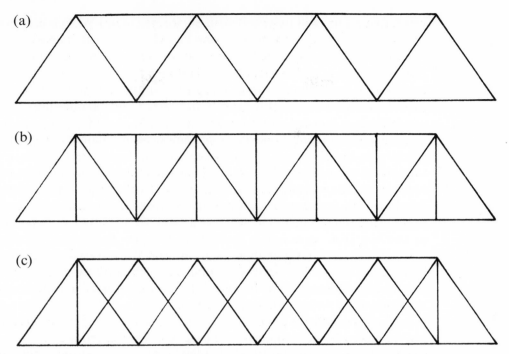

49  Forms of the Warren truss. a. The original form patented in England by James Warren and Theobald Monzani, 1848. b.c. Later modifications in which (b) posts and (c) a second set of diagonals have been added.

The great majority of Whipple trusses in railroad bridges were from the 1847 patent, having parallel chords and double-panel diagonals. One of the earliest of these Whipple built for the Rensselaer and Saratoga Railroad near Troy, New York, in 1852–53 (fig. 48).[11] The top chord and posts of the truss were cast iron, the diagonals wrought iron rods, and the bottom chord built up of a succession of wrought iron bars.[12] The bridge was set on a skew, so that the timber crossbeams between posts did not extend at right angles to the line of chords. The two trusses were tied together and braced against lateral sway by means of diagonal rods set in the horizontal plane between the transverse beams. Although still in sound condition, the bridge was replaced in 1883 chiefly because locomotive weight had doubled in the 30-year period. A decade after construction of the Troy bridge the Whipple truss was adopted for bridges of great size over the Ohio and Mississippi rivers and for twenty-five years had no serious rival in long-span structures.[13]

In addition to the trusses associated with his name, Whipple, according to his own claim, built the first Warren truss in the United States presumably without knowledge of its English precedent (fig. 49). The original Warren truss was patented in 1848 by two British engineers, James Warren and Willoughby Monzani, who had built the first one in 1846. The form as patented had two features which distinguished it from earlier types: there were no posts, or vertical members, and alternate diagonals sloped in opposite directions. The chief intention of its inventors was to design the simplest rigid truss whose primary members would be equal in length and hence most economically rolled and erected into a finished structure. The top chord, inclined end posts, and alternate diagonals (acting as posts) were compression members, the rest tension.[14] There were two later modifications, one the addition of vertical posts, the other the introduction of a second set of diagonals intersecting the first to give the appearance of a row of X's. It was undoubtedly the original form that Whipple developed. In the second edition of his treatise he wrote that he "built several small bridges upon this plan, to carry a railroad track over common highways, in 1849 or 1850, believed to have been the first application of this kind of truss."[15] He does not give their location. The Warren truss, curiously enough, is the only one with a natural counterpart. The hollow metacarpal bone of certain large soaring birds is internally reinforced with a system of diagonal struts identical with the human invention.

It would be difficult to determine whether Whipple or the English inventors set the example, but whatever the case, the Warren truss enjoyed a slow but steady climb to popularity after 1860. One of the earliest constructed of wrought iron (except for the cast iron end posts) was built by the Pennsylvania Railroad over the Juniata River near Tyrone, Pennsylvania (1869). Another that marked a return to the older wood-and-iron construction was built by the Louisville Bridge Company for a railroad line over the Blue River in Kentucky, 1871 (fig. 50).[16] The steel Warren truss began to appear in rapidly growing numbers in the last decade of the century, and continued a vigorous life throughout the twentieth. It reached its high point in one of the largest and handsomest truss bridges built in the United States, the great Pit River bridge of the Southern Pacific Railroad in Shasta County, California (1939–42).

## 3. BOLLMAN AND FINK TRUSSES

The building of the Baltimore and Ohio Railroad, the first railroad company in the United States, naturally called forth a variety of inventive talents. Behind them was the vigorous and influential figure of the road's second and perhaps greatest chief engineer, Benjamin Henry Latrobe II, the son of the celebrated Greek Revival architect. Born in Philadelphia in 1806, Latrobe studied mathematics and law at Georgetown College and at St. Mary's College in Baltimore. He began his professional career with the practice of law, soon

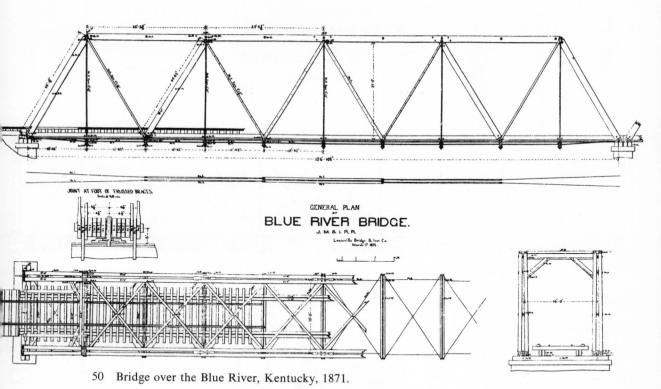

GENERAL PLAN
of
BLUE RIVER BRIDGE.
J. M. & I. R. R.
Louisville Bridge & Iron Co.
March 17, 1871.

JOINT AT FOOT OF TRUSSED BRACES.

50   Bridge over the Blue River, Kentucky, 1871.

found it distasteful, and abandoned it to join the engineering department of the Baltimore and Ohio in 1831. Because of his knowledge of mathematics he was rapidly advanced to the position of principal assistant to the chief engineer, Jonathan Knight. In this office and later as chief engineer himself, Latrobe played an essential role in the early construction of the railroad. His achievements began in 1832 with the survey of the Baltimore-Washington line. In the succeeding thirty years he was chief of surveying and construction of the lines of the Baltimore and Port Deposit Railroad between Baltimore and Havre de Grace and of the B. and O. from Point-of-Rocks, Maryland, through Harper's Ferry to Cumberland, Wheeling, and Pittsburgh, and designer of the famous Thomas Viaduct near Baltimore.[1] He originated the unit of freight transportation known as the ton-mile. After his retirement from active railroad work he served as a member of the committee which examined and passed on Roebling's plans for Brooklyn Bridge.

Among the men whom Latrobe trained in his office were two bridge designers whose inventions placed them in the front rank of the pioneers. The first of them, Wendell Bollman, began his career as a carpenter for the railroad; the other, German-born and German-trained Albert Fink, started as a draftsman in Latrobe's office. Bollman's bridges were used chiefly on the older, eastern

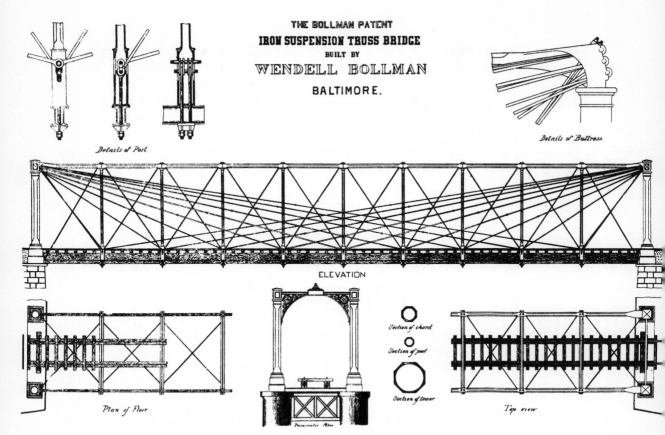

THE BOLLMAN PATENT
IRON SUSPENSION TRUSS BRIDGE
BUILT BY
WENDELL BOLLMAN
BALTIMORE.

Details of Post.

Details of Buttress.

ELEVATION

Section of chord

Section of post

Section of tower

Plan of Floor

Top view

51  The through truss patented by Wendell Bollman, 1850.

portion of the original main line, while Fink's were constructed on the western extension, in the region of the Ohio valley. Although the trusses invented by both men were originally designed for the familiar combination of wood and iron, they were quickly adapted to all-iron construction and were thus instrumental in the railroad company's early and extensive commitment to iron bridges. Both Bollman and Fink, who were familiar with earlier work in their field, seem to have approached the problem of truss design from the standpoint of increasing the strength of the Howe and Pratt trusses by increasing the number of members. In this respect Bollman clearly outdistanced everyone else.

The original Bollman truss was developed in 1850 (figs. 51, 52). Its basic element was a Pratt truss with timber posts and top and bottom chords and wrought iron double diagonals. Superimposed on it was a remarkable system of radiating wrought iron rods or bars extending from the upper end corners of the truss downward to the foot of every post. The portal frame, or end posts and laterals, was made of heavy cast iron pieces, often octagonal in section.[2]

Bollman's intention in this highly redundant and bewildering array of separate pieces was undoubtedly to combine the truss with a mode of support comparable to that of the suspension bridge.[3] The earliest of his bridges, located in the Potomac valley, were wood and iron. The first to be built entirely of iron was constructed in 1851 across Salt Creek in Muskingum County, Ohio, and thus may well have been, as Bollman claimed, the first iron bridge in that state. It was a single-span deck truss 71 feet in length.[4]

The longest of all bridges in which Bollman had a hand was the immense structure that carried the Baltimore and Ohio line across the Ohio River between Benwood, West Virginia, and Bellaire, Ohio, and through the town of Bellaire (1868–71). The Ohio River offered a formidable challenge to the railroad builders of the past century. Its great breadth and length, its annual and often devastating floods, and the hilly topography along most of its length repeatedly tested the bridge engineer's ingenuity and courage. Above Huntington, West Virginia, it stood in the way of many of the east-west trunk lines, while below that city it formed a barrier to the lines connecting the Great Lakes region with the Pocohontas coal fields and the South. Many of the largest bridges embodying the most advanced designs were built to span the long waterway. The Bellaire bridge, both in the size of the primary structure and in its elaborate approaches, was an excellent early example of how the builders solved the many problems that the river posed.[5] The main river crossing, about

52   The Bollman deck truss, 1850. Shown in full elevation at the bottom of the group of figures.

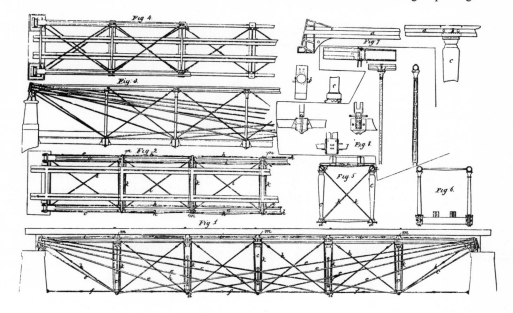

a half mile in length, included 14 spans divided between Bollman and Whipple trusses. The entire bridge, including the approaches, was nearly two miles long.[6] As interesting as the iron river spans were the approaches to them. In order to gain elevation from the low river banks it was necessary to build a long masonry arch viaduct over the rooftops of Bellaire and to turn the railroad line through a 270-degree loop on a narrow flat in Benwood, from which the track continues northward along the river bank to Wheeling.[7] It was a big bridge by the standards of the day and served the railroad well until the sheer weight of traffic forced its replacement at the end of the century. The Bellaire viaduct and the Benwood loop, however, still remain.

The fact that the engineers of the Baltimore and Ohio preferred the Whipple truss for the longer spans of the Ohio River bridge indicated that Bollman's invention was nearing the end of its day. Its popularity, indeed, had always been confined largely to the railroad that sponsored it. The construction of the Valley Railroad of Virginia, a B. and O. subsidiary, kept it alive for another decade, but its use was limited to spans of intermediate length.[8] By 1880, however, steel and the clear advantages of simpler forms left the Bollman truss behind.

Albert Fink, on the other hand, was destined for a more prominent role in bridge and railroad building as inventor, engineer, and executive. His initial work was exactly contemporary with that of his fellow engineer: his first patented design appeared in 1850 and his first major bridge was completed in 1852. Although much simpler than the Bollman, the Fink truss is more difficult to characterize in the relationship of form to function. The original design was a short-span deck truss with wooden top chord and posts and wrought iron diagonals (fig. 53). Two features, however, immediately distinguish it from its predecessors: first, the absence of a bottom chord, and second, the presence

53  The deck truss patented by Albert Fink, 1851.

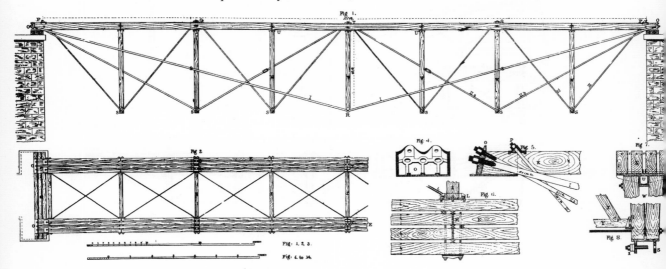

122

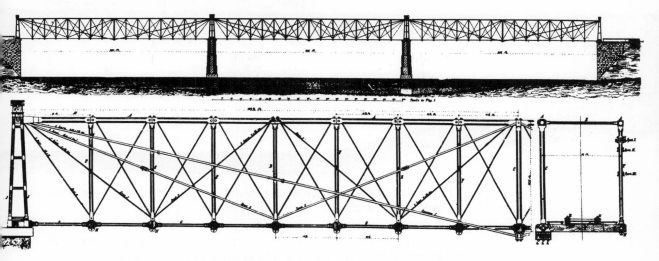

54 Bridge of the Baltimore and Ohio Railroad, Monongahela River, Fairmount, West Virginia, 1851–52. Albert Fink, engineer.

of a variety of diagonals which might be described from their distribution as half-panel, full-panel, and double-panel. The combination of features from the Pratt and Whipple trusses lay behind it, but it was simplified to the point of a pure truss in which the tension usually sustained by the bottom chord was carried by additional diagonal braces. Without a bottom chord the form was limited to deck trusses; for through trusses, however, the missing member was replaced.

The first major bridge of Fink trusses carried the Baltimore and Ohio line across the Monongahela River at Fairmount, Virginia (1852; West Virginia after 1863). Its three spans were composed of through trusses constructed entirely of iron, as were all the longer Fink bridges (fig. 54). The spans were exactly uniform in size and materials: top chord, posts, and end frames were of cast iron, and diagonals of wrought iron.[9] The track rested on continuous stringers laid on transverse timber beams to which the posts were bolted.

In 1857 Fink joined the Louisville and Nashville Railroad as engineer of bridges and structures and immediately began the design of the longest and most spectacular iron bridge in America at the time. Completed in 1859, it carried the main line of the L. and N. over the Green River near Mammoth Cave, Kentucky (fig. 55). The bridge was nearly 1,000 feet long between abutments and stood high above the valley beneath it. Its five spans, carried on masonry piers, were made up of Fink deck trusses of the original form.[10] The network of thin wrought iron rods in the trusses gave the bridge a fragile, sharply etched character possessing an odd kind of spider-web beauty that

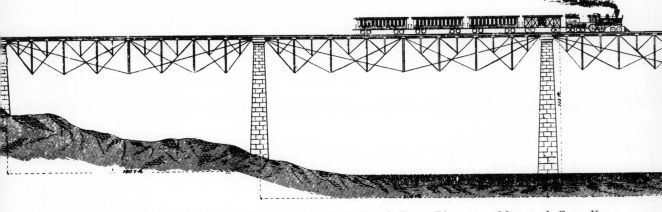

55  Bridge of the Louisville and Nashville Railroad, Green River, near Mammoth Cave, Kentucky, 1857–59. Albert Fink, engineer.

one misses in the heavier modern structures. But such delicate wrought iron work could not long sustain the heavy loads of rail traffic, and the Green River bridge had to give way to the massive trusses of steel. Fink's crowning achievement as an engineer was his bridge for the Pennsylvania Railroad over the Ohio River at Louisville (1868–70), for the channel spans of which he designed a new kind of truss that was to be the basis for many long-span railroad bridges constructed up to the present time.[11] Of the 27 spans of this mile-long bridge, however, 25 were deck trusses of the original form, like those of the Green River span, and were on the average about 180 feet in length. After the completion of the Louisville bridge Fink turned to railroad administration, eventually becoming a vice-president of the Louisville and Nashville.

## 4. SPECIAL INVENTIONS: TRUSS FORMS AND STRUCTURAL DETAILS

The mid-century year in which Bollman and Fink patented their respective trusses began a two-decade period of extraordinary inventive activity in the design and construction of bridges. Some of it produced results of permanent value for the structural art; the bulk of it, however, proved to be ephemeral or, at times, useless and even absurd. It was another demonstration of the extent to which creative ingenuity in the nineteenth century found realization in technical invention. The idea that economic necessity alone called forth these outbursts can hardly be supported. There were equally potent factors that took a less tangible form. One was the possibility of acquiring wealth, a universal dream which many inventors had been able to turn into reality. Another grew out of the supreme technical achievement of the age, the invention of the method of invention. One could create new forms with at least the appearance of a utilitarian nature by mastering a well-analyzed technique and by acquiring sufficient knowledge of the physical sciences. Finally, the sheer multiplicity

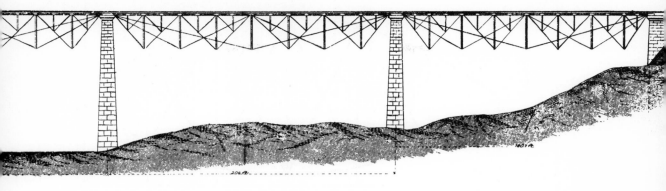

of new materials and processes produced a state in which chance associations of existing elements might result in new and practically successful patterns. The record of the nineteenth-century inventions that failed, however, is proof that much of this continuous stream was the product of naive enthusiasm rather than disciplined creative intelligence.

In the field of truss design the decade of the 1850's was a kind of interregnum between the pioneer age that extends from Palmer to Fink and the later and more lasting achievements that appeared in response to the railroads' insatiable demands for bridges that would stand up under the constantly expanding traffic. Most of the inventions fell into two classes: highly elaborate original forms that were generally of no value, and refinements, often slight, on the existing forms. In the latter case, as a matter of fact, some of the inventions differed so little from existing structures that one wonders on what basis the Patent Office granted licenses. Between them were valid solutions to difficult problems, some of which we shall treat under long-span bridges.

The first of the new productions came in 1851, when Edwin Stanley patented the original American lenticular truss (fig. 56). There had been German and

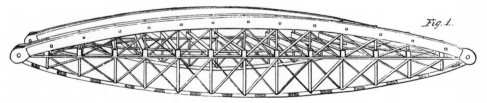

56   The lenticular truss patented by Edwin Stanley, 1851.

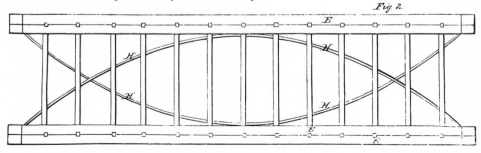

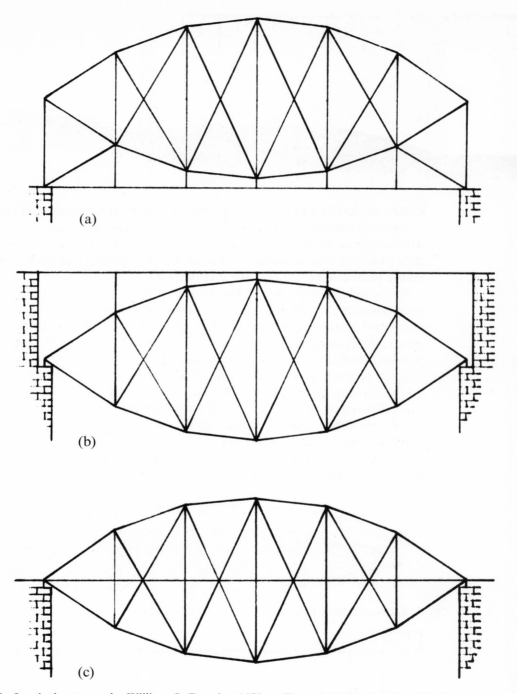

57  Lenticular trusses by William O. Douglas, 1878. a. Through. b. Deck. c. Semi-deck.

58  Smithfield Street Bridge, Monongahela River, Pittsburgh, Pennsylvania, 1884. Gustav Lindenthal, engineer.

British precedents, of which at least one was built by Robert Stephenson, whose authority as an engineer and builder gave it some prestige. Stanley's invention was a combination through and deck truss, the lower portion of which (below deck) was a reflection of the upper bowstring. The top chord was a massive timber or casting, while the bottom chord, posts, and double diagonals were lighter members of wrought iron. There does not seem to be any record of actual construction of the Stanley truss, and later adaptations of the form to iron throughout were probably based on European work, chiefly Brunel's famous Saltash bridge in England (1859). In 1878 William O. Douglas of Binghamton, New York, was granted a patent on a lenticular, or as he called it, a parabolic, truss with cast iron chords and posts (fig. 57). The truss was designed to be used in through, deck, or semi-deck positions, the last being one in which the roadway lies on the median plane of the truss, as in Stanley's invention.[1] In spite of its lateral bracing, the Douglas truss proved to be of inadequate stiffness and disappeared entirely after its brief fifteen-year life.

In 1884, however, Gustav Lindenthal, who was later to achieve international repute for his Hell Gate Bridge in New York, built a large and successful lenticular truss bridge to carry Smithfield Street over the Monongahela River in Pittsburgh (fig. 58) to take the place of a suspension bridge built in 1845 by John A. Roebling. Lindenthal's bridge still stands, carrying a heavy load of vehicular traffic. Its two 360-foot spans consist of through trusses of steel and thus belong to the pioneer group of steel bridges in the United States.[2] A second lenticular truss bridge was built at Pittsburgh to carry 6th Street over the

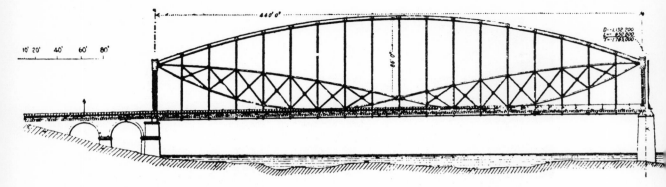

59   Sixth Street Bridge, Allegheny River, Pittsburgh, Pennsylvania, 1897.

Allegheny River, again to replace a Roebling suspension bridge (fig. 59). The bottom chord of the newer bridge is unique in that it is an inverted three-hinged arched truss, the two major parts of which are free to rotate about the end and center hinges.[3]

Following the Stanley truss there came a rapid succession of designs which may best be characterized as structural fantasies in their extreme redundancy and questionable arrangement of individual members. J. B. Gridley patented a truss (1852) which was in essence a Long truss on whose full-length auxiliary king-post there was superimposed a Pratt truss.[4] Either form, properly designed, would have been sufficient. George W. Thayer received two patents for trusses which outdid all the rest in their curious forms. The earlier (1845) was a kind of Pratt truss whose diagonal members extended beyond the top and bottom chords, for what functional purpose it would now be difficult to guess (fig. 60). The later patent (1854) consisted of a series of relatively small interlaced arches tied together by a continuous horizontal member passing through the points midway between their spring line and crowns (fig. 61).

60   The first truss patented by George W. Thayer, 1845.

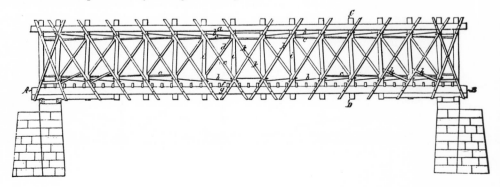

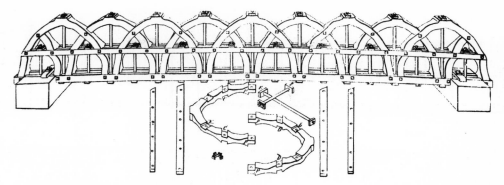

61   The second Thayer truss, patented 1854.

In the same year Samuel and Thomas Champion secured a patent on a modification of the Bollman truss, in which the top chord was omitted and the radiating diagonal braces spread out from the lower as well as the upper corners. The Gridley and Champion trusses, though structurally feasible, had an unnecessary multiplicity of members which added nothing to their utility and greatly increased their cost. The second Thayer truss was actually an interlaced arcade rather than a truss. It is doubtful whether it would have been a rigid structure, and the small size of the individual arches would have left them inadequate as compression members. Thus it is questionable whether it would have acted as either a truss or an arcade, although its inventor's aim was probably to combine the virtues of both.

The innovations toward the end of the decade were mainly characterized by associations of two or more basic forms. Abram S. Swartz of Buffalo, New York, patented a truss (1857) which was a development from the Whipple bowstring (fig. 62). It involved two additions, however, and one marked difference in the action of the truss itself. The cast iron top chord of the bowstring apparently was meant to function as an arch and thus to exert a horizontal thrust. This force was not sustained by skewbacks but by a horizontal wrought iron tie rod set below the deck between the ends of the arch. Apparently unsure of this sound technique, which is very nearly as old as the arch itself, Swartz added two long diagonal rods extending from the top of the

62   The truss patented by Abram Swartz, 1857.

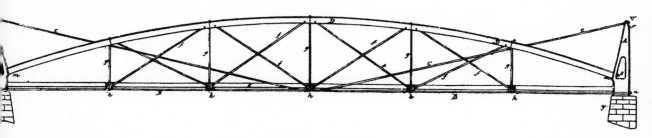

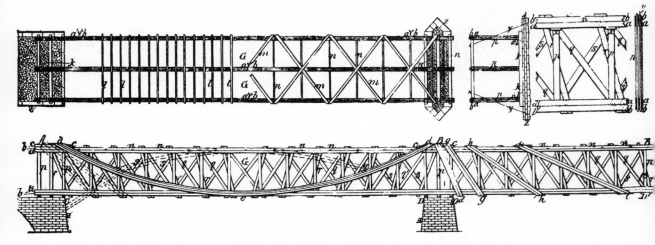

63   The truss patented by Stephen H. Long, 1858.

heavy end posts downward to the center of the bottom chord. The posts and diagonals under the arch must have functioned largely as stiffening members. The Swartz truss was another attempt to combine arch and truss into a single structure, but as such it looked back to an earlier day that the bridge builders had now passed. The principle of the tied arch, however, is perfectly sound and was to be used later on very large bridges.

The idea of combining fundamental forms continued to be attractive. In the same year that Swartz designed his truss, George S. Avery patented one very much like it. It was a bowstring with a top chord acting as a true arch, which, in this case, consisted of a series of parallel groups of concentric ribs. Once again, although the entire form was inefficient, it embodied a valid principle, that of a close array of parallel ribs. It was to be used on a large scale by the end of the century. Stephen H. Long (1858) tried the possibility of combining a truss with parallel chords and a parabolic wrought iron rib like an inverted arch or like the chain of a rigid suspension bridge (fig. 63). The patented design was thus a modification of the Burr arch and truss, in which the arched member was inverted. Lewis Eikenberry again returned to the arch-and-truss combination (1859) when he patented his so-called "compensating" truss (fig. 64). This was a flexible truss with a very close array of single diagonals, upon which he superimposed a pair of fixed arch ribs. The idea was that the flexibility would make possible the absorption without excessive stress of contraction and expansion attendant upon temperature changes. Archibald McGuffie two years later reached the ultimate of the complex types when he combined truss, arch, and suspension principles in a single form. Like most of its immediate predecessors, it died quickly and remained buried in the Patent Office.

While this flurry of experimentation was reaching its climax, other inventors took a more sensible approach. Several patents show repeated attempts to redesign the Howe truss with a view to giving it greater strength and rigidity, or to make it a determinate structure (fig. 65). Josiah Browne (1857) concentrated on connections, while Joseph W. Sprague (1859) substituted hollow iron tubes in all the compression members. Francis C. Lowthorp (1857) made the greatest number of refinements—massive box-like joints in the top chord, heavy cylindrical members in both chords, additional wrought iron bars in the bottom chord, the number of which in each panel increased toward the center (the point of maximum bending moment), and posts with end flanges and transverse stiffening plates (fig. 66).[5]

The Lehigh Valley Railroad sponsored one of the most widely used inventions of the mid-century. The road's chief engineer, John W. Murphy, built a single-span bridge over the Morris Canal at Phillipsburg, New Jersey, in 1858–59. A Whipple truss 165 feet long, it was the first pin-connected span built in the United States. Unturned wrought iron pins, one to a joint, took the place of the traditional bolted connections. In other respects the bridge followed the usual standards: compression members were cast iron, while the

64  The "compensating truss" patented by Lewis Eikenberry, 1859.

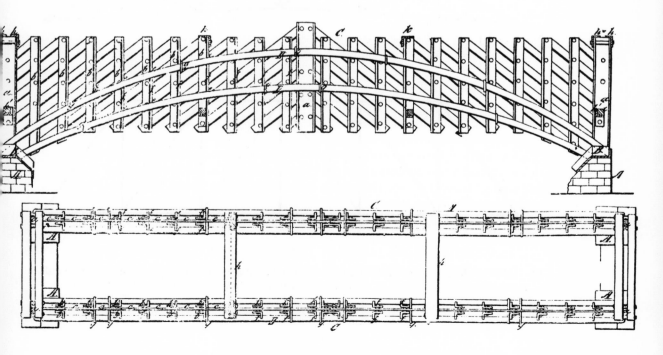

diagonals and bottom chord were made up of wrought iron bars with welded loops or eyes at the ends to receive the pins. The true eye-bar—that is, a solid bar with eyes at the ends forged integrally with the bar—was invented in 1861 by Jacob H. Linville, chief engineer of the Pennsylvania Railroad. The Phillipsburg bridge later served the Lehigh Valley at two other locations before it

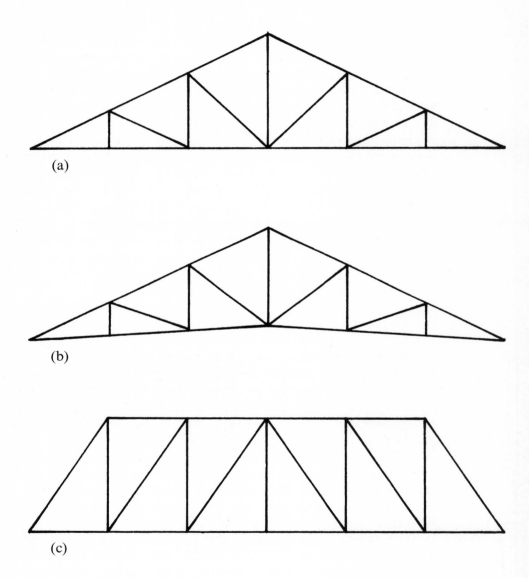

(a)

(b)

(c)

65  Later modifications of the Howe truss designed to make it a determinate structure. a. Standard triangular roof truss. b. Cambered roof truss. c. Standard trapezoidal bridge truss.

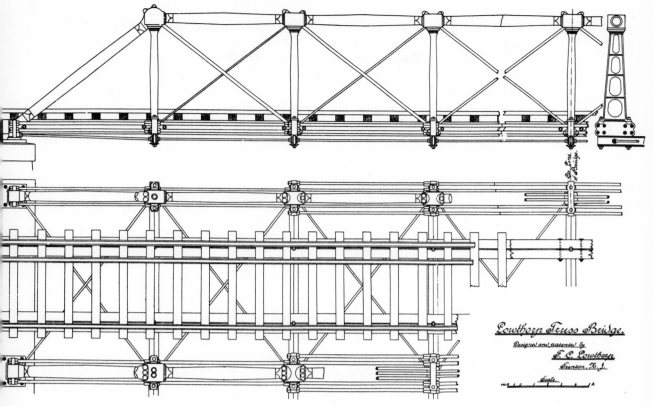

66  A modification of the Howe truss patented by Francis C. Lowthorp, 1857.

was scrapped in 1906: over the North Branch of the Susquehanna River at Towanda, Pennsylvania, and finally, over Cayuta Creek at Sayre. In 1863 Murphy built the first pin-connected truss with all structural members of wrought iron, a Whipple truss in which there were two sets of diagonals sloping in opposite directions. Wrought iron Whipple trusses built by Murphy embodied certain other changes in detail from the original form and were generally known as Whipple-Murphy trusses (fig. 47).

Pinned connections were much superior to bolted in their greater strength and the freedom of the member to rotate about the joint, thus reducing stresses at that point. They were later found to be unsatisfactory, however, because of wear of the pins and eyes with consequent excessive play of the individual members. Before the end of the century pins were replaced entirely by riveted joints, although this had the effect of making any kind of truss an indeterminate structure, since a riveted connection binds the members together over an area instead of bringing them together separately at a bolt or pin, and, being a fixed joint, tends to produce bending of members with consequent increased stresses.

The adaptation of the Town lattice truss to iron construction was made in 1859, when Howard Carroll built a bridge of this form for the New York Central Railroad. It was a short single span made entirely of wrought iron with riveted connections. Carroll used iron floor beams and track stringers for the first time in this bridge, in place of the usual wooden members. He and George E. Gray, both of the New York Central's engineering staff, built a number of iron lattice trusses for the railroad during the 1860's and 70's, all of which were limited to short spans of 40 to 90 feet. In 1864, however, the two engineers appear to have abandoned their original all-wrought iron truss for the traditional combination of wrought and cast iron. Their intention in adopting the riveted lattice truss was to build a rigid structure in which stresses were distributed over a large number of joints rather than concentrated on a few.

Karl Culmann, on the other hand, took a particularly unfavorable view of the iron lattice truss. He held that the thin compression members would buckle laterally because of their inability to withstand large compressive forces and in this respect were weaker than the wooden prototypes, which were much larger in cross section. The two attempts to correct this defect both proved unsatisfactory: the introduction of heavy cast iron members made the lattice truss so cumbersome that it was difficult to erect, while the introduction of vertical stiffeners completely changed the statical character of the truss and made its mode of action unpredictable. In spite of the weaknesses that Culmann pointed out, the lattice truss enjoyed a comparatively long life. During the 1880's it was used in one bridge of considerable size, the wrought iron span of the Pittsburgh, Fort Wayne and Chicago Railroad over the Allegheny River at Pittsburgh.[6] Designed by Felician Slataper, it had five spans of 178 feet each, probably the maximum for this type of truss. Before the end of the century the form had been simplified by reducing the number of separate members and began to be built in steel. In the new material it survived until the second decade of the present century.[7]

Among all the inventions of new trusses and modifications of existing ones the most specialized were the structures designed for the first elevated lines on Manhattan Island. The original proposal for such a railroad was made by the civil engineer John Randel in 1848, twenty years before construction of the first line. His project involved a continuous double-track iron bridge made up of four parallel longitudinal Howe trusses laced together by transverse members and stiffened by diagonals set between the trusses in the transverse plane (fig. 67a). This bridge was to be supported centrally by a pair of cast iron columns bolted together at their mid-point and located at the curb line of the sidewalk. The bridge was thus bracketed out from the columns. The great advantage of Randel's project was that it left the street free of obstructions to traffic and light. No elevated line of those now in use was ever

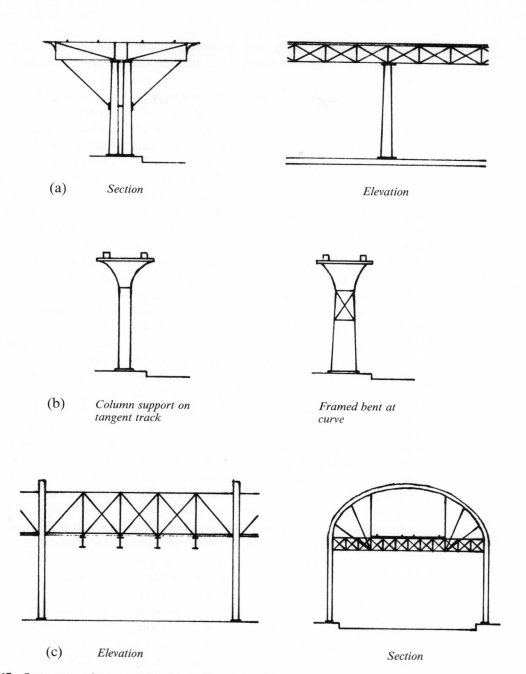

(a)     *Section*

*Elevation*

(b)     *Column support on tangent track*

*Framed bent at curve*

(c)     *Elevation*

*Section*

67  Supports and trusses of early projects for New York elevated railroads. a. Proposal for a line on Broadway, 1848. John Randel, engineer. b. The West Side and Yonkers Patent Railway Company, Ninth Avenue, 1867–68. Charles T. Harvey, engineer and builder. c. The Gilbert Elevated Railway Company, Sixth Avenue, 1878. Rufus Henry Gilbert, engineer and builder.

built in this way; yet there is no good reason why it could not have been done if the sidewalk were sufficiently wide and the cantilevers or brackets properly designed.

The first elevated to be put in service was built by Charles T. Harvey (1867–68) on the lower end of Ninth Avenue. Its official corporate name was the West Side and Yonkers Patent Railway Company. Following Randel's precedent, he located the cast iron columns at the edge of the sidewalk. His bridge, however, was a much simpler structure (fig. 67b). A pair of wooden stringers set on transverse wooden beams carried the rails of a single-track line. The beams were supported by curved brackets which spread out from two plates bolted to either side of the central column. Harvey recognized that his structure was insufficiently rigid to withstand the horizontal thrust exerted by trains on curves. As a consequence he altered the support at curves into the form of an iron bent, which consisted of two outward-curving cylindrical cast iron members laced together by a single pair of diagonals and laterals just above the mid-point. The cars of Harvey's railroad were pulled by a moving cable probably operated by huge steam-driven pulleys. The motive power was undoubtedly a source of much trouble. In 1871 the line was taken over by the New York Elevated Railroad Company, which substituted steam locomotives for the cable. Harvey's company was thus the beginning of the vast elevated system of New York City, still the most extensive of all, though now confined to the boroughs of Brooklyn, Queens, and the Bronx.

The most elaborate of the early projects was that of Rufus Henry Gilbert, who proposed a central line extending from the Battery to Harlem. The two tracks were to be carried between a pair of deep through longitudinal trusses (fig. 67c). They were Pratt trusses with double diagonals in all but the end panels and with the usual combination of cast and wrought iron members. The longitudinal trusses rested on transverse Howe trusses which spanned the full width of the street. Gilbert belonged to the school of bridge builders who sought safety by combining two or more structural forms. The most novel feature of his elevated was the addition of another set of transverse supports in the form of elliptical wrought iron arch ribs located above the transverse trusses. The latter were thus supported partly by the columns and partly by wrought iron tension rods set radially between the arch and the truss. But Gilbert's over-elaborate design was far too costly. A second project reduced the structure to a system of shallow longitudinal and transverse Howe deck trusses essentially like the elevated structures that exist today, where trusses rather than plate girders are used. This plan proving feasible, Gilbert organized the Gilbert Elevated Railway Company, which by 1878 completed construction of a line over Sixth Avenue from Morris to 59th Street. It formed the initial segment of the Sixth Avenue elevated of the B.M.T., which was demolished on Manhattan Island when the Independent subway was completed in 1936.

By 1875 the continuous girder and truss common to the metropolitan elevated were beginning to appear on the steam railroads, and questions of their economy and strength were being discussed in the engineering press.[8] The authors generally favored trusses rather than girders. The latter, nevertheless, grew in popularity, even for relatively long bridges, but the length of individual spans was generally limited to 40 or 50 feet. The girder bridge was particularly well adapted to the requirements of the metropolitan elevated railroad. A continuous plate-girder structure of wrought iron was built over Ninth Avenue in New York for the original line of what was later the Interborough Rapid Transit Company (1879). Structural members of this bridge were progressively replaced beginning in 1918, but the testing of certain pieces revealed that they were internally sound after nearly forty years of service under more than 100,000,000 wheel loads.

Although continuous truss bridges were rare in the 1870's, the form was nevertheless adopted for one very long bridge in 1882. Constructed by the New York, Lake Erie and Western Railroad over Kinzua Creek in McKean County, Pennsylvania, the bridge was 2,050 feet long overall and the rail stood 302 feet above the surface of the stream.[9] High, narrow wrought iron bents carried a pair of continuous Howe trusses of the same material. Primarily the work of the Erie's chief engineer, Octave Chanute, it was a novel and daring experiment which aroused a good deal of interest in Great Britain as well as America. In England bridges of this type were regarded as peculiar to the United States and were long known as the "American railway viaduct." In both the truss and girder form they are common over V-shaped valleys of unusual width and depth, and consequently many of the largest of them span western canyons.

George H. Pegram, a St. Louis engineer, in 1887 invented a locally popular but short-lived truss for a wide range of span lengths (fig. 68). Its distinguishing feature was the inclined posts, whose angle of inclination increased progressively and symmetrically from the center panel to the ends. Pegram's aim was to offset the one disadvantage in trusses with curved or polygonal top chords, namely, the high cost of fabrication resulting from the use of members of many different lengths. In his truss the separate members of the bottom chord were of equal length, as were those of the top chord, although shorter than their counterparts in the lower. Equality in the length of posts was maintained by setting them at varying angles of inclination. Pegram designed the truss in a number of variations on the basic form—with single and double diagonals, diagonals crossing two or more panels, an intermediate chord extending through the horizontal center line of all panels from end to end—

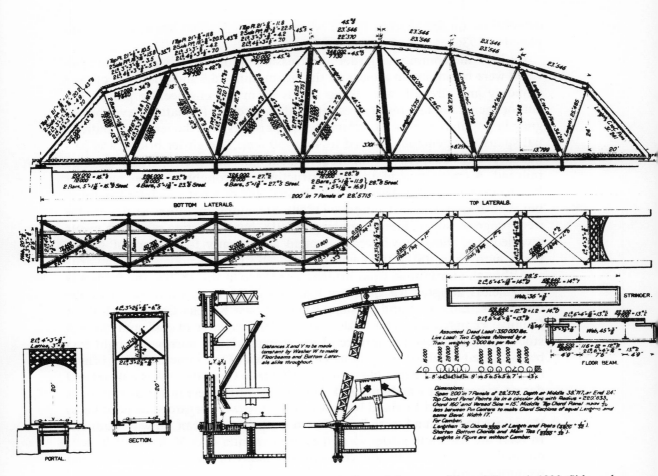

68   Bridge of the Fort Scott and Eastern Railway, Marmaton River, Missouri, 1890. Side and end elevations and details of connections of the Pegram truss.

and proposed it for spans up to 650 feet. Beginning about 1890 a number of bridges with Pegram trusses were built on the lines of the Missouri Pacific Railway and its subsidiaries, twenty of them in the years 1889–90 alone. The longest single span among them was the bridge over the Marmaton River in western Missouri, built by the Fort Scott and Eastern Railway (fig. 68). All members were wrought iron, the diagonals being rods and the posts built-up members of plates and angles laced together by iron straps.[10] The largest single installation of Pegram trusses is in the trainshed of St. Louis Union Station (1891–94), where they continue to function as the main supporting members of the enormous roof.[11]

The last patented truss form of the nineteenth century, other than special types introduced for long-span railway bridges, was developed in 1892 by the

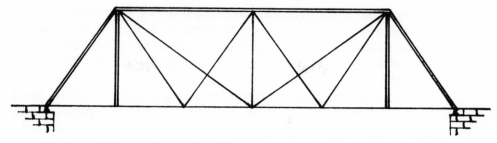

69 The truss patented by W. E. Stearns, 1892.

Kansas engineer W. E. Stearns (fig. 69).[12] It was, in a way, a simplification of the Fink truss in which the posts were omitted at alternate panels and a single diagonal was added across two panels. The compression members of the Stearns truss, which was designed for steel construction, were usually built-up box forms of plates, but for heavier bridges they were open-web members with a latticework of steel straps between the plates. The Stearns truss was designed for short spans and was common in highway bridges around the turn of the century.

The twenty-five years from 1855 to 1880 saw a series of extremely important developments which completed the revolution that transformed building from an empirical art to a scientific technique. On the basis of the pioneer work of Whipple and the European engineers and theorists, stress analysis of determinate trusses reached a mature level in both analytical and graphical methods by 1870. Accurate solutions of the more difficult problems of indeterminacy were achieved by 1880. At the same time the European work began to form the core of American engineering texts, the best of which quickly reached a level that made Whipple's treatise seem crude by comparison. What remained to be done was the adoption of the techniques of experimental science in the process of manufacture, the exact determination of standards of performance, and the clear and accurate presentation of such standards in written specifications. A number of techniques were developed around the mid-century for making a direct empirical measurement of the strain imposed on a given member by a static load and the impact of a moving load. The American engineers Plymton and Murphy made models of trusses in which any member could be removed and replaced by a spring balance that indicated the actual stress in that member. Eventually it was possible to introduce strain gauges into the finished structure and thus avoid the measure of error that is always present in translating stresses from model to actual structure. By 1867, after more than a century of experimentation, testing machines had been developed to the point of practical utility and were installed in the shops of the Phoenix Iron Company, the Keystone Bridge Company, and the Carnegie Steel Company. With such machines full-scale members could be submitted to experimental investigation. By subjecting them to tensile and compressive loads it became possible to determine the load level at which deformation, yield, and ultimate rupture occur, and by means of metallographic examination, to see the internal changes that take place under such conditions.

Since the manufacturers were now in a position to obtain exact knowledge of the behavior of their product, the railroad companies could set precise standards and require that they be adhered to. Such standards came to be embodied in written specifications of material, construction, workmanship, and performance. The first specifications for bridge design were prepared by Clarke and Reeves of the Phoenix Iron Company in 1871.

The crucial factor in design and in establishing standards of performance is the load the bridge is required to carry. By 1860 the practice had become general of designing all parts of the railroad bridge for a uniform load of one ton per lineal foot of track. In 1870 a heavier unit load was adopted for the floor system (up to two tons per foot), but the lower figure was retained for the main trusses. But this technique represented a crude empiricism. An exact determination based on the actual distribution of train load was necessary. The practice of specifying precise wheel-load concentrations was begun in 1875 by L. F. G. Bouscaren, chief engineer of the Cincinnati Southern Railway, a company which had great need of the bridge builder's talents.[13] Bouscaren used the engine and train diagram to calculate loads at the wheel contact points. After the size and shape of each member had been determined and plans and specifications sent out for bids, Bouscaren then required that bidders submit full-size sample members to test in order to determine ultimate strength and elastic limit. George S. Morison took the next step when he required complete stress tables from bidders. Theodore Cooper completed the development of the modern bridge specification in 1878 when he introduced the practice on the Erie Railroad of indicating the maximum allowable working stress in each member of the structure in the light of the action it was designed to provide. He made the ironic claim that he was the first to omit "that relic of ignorance, the factor of safety."[14] Further, he developed the simple method of representing the type and extent of train-wheel loads which is in common use today. And finally, this energetic and creative man—engineer, inventor, scientist, historian—discovered the phenomenon known as Cooper's lines, marks often appearing on the surface of a test piece submitted to a distorting load which are useful in indicating lines of maximum strain.

By 1880 the modern program of design and manufacture was complete and had become the accepted standard for all railroads and builders—theoretical stress analysis, comprehensive stress tables, plans, notes, and specifications, competitive bidding, testing of full-scale members, regular and thorough inspection, metallurgical analysis, and the training of mill and construction workers. The railroads were at last in a position to tackle with assurance their really big jobs, the long-span iron and steel bridges and the great trainsheds of the metropolitan terminals. For all the abuses that marked economic expansion in the past century, it was the heroic age of iron construction, and one can only be impressed by the final achievement, which could come about only through systematic co-operation among engineers, builders, manufacturers, and workers.

## 5. LONG-SPAN BRIDGES

The grouping of a number of bridges on the basis of span length into a distinct class is to some degree an arbitrary designation, especially when one's concern is to trace their historical development. At the same time, when the single truss reached a length of 400 feet, the designers began to develop special truss forms which clearly differentiated the long-span bridges from the smaller structures. The truss might be simple, continuous, or cantilever, but the peculiar problems attendant upon building the large spans required extensive redesign of truss forms previously in use. Cantilever bridges form a distinct subclass of long-span bridges, with a history of their own, and accordingly we shall treat them in a separate section.[1] Most of the bridges we shall consider here consisted of a series of simple through trusses. When we trace the evolution of long-span bridges, we find the usual progressive and organic development which begins with already well-established forms and materials and ends with entirely new types. As we have already noted, it was the Whipple truss that was initially used for long-span crossings, and for twenty-five years it had no serious rival.

The history of long-span bridges may be said to have begun when it was necessary to build new or to replace the original Ohio River bridges with structures sufficiently massive to support the traffic loads that might reasonably be expected within the remainder of the century. As a matter of fact, most of the railroad bridges over the Ohio were iron structures from the beginning. Iron was becoming common when the earliest of them were built, and the proximity of the Pittsburgh iron industry along with waterway transportation from the mill to the site led to the early use of iron. The cost of transporting iron members by rail to the Mississippi was so high that the builders of the initial group of spans over the larger river had no alternative but to use wood. The first of the long-span bridges over the Ohio was built at Steubenville, Ohio, by the Pittsburgh, Cincinnati, Chicago and St. Louis Railroad after the design of the company's chief engineer, Jacob H. Linville (1863–64).[2] The seven spans were composed of Whipple-Murphy trusses with double diagonals and the traditional combination of cast and wrought iron members (fig. 70). In spite of the unprecedented length of the channel span—320 feet—the trusses differed little from earlier examples. The Steubenville bridge was replaced by the present structure in 1927, locomotive weight in the intervening sixty-three years having multiplied three times.

Whipple trusses of original form and shorter length were used for the first iron bridge over the Mississippi River, that of the Chicago, Burlington and Quincy Railroad at Quincy, Illinois, 1866–68 (fig. 71). Designed by one of the foremost bridge engineers of his time, Thomas C. Clarke, it was extraordinarily long, having 18 spans with a total length between abutments of 3,189 feet. The maximum length of a single span was 250 feet.[3] The length of the iron Whipple truss increased drastically in 1877, when the Ohio River bridge of the Cincinnati Southern Railway at Cincinnati was completed. The big structure was designed by L. F. G. Bouscaren of the Cincinnati company and J. H. Linville of the Pennsylvania and its affiliates.[4] Its main channel span reached a new record length of 517 feet. Whipple trusses of cast and wrought iron carried the four spans of its 1,600-foot river crossing.

70  Bridge of the Pittsburgh, Cincinnati, Chicago and St. Louis Railroad, Ohio River, Steubenville, Ohio, 1863–64. Jacob H. Linville, engineer. Elevation of the channel span and details of connections.

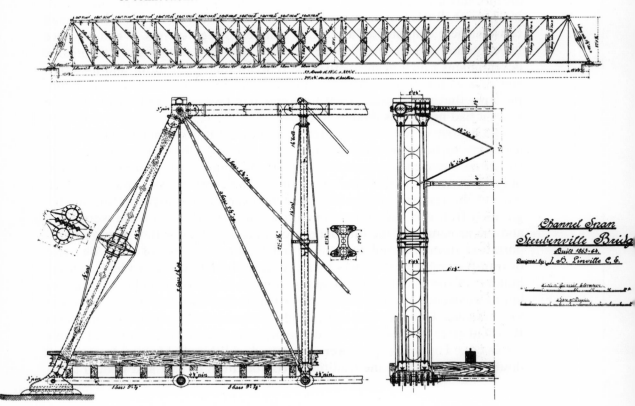

71 Bridge of the Chicago, Burlington and Quincy Railroad, Mississippi River, Quincy, Illinois, 1866–68. Thomas C. Clarke, engineer.

With these impressive demonstrations of its soundness, the Whipple truss was the logical choice for the first American bridge to be constructed entirely of steel, the Missouri River crossing of the Chicago and Alton Railroad at Glasgow, Missouri (1879).[5] A decade earlier James B. Eads had made the initial decision to use steel when he adopted it for the tubular arches of his Mississippi River bridge at St. Louis. He chose it because the iron available to him was not capable of the compressive stresses he required.[6] The chief engineer of the Glasgow bridge, William Sooy Smith, turned to steel for exactly the same reason: one did not need to look far ahead to see the day when the normal working stresses in a railroad bridge would far exceed the allowable limits of cast and wrought iron.

The design and construction of the Glasgow bridge constitute an extremely important but little known chapter in the history of the bridge-building art. Smith's decision to use steel followed five years of inquiry into the relative merits of the available ferrous metals. In 1872 the American Society of Civil Engineers met at Chicago chiefly to consider the question of the failures of iron bridges because of the tendency of the metal to crystallize under heavy strain, especially when produced by sudden impact. Smith proposed successfully that the United States government build a testing machine and appoint a committee of engineers to make exhaustive tests of structural iron. The membership of the committee included, in addition to Smith as chairman, James B. Eads, Albert Fink, and General George B. McClellan. The results of these tests convinced Smith that steel was far superior to cast and wrought iron as a structural material.

During the course of this research the committee received a letter from Abram T. Hay, an iron founder of Burlington, Iowa, who remains one of the most obscure figures in the history of structural materials. Some time in the early 1860's Hay had invented an electric furnace for producing high-grade steel with exceptional physical properties. Hay demonstrated to Smith's satisfaction that he could produce a steel with a tensile strength of 70,000 to 90,000 pounds per square inch. In 1877 the engineer was appointed chief of design and construction for the Glasgow bridge, and, to the scandal of the profession, adopted Hay steel as the material for the river trusses. The metal was manufactured to Hay's specifications by the Carnegie Steel Company in Pittsburgh.

The construction of the pier foundations for the bridge began in May 1878, and the whole structure was opened to traffic in March 1879. Before completion, however, catastrophe provided another test of Hay's steel. During erection of one of the river trusses, the falsework failed and the 160-ton span fell into the water. Many of the members of the truss were bent and twisted but none suffered even partial fracture. The completed structure was divided between the five 314-foot Whipple trusses of the river crossing and the iron Pratt trusses and wooden trestlework of the approaches.[7] A pioneer work of great significance for the subsequent development of structural techniques, the Glasgow bridge enjoyed a short life of only twenty years. Increased weight of traffic required its replacement in 1899, although the bridge was perfectly sound.

In spite of its good performance, the Glasgow bridge did not convince the builders of the advantages of steel. As in the case of the tall building, the stronger metal did not enjoy steady popularity until the last decade of the century. Its high cost was still the major factor in prohibiting widespread use for the entire framing of bridges and buildings. During the 1880's the practice was to employ it for certain members of the truss, chiefly those subjected to high compressive stresses.[8] Such a combination of steel and wrought iron characterized the Whipple trusses in the Ohio River bridge of the Illinois Central Railroad at Cairo, Illinois (1887–89). In this structure, begun the year before Whipple died at the age of 84, the now celebrated engineer's invention reached its greatest size and very nearly the end of its active life in railroad service. Designed by George S. Morison and Alfred Noble, the trusses of the three river spans reached a length of 519 feet and thus exceeded in size anything previously built on the Whipple patent. The diagonals, a single one across each pair of panels, were wrought iron, but all other members were steel.[9] The piers of stone masonry rested on piles extending to bedrock beneath the river bed. As remarkable as its great size was the unprecedented speed with which two sets of trusses were erected: the first span was completed in six days, and the second in four and a half. All spans were erected on timber falsework, in itself a considerable feat of bridge building in wood.

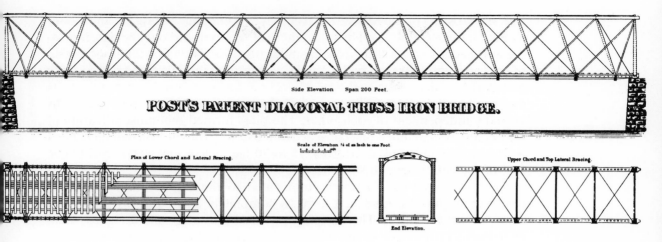

72 The truss patented by S. S. Post, 1865.

The long-span bridge appeared in other forms before it found those specifically adapted to its peculiar requirements. In several cases wrought iron Warren trusses were chosen, originally for the first International Bridge over the Niagara River between Buffalo and Fort Erie, Ontario (1866–70). Designed by Thomas W. Kennard, bridge engineer of the Atlantic and Great Western Railroad, it was built to connect the Buffalo branch of that company with the Grand Trunk Railway of Canada.[10] More noteworthy than the trusses of International Bridge, however, was its elaborate pier construction, which best represented such construction on a large scale and under extremely difficult conditions before the use of caissons in American bridges.[11]

Another bridge engineer of the Erie, S. S. Post, invented a truss in 1865 that enjoyed a brief but fairly vigorous life in long-span bridges (fig. 72). The Post truss was of rectangular profile and differed from the Whipple truss chiefly in the fact that its posts were inclined slightly from the vertical. Because of this double system of sloping intersecting members set at two different angles to the normal, the distribution of stresses was ambiguous and hence difficult to predict under the action of moving loads. Its early popularity was the result of what appeared to be greater rigidity under live loads, and for about fifteen years a considerable number of them were built in cast and wrought iron, the first at Washingtonville, New York, on the Newburgh branch of the Erie (1865).[12]

Although the Post truss had not been tested in heavy service, the builders of the Union Pacific Railroad decided to use it for the largest bridge on their line, the crossing of the Missouri River between Omaha, Nebraska, and Council Bluffs, Iowa (1868–72). The total length of this extraordinary bridge, including approaches, was a little over 2½ miles (figs. 73, 74).[13] The 250-foot trusses of cast and wrought iron had a single system of diagonals that crossed three panels rather than the usual two. There was no sway bracing between posts and none at the portals. The two parallel trusses forming one span were thus virtually independent of each other. The piers formed the unusual feature of the Omaha bridge. Each one consisted of a pair of wrought iron cylinders filled with concrete and sunk to bedrock 75 to 80 feet below low water level.[14] The cost of the entire structure was $1,750,000.

The absence of sway bracing contributed to the disaster that struck the bridge in August 1877, when a tornado completely destroyed two spans and damaged several others. The company replaced it as originally designed, then, realizing its inadequacy at last, removed it and substituted a double-track steel and iron bridge on masonry piers in 1886. Thirty years later it too proved inadequate, and the present structure was built at the same site (1916). The weight increase of the successive spans provides an index to the continuously growing loads that such bridges were required to carry. The ironwork of the original one could not have weighed more than 1,200 tons (a rough estimate), that of the second design weighed 1,950 tons, and the third 3,580 tons. Not all of the weight increase can be attributed to the requirement of meeting train loads, some of it being the result of wind and sway bracing.

The Post truss reached its maximum length in the Missouri River bridge of the Missouri-Kansas-Texas Railroad at Booneville, Missouri (1874). Like those of the Omaha bridge, the iron trusses had triple-intersection diagonals. The maximum length of the fixed spans was 256 feet, but the swing span was 360 feet long. The capacity of the Booneville bridge was called into question within a few years of its construction, with the result that the cast iron top chord was replaced in 1884 by a built-up member of wrought iron. A complete replacement by steel trusses followed in 1894–96, and another in 1932.[15]

The emancipation of the long-span truss from the pioneer forms of 1840–50 came with Albert Fink's bridge for a subsidiary of the Pennsylvania Railroad over the Ohio River at Louisville, Kentucky (1868–70). The river at this point offers a special challenge to the engineer: not only does it carry a great volume of water subject to the annual floods for which it is notorious, but it spreads out into a large embayment that is nearly a mile wide at its maximum extent. Further, the volume of waterborne commerce meant that the length of the channel spans had to be increased well beyond the standard at the time. Fink met the challenge head on: his finished structure, 30 feet short of a mile long, was divided into 27 spans. The two channel spans, respectively 370 and 400 feet in length, were carried by through trusses whose design became the basis

73    Bridge of the Union Pacific Railroad, Missouri River, Omaha, Nebraska, 1868–72.

74    Missouri River bridge of the Union Pacific Railroad. A construction view showing the timber falsework from which the trusses were erected.

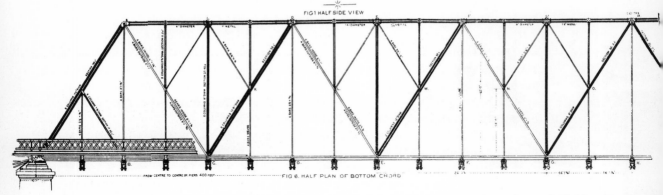

75 Bridge of the Pennsylvania Railroad, Ohio River, Louisville, Kentucky, 1868–70. Albert Fink, chief engineer. Half-elevation of the channel truss.

of a large proportion of subsequent railroad bridges (fig. 75). Derived in part from the principles of the Pratt and Whipple trusses, chiefly in the shape and disposition of the diagonals, the form that Fink developed differed from its predecessors by virtue of its subdivided panels, in which the location, cross-sectional profile, dimensions, and number of individual members were precisely calculated on the basis of the stresses they were to carry.[16] The huge Louisville bridge enjoyed a comparatively long life. It withstood floods and traffic loads until 1919, when the railroad company completed its present bridge at this location.

The engineers of the Pennsylvania Railroad immediately saw the merits of Fink's design. Because of the number and diversity of separate members and the points of multiple-intersection, however, it was difficult to analyze and costly to erect. As a consequence, they sought to simplify the design by reducing the number of intermediate members within any one panel. In 1871 they developed the so-called Baltimore, or Petit, truss, the panels of which were subdivided into fewer and simpler units by a half-diagonal and a half-vertical member (fig. 76). By 1875 it had been modified into the Pennsylvania truss (also known as the Petit), which had the same web system, or pattern of members between the chords, but a polygonal top chord in place of the parallel chords of the older form (fig. 76). The substitution of an increasing depth from end to center in place of uniform depth was important in the economy of construction. With the exception of the bowstring, lenticular, and McCallum trusses, all the basic types invented from 1840 to 1870 had parallel chords, a characteristic which did not reflect the increase in bending moment from the ends to the center of a simple span.[17] If a truss of uniform depth had sufficient rigidity at the center, then it had an increasingly redundant quantity of material in the direction of the end. The addition of a second set of diagonals in the center panels of the Pratt and Whipple trusses grew out of a recognition of the actual change of bending moment through the length of the truss. The polygonal top chord was a more precise reflection of the true state of affairs and it became a permanent feature of most large through spans. Pegram's invention, we have already noted, was an attempt to offset the one disadvantage of the polygonal form—that is, the high cost of manufacture arising from the number of different sizes of the individual members.[18]

It was a variation on the Pennsylvania truss that established a new record for the length of a simple span, achieved by the Chesapeake and Ohio Railway, again to bridge the Ohio River at Cincinnati (1886–88).[19] The steel and wrought iron structure was designed by the engineers of the Phoenix Bridge Company, fabricators of the steelwork, under the direction of William H. Burr, who acted as chief of design and construction.[20] The entire width of the river was crossed in three immense spans, the two at the ends 476 feet long, the one over the channel 545 feet long and 84 feet in depth of truss (fig. 77). A combined rail and highway bridge, it carried a double-track railroad line between trusses and a roadway and sidewalk on cantilevered beams extending outward from either side. To meet the conditions imposed by the different kinds of traffic and the

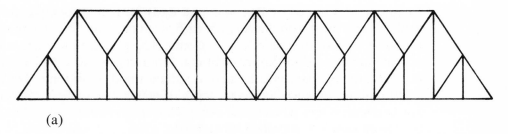

(a)

76  Forms of the Petit truss, designed by the engineering staff of the Pennsylvania Railroad. a. Baltimore truss, 1871. b. Pennsylvania truss, 1875.

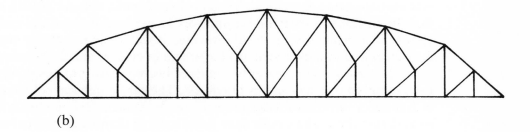

(b)

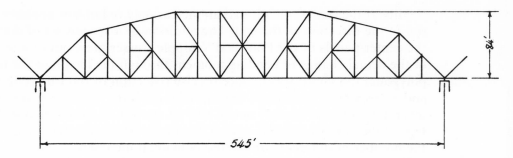

77  Bridge of the Chesapeake and Ohio Railway, Ohio River, Cincinnati, Ohio, 1886–88. William H. Burr, chief engineer. Side elevation of the channel truss.

radically eccentric distribution of loads, the bridge was designed for an extra-ordinarily complex system of loading requirements.[21] The trusses were erected on timber falsework, and construction progressed without trouble until the bridge was nearly completed. Then, on the morning of August 26, 1888, the falsework suddenly gave away and dropped part of the steelwork into the river. The accident was the consequence of a large accumulation of driftwood thrust against the timbers, the debris having been carried down by an unheard-of late summer flood in several tributaries of the Ohio.

Pier construction of the C. and O.'s Cincinnati bridge followed the advanced techniques developed by Roebling and Eads for their Brooklyn and St. Louis bridges. The piers were faced with with large cut stone blocks in mortar sur-rounding a core of loose rubble masonry. The foundations were solid blocks of concrete poured in timber cribbing. Examination of the pier foundations in 1929 revealed that the cribbing was still in sound condition.[22] The piers have withstood extreme variations in depth of water, as much as 75 feet between low and high stages. During the worst Ohio River flood, that of January 1937, they were almost completely submerged.

The life of the C. and O.'s Cincinnati bridge was ended for rail service chiefly by the growth of coal traffic. In addition to the freight and passenger trains of the Chesapeake and Ohio, the structure carried about half those of the Louis-ville and Nashville as well. An investigation of traffic volume in 1916 revealed that the bridge was carrying locomotives 55 per cent heavier and train loads 100 per cent heavier than those for which it was designed. By strengthening the trusses and severely restricting the weight of engines and the speed of trains, the railroad kept it in service for another twelve years, but eventually it had to be replaced by a new bridge (1928–29). The earlier one was sold to the state of Kentucky for highway use and still stands immediately alongside the later span. From the highway one may see a striking demonstration of how even the largest and best designed structures of the nineteenth century seem small and flimsy beside those of the twentieth. The 1929 bridge, one of the largest of its kind ever built, is staggering in its size and weight and wholly overshadows its companion.

Before the end of the century the length of a simple span increased again, and it was once more the Ohio River that provided the necessity. The Louisville and Jeffersonville Bridge Company, a subsidiary of the Cleveland, Cincinnati, Chicago and St. Louis Railroad, built a single-track bridge over the river at Louisville with three main spans of 547-foot length (1889–95).[23] The remainder of the river crossing was divided into shorter spans, the longest being 341 feet. The trusses of the L. and J. bridge were identical with those of the Chesapeake and Ohio span at Cincinnati, and the largest was almost similar in dimensions, having an over-all depth of 80 feet. The existence of big steel bridges such as these at the end of the century and their satisfactory performance over many years indicate that the science of long-span structures had become mature. The process of construction, however, was still highly unsafe, a state of affairs tragically emphasized by the catastrophes that struck the Louisville and Jeffersonville bridge. Financial difficulties at the start held up construction for several months. It was scarcely under way when, on January 10, 1890, a pier caisson collapsed under water pressure and carried twelve men to death by drowning or suffocation. In the same year a caisson section was being lowered into position when a wooden beam broke and killed four more. These accidents served as a prelude to the terrifying climax. On December 15, 1893, a violent windstorm hit the central long span and destroyed the falsework. The mass of steel fell into the water, taking 21 lives on the way. Then, as incredible as it seems, later during the same day the storm carried the first completed span off the piers and into the water. The earlier accident kept the remainder of the crew off the bridge, so that no lives were lost in the final disaster. The total had run to 37 deaths, a near-record in this still hazardous work.

The causes of the collapse of two spans in one day were easy to discover when the inevitable backward look was taken. In the first case the wind overturned a traveling crane on the falsework, the impact of which cut down some of the timber supports. But the damage would have been much smaller if the falsework had been adequately braced in the longitudinal direction. The common practice at the time was to "squeeze" the falsework between piers and to regard this technique as providing satisfactory bracing. Obviously it did not. The second span, presumably fixed in place, fell as the result of vibrations which sheared an end post at a spliced joint near its mid-point. Again, however, it was not the wind that was entirely to blame. The joint in question had not been riveted but was fastened only with temporary bolts. Further, sway bracing had not yet been installed in the bottom frame of the truss. The moral was simple: "never trust a bolted joint any longer than is necessary to put a riveted one in its place; and as soon as a structure is erected lose no time in placing and securing all its wind bracing."[24] The Louisville and Jeffersonville bridge was finally completed and served the railroad well enough for nearly thirty-five years. Like its model at Cincinnati, it was replaced in 1929.

## 6. THE CANTILEVER BRIDGE

The longest clear spans among truss bridges at the end of the nineteenth century were achieved by combining a pair of cantilevers with a suspended, or floating, span. Although the disposition of web members in a cantilever truss may differ little from that of a simple structure, the over-all form and the general action are sufficiently different to warrant placing it in a special class. Moreover, its history for most of its early life follows a distinct course, separate from the main line of development. It is curious and somewhat inexplicable that none of the major inventors of truss forms in the nineteenth century worked with the cantilever. It was the last quarter of the century, as a matter of fact, before it was given a large-scale demonstration in railroad practice. And it was the last decade before the engineers realized that it could be employed in spans very much longer than the longest of simple trusses. The fact that the cantilever is supported at only one end probably had something to do with the reluctance to use it under heavy rail traffic.[1] A sense of the validity of the form has a more immediate kinesthetic basis than the beam, since a bracket bears a much closer resemblance to the human arm than a lintel. Yet the problem of translating this intuitive realization into an adequate structure must have seemed most perplexing until well into the second half of the century.

Wooden cantilever bridges of crude form have been built since remote antiquity and have appeared in cultures with an extremely primitive technology. The form was recognized and understood during the Renaissance and was discussed at length in the first systematic work on bridge building, Hubert Gautier's *Treatise on Bridges* (1728). Among American builders, it was Thomas Pope who first discovered the form and proposed to construct usable bridges on the basis of it. In his *Treatise on Bridge Architecture* (1811) he printed an illustration of a cantilever bridge at Wandipore, India, constructed about 1660.[2] On the evidence of this print the two cantilevers appear to have been built up of massive timbers laid longitudinally, one above the other, each one somewhat longer than that immediately below it. The cantilever was thus a composite beam of corbeled construction. Pope's own projects for bridging the Hudson and East rivers were clearly based on the Wandipore structure, although he combined with it the principle of the arch. Some historians hold that Wernwag's bridges were in reality cantilevers, but such details as we have suggest that they were homogeneous arched trusses with only the natural cantilever action of any end segment of a fixed arch. Neither Wernwag nor Pope seems to have had any immediate influence in the direction of cantilever construction, and the record shows no work of this kind other than very crude vernacular essays until the 1860's.

Shortly after the Civil War a corporation was organized in Boston with the name of the Solid Lever Bridge Company. Its chief designing engineer was C. H. Parker, who achieved some reputation for redesigning the Pratt truss by adding a polygonal top chord, a modification often known as the Parker truss. In 1867 the company began to build cantilever bridges in both wood and iron throughout New England and the Canadian province of New Brunswick, but its active life does not appear to have extended beyond 1871. The name of the organization and such descriptive fragments as we possess on the wooden structures establish beyond doubt that Pope's design lay behind them. Their arched decks were supported on solid cantilevers built up of corbeled timbers securely anchored in the masonry of the abutments. Parker's design for the iron structures shows a much higher level of sophistication. A wrought iron Warren truss with posts, it had a level deck and a downward curving top chord which conformed to the decreasing bending stress from abutment to free end (fig. 78). Parker seems to have understood correctly the distribution of stresses in the top and bottom chords of the cantilever. His method of anchoring the truss consisted of a set of tension rods which extended downward from the end frame and were fixed in the masonry of the abutment wing wall. If the illustration is typical, the bridges did not have true anchor spans. The free ends of the two cantilevers carried a suspended truss. Thus most of the essential features were there, providing a sufficient basis for adaptation to large-scale railroad requirements.

The widespread interest aroused by the long preliminary discussion and ultimate construction of Brooklyn Bridge (1869–83) gave rise to numerous proposals for spanning the East River between Manhattan and Long Island. At

78  An iron cantilever bridge of the type built by the Solid Lever Bridge Company, 1867–71. C. H. Parker, designing engineer. The bridge is shown in the course of construction.

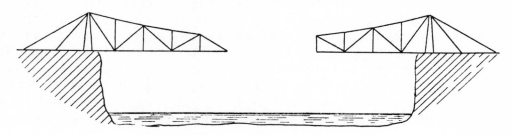

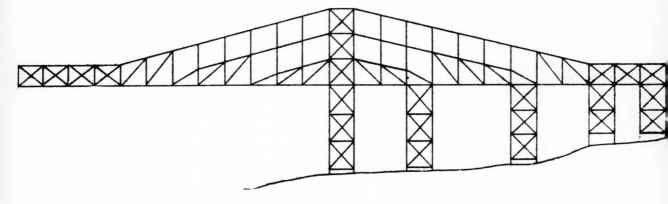

79   Project for a cantilever bridge over the East River at Blackwell's Island, New York City, 1872. Charles MacDonald, designing engineer. From left to right, side elevations of the floating span, cantilever, and anchor span.

least two of the projects, for a crossing at Blackwell's Island, were cantilevers. The first was submitted in 1867 by W. P. Trowbridge, and the second in 1872 by Charles MacDonald (fig. 79). The latter reached the point where a corporation known as the New York and Long Island Bridge Company was organized to undertake construction. Trowbridge's design was a structural fantasy, while MacDonald's was clumsy and dangerous. The main defect of the latter was that the cantilever and anchor trusses lacked adequate rigidity. But the basic elements of the long-span cantilever bridge—cantilever, anchor, and floating spans—were grasped in a way approximating their proper form. It was another fifteen years, however, before the mature concept reached a practical demonstration.

Meanwhile, the evolution continued along an irregular path. The next step was taken by Joseph M. Wilson, engineer of bridges and buildings for the Pennsylvania Railroad, when he designed the bridge to carry 40th Street over the railroad's tracks in Philadelphia (1874).[3] The structure involved the cantilever principle, but it was a curious hybrid in which the suspension bridge provided the other strain (fig. 80). Wilson described his span as a modification of the so-called straight-link suspension bridge invented in England by R. M. Ordish and patented in 1857. The 40th Street bridge had no suspended span, consisting only of two cantilevers and their respective anchor spans.[4] The main vertical supports were four towers at the corners of the central span. They were built up of wrought iron plates and angles laced together by a latticework of iron straps and encased in highly ornamented cast iron shells. The main span was in part a continuous suspension bridge, in part two cantilevers without a floating span.[5] Such a structure would not have been rigid throughout, but flexibility was what Wilson consciously intended. The 40th Street bridge was strengthened in 1913 and eventually replaced.

The decision to use the cantilever principle for a large railroad bridge was made in 1876 by two bold and imaginative engineers, L. F. G. Bouscaren and Charles Shaler Smith. The occasion was the necessity of bridging the Kentucky River for the Cincinnati Southern Railway at Dixville, Kentucky. Bouscaren, as we have noted, was chief engineer of the railroad company. Smith had learned his art in association with some of the leading engineers of his day. After an apprenticeship as surveyor with various roads, he became in 1855 assistant to George McLeod, then chief engineer of the Louisville and Nashville Railroad. Two years later he was made resident engineer under Albert Fink, at that time engineer of bridges and buildings for the L. and N. Smith continued his career during the Civil War as a captain of engineers in the Confederate Army. In 1866 he formed a bridge-building partnership with Benjamin and Charles Latrobe, an organization later incorporated as the Baltimore Bridge Company. As chief designer of the firm he acted as consultant to Eads on the St. Louis bridge (1868–74) and as co-designer with Bouscaren on the Dixville bridge (1876–77). He had a long line of bridges to his credit before his death at the age of 50 in 1886.

80 Bridge carrying 40th Street over the tracks of the Pennsylvania Railroad, Philadelphia, Pennsylvania, 1874. Joseph M. Wilson, engineer.

The chief problem at Dixville was that of erecting the trusses. The Kentucky River gorge at this point is 1,200 feet wide and 275 feet deep. The river has always been subject to flash floods of disastrous proportions, a maximum rise of 40 feet in one day having already been recorded when the two engineers made their preliminary survey. The use of falsework under such conditions was out of the question. Smith originally planned to build a continuous Whipple-Murphy deck truss, 1,125 feet long, extending over three spans of 375 feet each. The masonry towers for an earlier structure still stood at the tops of the cliffs, having been built in 1854 for a Roebling suspension bridge that was never completed.[6] Bouscaren made the proposal that hinges be introduced into the truss at two points, one at each end of the bridge between the shore and the nearest pier (fig. 81).[7] The major factors behind this decision were, first, improvement in the efficiency of the truss action; second, prevention of excessively high stresses resulting from pier settlement; and, third, the successful construction of Eads Bridge at St. Louis by the method of cantilevering the arches out from the abutments and piers. Because of the great length of span in the St. Louis bridge, the cantilevers extended outward a maximum of 260 feet before being joined as fixed arches. By adopting Bouscaren's suggestion Smith turned the bridge into a combination of types which were, in succession from shore to shore, a semi-floating span fixed at the abutment and hinged at the free end, a 75-foot cantilever, a fixed-end truss acting as anchor span to the cantilever, and so on in reverse order to the opposite shore. The material throughout was wrought iron. There was little precedent for a bridge of this kind, and Smith and Bouscaren staked their reputations on it. They saw it through to successful completion, and the bridge gave the railroad nearly thirty-five years of service before it was replaced in 1911 on the same masonry.[8]

Conditions similar to those at Dixville exist along the Niagara River immediately below the Falls, where the swift current and deep water of a flood are

81  Bridge of the Cincinnati Southern Railway, Kentucky River, Dixville, Kentucky, 1876–77. L. F. G. Bouscaren and C. Shaler Smith, engineers. In this diagram the portions of the top and bottom chords at the hinge panels are omitted to mark the location of the hinges.

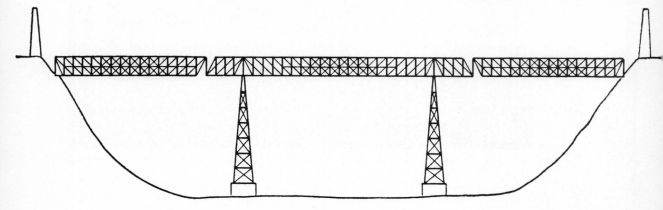

82  Bridge of the Michigan Central Railroad, Niagara River, Niagara Falls, New York, 1883. Charles C. Schneider, engineer.

permanent characteristics of the stream. Accordingly, when Charles C. Schneider built the steel and wrought iron bridge of the Michigan Central Railroad at this point, he adopted the cantilever principle and used it systematically and without ambiguity throughout the structure (fig. 82). In spite of its size, the bridge was erected in eight months, between April 15 and December 20, 1883. The bridge was divided symmetrically about the center into two cantilevers with their associated anchor spans and one floating span between the cantilevers.[9] The trusses were carried on a pair of high steel bents, whose four posts rested on masonry footings. The Niagara bridge was more distinctly modern in appearance than most of its predecessors by virtue of the simplicity of form and the greater weight of the individual pieces. The railroad replaced the bridge with a steel arch in 1925.

After the Niagara bridge the cantilever truss quickly reached its maturity in one of the great bridges of the century, the double-track railroad crossing of the Hudson River at Poughkeepsie, New York (fig. 83). Built by the Hartford and Connecticut Western Railway, the charter for construction of the bridge was granted in 1873, and work under an initial design was begun by the Poughkeepsie Bridge Company in 1878.[10] But financial difficulties forced suspension of construction in the early 1880's. The delay continued until 1886, when the properties of the original builder were purchased by the Manhattan Bridge Company and construction was resumed in co-operation with the Union Bridge Company of Buffalo and Dawson, Symmes and Usher, foundation engineers of New York City. The bridge was substantially redesigned by the structural engineers J. F. O'Rourke, P. P. Dickinson, and A. B. Paine.

The decision to build this enormous and costly structure on the part of a small railroad company rested on a farsighted appraisal of its potential importance. The original aim was to link the New England industries with the anthracite fields of Pennsylvania, an intention based on the estimate that as early as 1886 the coal traffic would amount to 3,000,000 tons per year. The new builders pushed construction steadily and opened the bridge to traffic in 1888, a long-span steel cantilever structure, which for its age was virtually in a class by itself. Proof of its high quality of design and workmanship is that, although it has twice been strengthened, it has never been replaced. Its total length of over a mile was a record for a steel structure, as was the 548-foot length of its channel span.[11] The cantilevers and anchors are modifications of the Warren truss with posts. The trusses of the connecting span are a special form with subdivided panels each containing a pair of diagonals. The piers, of coursed limestone surrounding a concrete core, rest on elaborate foundations of timber, iron, and concrete.[12] The concrete of the timber crib was poured by bucket from a barge anchored above the position of the foundation. The approaches of the bridge are carried on steel bents whose posts rest on concrete footings.

The builders of the Poughkeepsie bridge faced every kind of difficulty in the extreme: a deep, wide tidal river, great depth of bearing rock, height of the palisades which fixed the level of the deck, and sheer length of the whole structure. They met them well. The bridge was strengthened in 1906–7, and the two tracks were combined into a gauntlet in 1917 to avoid eccentric loading, but otherwise the bridge has required only routine maintenance and repairs. Today it not only fulfills its original role, but also serves as the key link in an important through freight route between the Ohio valley, the Pocohontas region, and the New England cities.[13]

83  Bridge of the Hartford and Connecticut Western Railway, Hudson River, Poughkeepsie, New York, 1886–88. P. P. Dickinson, J. F. O'Rourke, and A. B. Paine, engineers. Left to right, side elevations of the connecting, cantilever, and anchor spans.

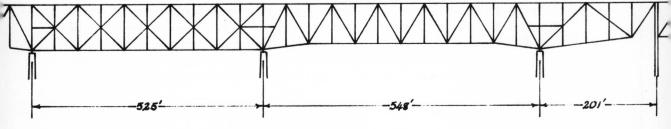

84  Bridge of the Kansas City, Fort Scott and Memphis Railroad, Mississippi River, Memphis, Tennessee, 1888–92. George S. Morison and Alfred Noble, engineers.

The cantilever truss reached its greatest size in the United States before the end of the century with the construction of the first Mississippi River bridge at Memphis, Tennessee. The extraordinary possibilities of the form were being demonstrated by the British engineers Benjamin Baker and John Fowler, who were then building the Firth of Forth bridge (1879–90), with two spans of 1,710 feet each and a maximum truss depth of 330 feet. The initial proposal for a crossing at Memphis was made in 1884, and a bill authorizing construction was presented in Congress but failed to pass, in part because of the opposition of the steamboat lobby. Two years later the Kansas City, Fort Scott and Memphis Railroad organized a building corporation and provided it with sufficient capital to carry out the huge project.[14] A second bill authorizing construction was passed by the Congress in 1886. The steamboat interests, however, were not willing to admit defeat. They demanded that the channel span be at least 1,000 feet in length and were prepared to use the courts to secure their alleged rights in the matter. To settle the issue the government appointed an impartial board of engineers. After a year of investigation the board concluded that the interests of all parties concerned would be satisfied by a channel span of about 800 feet. Their conclusion accepted, the railroad began construction in October 1888 and opened the bridge to traffic in 1892 (fig. 84). Its designing engineers, George S. Morison and Alfred Noble, were in the front rank of their profession at the time, and they planned the structure on a heroic scale.

The Memphis bridge is a steel structure 1½ miles in length overall. Its most striking features are the mile-long west approach of deck-girder spans and the 791-foot channel span.[15] Except for a Warren deck truss at the west bank of the river, the trusses are of a unique form difficult to categorize according to any of the standard types. The panels are unusually long, and the great bulk of the load is carried by the massive double diagonals, which cross from the center of one panel to that of the next. The over-all elevation of the river trusses presents an asymmetrical profile because of the absence of a cantilever-anchor pair at the west end to balance those at the east. In addition to the usual sway bracing in the top and bottom frames there is a dense latticework of light members set transversely between pairs of opposite diagonals. The four river piers of the bridge are of stone masonry resting on reinforced concrete foundations. The piers were built up in caissons from a stratum of hard clay underlying the mud, sand, and gravel of the river bed. The foundation of the deepest pier lies 131 feet below mean high water. The single track of the bridge is set in a deck of wooden planking flush with the top of the rail. In full use today, the Memphis bridge remains the only rail link between the city and the western lines.

After the Memphis bridge the cantilever spans erected during the remainder of the century seem anti-climactic. One, however, was spectacular because of its unusual height, the Pecos River bridge of the Galveston, Harrisburg and San Antonio Railway between Comstock and Langtry, Texas (1891–92).[16] The river at this point, close to its confluence with the Rio Grande, flows through a deep limestone gorge, which necessitated carrying the structure on high steel bents (fig. 85). Nearly the entire length of the bridge was composed of a succession of short girder and lattice spans arranged in alternating order.[17] The cantilevers, anchors, and floating span were Warren deck trusses. The bridge was strengthened in 1910 by substituting heavier members in the cantilevers and by replacement of the lattice trusses with plate girders. The entire structure was replaced by the present span in 1944.[18]

The construction of many cantilever bridges in the last decade of the nineteenth century demonstrated the high level of technical skill that the bridge builders had achieved. At the same time, it brought forth with equal force the problem of the aesthetic treatment of such bridges. It seemed hopeless, and in most cases the designers simply gave up and dismissed the problem as impossible of solution. Yet some engineers and a few journalists of the engineering press were seriously concerned with the matter. There was much criticism, based on the conviction that the engineer could create an aesthetic form if he consciously sought it as one end of his design:

Although the construction of iron and steel bridges [wrote the editor of *Engineering Record*] has reached a point at which the design meets every reasonable

85 Bridge of the Galveston, Harrisburg and San Antonio Railway, Pecos River, Comstock, Texas, 1891–92.

requirement of economy and safety, it is a fact which impresses at least some engineers as well as other people that graceful lines and the elements of beauty are almost absolutely lacking in that class of structure. There are some large bridges, it is true, in which the massiveness of the members and the magnitude of the entire work impress a beholder with an idea of grandeur which is more or less awe-inspiring, but even in those cases it can scarcely be said, even with the greatest stress of professional charity, so to speak, that there are any lines of real beauty or grace. . . . We believe the time is near at hand when the engineer's functions will not be considered complete . . . unless he makes the combination [of beauty and utility] which has heretofore been so rare. As a matter of fact, structural lines have meaning, and if they are so disposed to make that fact clear in a graceful manner, as they may be in almost every case, a structure will result in which the beauty of intelligence, at least, will appeal to the eye. It has been considered about impossible to make a cantilever structure a thing of beauty, but we believe even that, under proper treatment, is quite within the limits of possibility, although such ugly outlines as those of the principal cantilevers in this country and abroad might seem to justify the alleged hopelessness of the problem. If graceful effects are ever to be reached in bridge design it must be through a very advanced professional preparation on the part of the designers, and as there has been very great progress in that direction in the past few years we believe that there is much encouragement for the hope of escape at least from the reproduction of a good deal of structural ugliness which has been imposed upon the public up to the present time.[19]

It was one thing to demand beauty in the truss bridge, but a much more difficult problem to suggest how it might be achieved. Nearly all those who raised the question were committed to some kind of functionalist theory in which aesthetic quality was held to be a natural consequence of structural rightness and maximum efficiency of form. There were usually two aspects to this doctrine. One was that the exactitude of empirical form, without ornament or structural redundancy, is in itself visually aesthetic. The other, as the foregoing quotation shows, was based on an unconscious Platonism in which a bridge, for example, represents a concrete expression of reason manifesting itself in abstract analysis. In neither case, however, have we reached the essence of aesthetic form. The initial question is whether an empirical form like the cantilever truss has any elements which might be said to be the primary ingredients of an aesthetic experience, or of an object of beauty. The older trusses of cast and wrought iron, though often homely in their heavy-handed vernacular way, offered a vigorously articulated pattern of heavy compression members in a kind of structural counterpoint with thin tension rods. In the best of them this relationship could produce a clean, sharply etched abstract pattern of pleasing character. The steel railroad truss, on the other hand, is a stable and heavy thing, as permanent as a topographic feature, whose massive geometry seems far removed from the beauty Euclid is alleged to have looked upon. Yet in bridges of great size it has a kind of primitive dignity and power, black and spare, somehow moving in the sturdy rightness of its form. The conclusion seems inescapable that this is as close to aesthetic character as the truss bridge can come.[20]

# V

# THE SUSPENSION BRIDGE

## 1. THE PIONEER WORK OF FINLEY AND ELLET

The suspension bridge is of great antiquity in the Orient, but it was the last of the basic forms to appear in Europe. It was originally invented in China, apparently as early as the first century B.C., when it was built with cables of rope. Iron chains must have been developed early in the history of the type, since the first accurately dated reference (A.D. 580) suggests that the use of iron had been common for a long time. There is no evidence that even the idea of such a bridge occurred to anyone in classical or medieval Europe. The first European illustration of a Chinese suspension bridge was published by Fausto Veranzio in 1595, but none was built until 1741, when an iron-chain footbridge was constructed across the River Tees in Durham County, England. Not only was this the first permanent suspension bridge in the western world, but there is good ground for believing that it was the first bridge in which iron was used for a structural element. Yet it was not immediately popular in its native land; as a consequence, it later proved to be the one structural form in which the United States could claim leadership.

The iron-chain suspension bridge with a level, rigid deck suitable for vehicular traffic was the invention of James Finley, a native of Fayette County, Pennsylvania, who spent most of his professional life as a judge and justice of the peace. In 1796 he invented a flexible cable or chain of wrought iron links, which was essentially like that of the Durham County bridge. His original invention came in 1801, when he developed a bridge with a permanently level deck, whose rigidity was maintained either by longitudinal wooden trusses or iron girders and transverse wooden beams. There is no evidence, however, that any of Finley's bridges were built with iron girders as deck stiffeners. He gave his invention its first practical demonstration in the same year but did not receive a patent until 1808. About forty bridges were built on his patent between 1808 and 1816, when the invention of the wire cable eventually ended the life of the iron-chain bridge.

The two fundamental problems which Finley had to solve were the methods of determining the exact length of the cable and the length of each hanger or suspender necessary to maintain a level deck. His approach was simple and directly empirical, as his own description indicates:

To find the proportions of the several parts of a bridge of one hundred and fifty feet span, set off on a board fence or partition one hundred and fifty inches for the length of the bridge, draw a horizontal line between these two points representing the underside of the lowest tier of joists—on this line mark off the spaces for the number of joists intended in the lower tier, and raise perpendiculars from each, and from the two extreme points, then fasten the ends of a strong thread at these two perpendiculars, twenty-three inches and one quarter above the horizontal line —the thread must be so slack that when loaded, the middle of it will sink to the horizontal line; then attach equal weights to the thread at each of the perpendiculars—and mark carefully where the line intersects each of them.[1]

The simplicity of Finley's method of design is a fine example of vernacular naïveté, especially in the substitution of a fence for a drafting table. His description is a little ambiguous at one point because he fails to state that the perpendiculars should be equally spaced along the horizontal line, although this is plainly what he means. The load points are hence equally distributed along the deck but not along the chain, which as a consequence falls in a parabola rather than a catenary.

Finley's first bridge was built over Jacob's Creek at Uniontown, Pennsylvania (1801). Its span between towers was 70 feet, the over-all width of the roadway 12 feet 6 inches, and the height of the towers above the deck about 15 feet. The deck was stiffened with shallow longitudinal trusses of wood; cables and suspenders were wrought iron chains. The first American suspension bridge, it was also the first modern bridge of its type, since all the essential features remained throughout the history of the form—hangers or suspenders of varying length to maintain the deck in a fixed line, level or bowed slightly upward, the rigid deck with stiffening members, and the parabolic curve of the cables.

A somewhat larger bridge over the Potomac above Georgetown, Maryland (1807), was the one that brought Finley his fame (fig. 86). The span could not

86   Bridge over the Potomac River above Georgetown, Maryland, 1807. James Finley, builder.

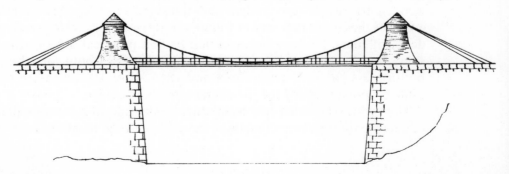

87  The second Essex-Merrimac Bridge, Merrimack River, above Newburyport, Massachusetts, 1810. Finley and Templeman, builders.

have been more than 100 feet and the towers were about 25 feet high. The latter were weatherboarded timber bents of odd form, squat and concave at the sides. Since the towers rested directly on the high abutment walls, there were no anchor spans, the chains being anchored in the masonry of the long wing walls extending back from the abutments.[2] Because of the difference in elevation between the river banks at the site, one approach of the George-town bridge had to be built at a steep grade on an embankment. As a consequence, the abutment at this end was a completely enclosed square of battered masonry walls surrounding an earth fill. Although the structure disappeared long ago, the neighborhood of its location is still known as Chain Bridge.

Without any effort on Finley's part the Georgetown bridge received international attention. Albert Gallatin's report to Congress on the roads and canals of the United States (1808) contained a description of the span. Thomas Pope, in his *Treatise on Bridge Architecture* (1811), gave an account of it, together with adverse criticism based on the contention that, if one link in the chain broke, the whole bridge would collapse. Two French authors of early works on suspension bridges, Cordier and Navier, who knew Gallatin's report and Pope's treatise, gave Finley full credit for invention of the level-deck suspension bridge. Louis Navier was the leading figure in the science of structural materials at the beginning of the century, and his classic *Memoir on Suspension Bridges* (1823) was the authoritative work on the subject. More than this, there seems to be good ground for believing that Thomas Telford knew Pope's book and hence something of Finley's work. If this was the case, then it may be that Telford's celebrated suspension bridge across Menai Strait (1818–26) was derived from the work of an obscure Pennsylvania judge.[3]

Finley's next bridge was of much greater length than anything he had previously attempted. It was a footbridge across the Schuylkill River at Philadelphia (1809) with a span between towers of 308 feet. It was similar to the others in all respects—wrought iron chains, wooden stiffening trusses and towers. For some reason the bridge was found unsatisfactory and was replaced in 1816. The largest of Finley's bridges in total weight was the Essex-Merrimac span a few miles above Newburyport, Massachusetts (1810), constructed in collaboration with a local builder named John Templeman (fig. 87). The double roadway of planking on wooden transverse beams spanned 244 feet between towers. The total load was divided among four groups of wrought iron chains, one group on either side of the roadway and two at the center. Each chain was 516 feet long between anchors. The suspenders were solid wrought iron rods. The A-shaped wooden bents that constituted the towers rested on masonry anchor piers. The approaches to the main span were pile-and-girder structures of the traditional form. The chain links of the Essex-Merrimac bridge were forged on the site, and in spite of the fact that they were only once painted, they survived in sound condition for 100 years. Weight of traffic required that the bridge be closed in 1909. Its long life offered many opportunities for investigation of structural details in the Finley bridge, but no one appears to have taken the trouble, with the result that we know very little about such elements as chain saddles, anchors, and connections between chains and suspenders.[4]

An invention of the greatest importance for mechanical and structural techniques very nearly ended the active life of the chain bridge in 1816. In that year Josiah White and Erskine Hazard, ironworkers, anthracite mine operators, and owners of a Philadelphia wire mill, manufactured the first wire-rope cable in the United States of sufficient strength to be used in the suspension bridge. White and Hazard put their invention to immediate use in the Schuylkill River bridge built to replace Finley's earlier structure at the same site. But there was much to learn about cable-bridge construction, and the knowledge was to be developed largely by French investigators, of whose work the Philadelphia wire manufacturers remained wholly ignorant. Each cable of the Schuylkill bridge consisted of only three ⅛-inch brass wires bound at intervals into a fairly tight unit. The bridge was longer than Finley's, having a span of about 400 feet between towers, but it was only 2 feet wide. The roadway was limited to foot traffic, and no more than eight persons were allowed on the deck at any one time. White and Hazard had reason to doubt the strength of their wire, for in the winter of the same year their bridge collapsed under a load of snow and ice.

88  Bridge over the Merrimack River, Newburyport, Massachusetts, 1826–27. Thomas Haven, builder.

This misfortune was the major factor in deterring builders from making immediate practical use of the great advantages inherent in wire-rope cable. Not only did it offer flexibility and elasticity, but with properly drawn wire it provided far greater strength that that of solid pieces of equal cross-sectional area. When wire is drawn, its tensile strength is increased, up to a certain limit, with each successive drawing or reduction in its diameter. If a large number of finely drawn wires can be compacted into a unit so tightly bound that there is no wear from slippage between wires, the resulting mass will possess a tensile strength many times greater than a bar or rolled shape of equal cross-sectional area of metal. The failure of White and Hazard's bridge was probably in part a consequence of the inadequate binding of the wires. Further progress in the use of wire cable came after the achievements of French engineers—the construction by Marc Seguin and Gabriel Lamé of the first wire-rope suspension bridges in Europe (1824–26), and the method of spinning the cable at the site, invented by Louis Vicat (1829).

What was probably the last of the chain suspension bridges was at the same time the first multispan bridge of its type. It was built by Thomas Haven to cross the wide estuary of the Merrimack River immediately below Newburyport, Massachusetts, 1826–27 (fig. 88). The bridge was about 1,000 feet long overall, and was divided into three main and two anchor spans, with a short draw span at one end. One anchor span was 150 feet long, the rest of them under the cable 200 feet each. The level deck of the bridge was thus carried by a pair of continuous chains which passed over four pairs of towers between the anchors in the abutment walls. The towers, weatherboarded timber bents resting on masonry piers, stood 31 feet above the deck. In theory Haven's adaptation of the suspension principle to a multispan bridge was sound: since the tension in the cable between any pair of towers would act in a direction opposite to that between the adjacent pair, the horizontal components of the tension at each saddle would balance each other. Any one span might thus be regarded as an anchor to the one adjacent to it. Traffic and wind loads on the bridge, however, would naturally subject it to an unequally distributed load, with the result that tension on one side of a tower would momentarily be greater than that on the other. The tower would then be subjected to twisting or overturning forces which might be sufficient to cause serious damage. For this reason multispan suspension bridges have been extremely rare since 1850. The only one of great size that exists today—Bay Bridge, San Francisco —has two spans with a common anchor pier at the middle of the crossing.

The American revival of the wire-cable suspension bridge was the work of a man of most unusual but often thoroughly frustrated talents. He was Charles Ellet, engineer, mechanical inventor, and geographer, who was born near Bristol, Pennsylvania, in 1810. He had little formal schooling but managed to teach himself elementary mathematics and French. The boy's father, a Quaker, was opposed to his son's adolescent interest in engineering, with the result that he left home at the age of 17 to become a surveyor's assistant on the Chesapeake and Ohio Canal. Ellet was appointed surveyor in 1828, a position he held until 1830, when he went to Paris for a year's study at the École Polytechnique. He was thus the only American builder of his time who enjoyed first-hand association with the brilliant group who had already made the French institution the finest scientific school in Europe.

Ellet returned to the United States full of schemes for bridge projects, very few of which came to fruition. He took up his original profession of surveying and advanced rapidly to prominence as an engineer. For twenty-five years, up to the beginning of the Civil War, he served as chief engineer in charge of construction for a number of eastern railroad and canal companies. He built an ironclad ram for the Union which saw service in the action at Memphis in 1862. During the engagement Ellet received injuries which proved fatal, and he died within a few months of the battle.[5] Ellet's best creative talents were either denied expression or, if used, led to misfortune and disaster. Most of his bridge projects were rejected, his plans for flood control and coastal harbor defense were neglected, he saw his greatest bridge go down in a storm, and finally, he was fatally wounded in military action involving his only invention that the government accepted.

As a student at the École Polytechnique, Ellet was profoundly impressed by the work of the men who created the modern cable suspension bridge and developed the first body of theory on its mode of action—Lamé, Seguin, Vicat, and Navier. His extraordinary imagination fired, he began at the age of 22 to offer his many proposals for suspension bridges of unheard-of span length. His first was a project to construct a highway bridge over the Potomac River at Washington with a span between towers of 1,000 feet. The proposal was submitted to Congress in 1832 and was quickly turned down. A few years later he entertained a more ambitious scheme, a project for a suspension bridge with a 1,200-foot span over the Mississippi River at St. Louis (1839–40). His next three bridges were carried to completion, but two of them lasted only six years. There was another unbuilt project for a railway span over the Connecticut River at Middletown, Connecticut (1848), and a second for the Potomac at Washington (1852), which was his swan song as a bridge builder.

The first of Ellet's completed bridges was built over the Schuylkill River at Philadelphia (1841–42) to replace Wernwag's Colossus. It was a roadway

89 Bridge over the Schuylkill River, Philadelphia, Pennsylvania, 1841–42. Charles Ellet, engineer.

bridge, for vehicular as well as foot traffic, and had a clear span between towers of 358 feet (fig. 89). The towers were either slender weatherboarded timber bents or solid built-up columns of wood which stood 50 feet above the deck. Since they were set on the abutments, there were no anchor spans. The chief supporting members were ten cables of wrought iron wire, five to a side, which were not bound throughout their length into a compact unit and were unwrapped. The length of the suspenders, also of wire-rope, was calculated to maintain a slightly bowed deck, with the aid of wooden stiffening trusses which also acted as rails. The Schuylkill bridge was a preliminary essay to Ellet's greatest completed structure, the highway suspension bridge across the Ohio River at Wheeling, West Virginia (1846–49; Virginia at that date). Its main span, 1,010 feet long, was hung by cable suspenders from two parallel groups of six cables, the twelve together containing 6,600 wires. The cables were hung from masonry towers, the first of stone to be built in the United States for a suspension bridge. The original suspenders were inclined slightly from the vertical. Longitudinal stiffening trusses of wood helped to maintain the rigidity of the level deck. In its reconstructed form the Wheeling bridge has survived more than a century of use, carrying vehicular traffic to this day.

Of all the American bridges that he studied, Culmann was most impressed by the Wheeling span, and it was partly on this basis that he recommended the use of the suspension bridge for railroad service. There is no question that Ellet's bridge was a mature work of structural art for its type and day, but there were two possible sources of failure in it: first, the likelihood of weaknesses and flaws in some 2,000 miles of wrought iron wire, and, second, inadequate binding of the cables, with the result that the separate strands could not act as a unit and were liable to deterioration from friction. These and other less predictable variables led to nearly complete destruction of the bridge by storm in 1854. John A. Roebling, already at work on his Niagara span, was invited to rebuild the structure, of which only the north cables remained.[6] He built a much stronger bridge by compacting the cable strands and wrapping them in a continuous helix of coated wire, and by introducing an auxiliary system of suspenders in the form of radiating cables extending from the tops of the towers outward and downward to the deck (fig. 90). It was a device that he used in a more elaborate way on all his large bridges. The suspenders were hung from iron clamps encircling the cables.

Ellet's final work to reach the stage of construction again found Roebling at hand to take over when trouble came. It seems an unkind fate, yet for all the value of Ellet's pioneering, there is no question of the superiority of the great German-born engineer, who had the advantage of a full training in a German technical school. In 1847 the directors of the American and Canadian Niagara Bridge Company offered Ellet the contract for a bridge to span the river two miles below the Falls. The site is the kind which requires either a suspension, arch, or cantilever span, but at the time only the suspension

90  Bridge over the Ohio River, Wheeling, West Virginia. Originally built by Charles Ellet, 1846–49; reconstructed by John A. Roebling, 1854. The photograph shows Roebling's bridge.

91 Bridge over the Niagara River, Niagara Falls, New York, 1847–48. Charles Ellet, engineer.

bridge could be built with a span long enough to cross the river without intermediate supports. The high cliffs on either side of the gorge fixed the height of the deck. The deep water and swift current of the river and the ice jams of mid-winter made it impossible to construct piers or falsework between the banks. These factors meant that the typical railroad truss bridge was out of the question. In the face of these formidable difficulties, Ellet began the job and by 1848 had erected a light footbridge with a 770-foot span and a 9-foot width (fig. 91). His plan was to use it as an auxiliary service span for construction of a wider and heavier structure designed to carry both road and rail traffic. Its flimsy character and the absence of stiffening trusses indicated its temporary nature. Before he could begin work on the larger bridge, however, he was involved in a dispute with the company's directors and resigned in 1848 rather than accept their terms. The footbridge stood until 1854, having been used by Roebling for three years as the auxiliary for which Ellet intended it. But it was Roebling, of course, who took up the contract after Ellet's resignation and who thus had the honor of building the first railroad suspension bridge.

## 2. FROM JOHN ROEBLING TO THE END OF THE CENTURY

That John Augustus Roebling stood in the front rank of creative engineers in his time has never been seriously disputed. At the same time he possessed a greatness of mind and moral character that made him the embodiment of the highest ideals of his profession. His courage and his sense of civic responsibility, as well as his inventive genius, produced a life as admirable as his art.

Roebling was born in 1806 in the town of Mühlhausen, Thüringen, at the time one of the many cities and principalities of Napoleon's Confederation of the Rhine, but after the Congress of Vienna a part of the kingdom of Prussia. He received his higher education at the Royal Polytechnic School in Berlin, from which he graduated in 1826 after a program of study embracing architecture, civil engineering, and philosophy, the last under Hegel. He began his professional career as an engineer of public and military works for the Prussian government, a position he held until 1829.

But the Prussian state hardly provided a congenial atmosphere for a man of Roebling's beliefs and temperament. A republican of liberal convictions, his name on the police lists as a suspected subversive, he was not long tolerated as a civil servant. Finding his own career blocked, disappointed in the failure of the liberal movement in the German states, he came to the United States in 1831. In his adopted land, perhaps with the hope of helping to realize the ideal on an agrarian republic, he abandoned engineering and took up farming. Fortunately he made a poor job of it and wisely decided to return to the art for which he was so brilliantly suited.

His engineering work in America began in 1837 with a surveyorship on the construction of the Beaver River Canal in Pennsylvania and Ohio. From there he went to the Pennsylvania Railroad, then building its line through the Alleghenies from Harrisburg to Pittsburgh. He worked first as surveyor, later as assistant in the bridge department. With the work of Finley, Ellet, and the European pioneers behind him, Roebling was early impressed by the possibilities of the suspension bridge, on which he had written a dissertation as a student. By 1840 he had developed the method of manufacturing wire-rope cable, which was to be his chief industrial contribution.

It was on the basis of this invention that he received, in 1844, his first commission for a bridge, an aqueduct to carry the state-owned Pennsylvania Canal over the Allegheny River in the northwestern corner of the state. Roebling designed a wooden aqueduct of seven spans hung from a pair of continuous wire cables suspended between anchors from a series of timber bents. The aqueduct was condemned by most engineers of the time, not only because of the novelty of the structural system, but also because Roebling used it for the heaviest load that any bridge could be called upon to carry.

172

Extending out from each side of the wooden flume was a tow path carried on triangular brackets fixed to the girders at the bottom of the side walls. A portion of the weight of each span was carried by the trusses in the walls of the flume, a reduction of the load on the cables which Roebling was to accomplish by various methods in all his bridges.[1] A massive and complex structure, the Allegheny aqueduct was constructed in nine months, between August 1844 and May 1845. But the life of the Pennsylvania Canal was nearing its end. Competition from the railroads forced abandonment of the remarkable waterway in 1861, and Roebling's aqueduct was demolished the same year.[2]

The success of the Allegheny aqueduct offered an immediate advantage to the canal builders—that is, a method of reducing the expense of the costliest part of canal construction. The aqueduct was a necessity at any intersection with another artery, such as a highway or railroad, but such structures were generally quite short. A river crossing, however, might require either a trussed or masonry span of great length and weight or a double flight of locks into and out of the valley. Either alternative involved a prohibitive expense, and Roebling offered a way out of the dilemma. The Delaware and Hudson Company, which was faced with an unusual number of deep valley crossings, was the first to make systematic use of his ability. The company was established in 1823 to transport anthracite coal from the Pennsylvania mines to the river terminals in the region, its initial impetus stemming from the War of 1812, which cut off the British coal supply. The original Delaware and Hudson Canal was completed in 1828 and quickly came to be regarded as an engineering marvel for the young Republic. Most famous of its features was the inclined railway built to lift canal boats over the ridge between Carbondale and Honesdale, Pennsylvania.

The improvement and extension of the waterway in the decade of the 1840's led to the company's commissioning Roebling to build four suspension aqueducts respectively over the Rondout, Neversink, Delaware, and Lackawaxen rivers in northeastern Pennsylvania (1845–50) to eliminate the flights of locks at these crossings. The structures which he designed were wooden aqueducts with floors of planking laid on transverse beams and side walls of trusses covered with diagonal sheathing. The continuous wire cables rested on cast iron saddles set into squat stone posts extending above the piers to a height equal to that of the side walls. The longest of these aqueducts, the Delaware, was over 1,000 feet from end to end, and its 8½-inch cables were consequently the largest. The wrought iron wire of the cables was apparently neither coated nor wrapped. All transportation on the canal was taken over by the Delaware and Hudson Railroad by the end of the century, and most of the aqueducts were demolished with the waterway's abandonment. The one over the Lackawaxen River, however, survived until the mid-twentieth century, carrying automobile traffic as late as 1952.

Roebling's first commission for a vehicular bridge came shortly after he began his work with the Delaware and Hudson Company. In April 1845 fire destroyed a large area of commercial waterfront buildings in Pittsburgh, together with Wernwag's Smithfield Street bridge over the Monongahela River. Roebling received the contract to build the new span, and completed the work early in 1846. It was 1,500 feet long between abutments, divided into six river and two anchor spans. The deck was carried by vertical suspenders of wrought iron rods which were hung from the two pairs of wire cables. The towers of the bridge were built of four hollow cast iron posts inclined inward, laced together by a latticework of wrought iron straps and anchored to the pier masonry by bolts. The railings were designed as shallow lattice trusses to function as stiffening members. Part of the total load was carried by stays of wrought iron eye-bars radiating downward and outward from the tops of the towers. The stays were fixed at their lower ends to the transverse beams which supported the deck. Cables for the Smithfield Street bridge were spun on the shore in the parabolic form they would assume on the bridge and fixed in place on the towers from flatboats carrying scaffolding. Although the bridge was perfectly sound, the weight of traffic required the replacement of this handsome pioneer work in 1883.[3]

In 1848 Ellet resigned from the Niagara River project. The original company was reorganized into two, the Niagara Falls Suspension and the Niagara Falls International Bridge companies. With sufficient capital to carry the program through, they offered Roebling the contract in 1851. Four years later he completed the world's first railroad suspension bridge, in the face of nearly unanimous engineering opinion that such a bridge could not possibly succeed (fig. 92). The dissenting voice, as we have seen, was that of Karl Culmann, who based his recommendation on Ellet's Wheeling bridge. Robert Stephenson, referring to his own tubular bridge, paid Roebling the highest compliment: "If your bridge succeeds, mine is a magnificent blunder."[4]

The Niagara span was a double-deck structure, the upper for the trains of the Grand Trunk Railway, the lower for vehicles and pedestrians. The masonry towers were built at the top of the gorge, and between them stretched a level span 821 feet in length. Four 10-inch cables of 3,640 wires each, two to a side, carried the wire-rope suspenders that supported the decks. At their low points the two cables on one side were widely separated, the top pair carrying the suspenders for the upper deck, the bottom pair carrying those for the lower. Massive wooden posts and diagonal iron rods between the decks formed deep stiffening trusses, which were assisted by an additional pair of shallow trusses under the railroad deck. As in all of Roebling's bridges, the total load was divided between the cables and an extensive system of radiating stays. The enormous quantity of wire required for the Niagara span was manufactured in England, probably a consequence of the fact that the project

92  Vehicular and railroad bridge over the Niagara River, Niagara Falls, New York, 1851–55. John A. Roebling, engineer.

was in part a Canadian enterprise. By the 1890's the weight of rail traffic had outgrown the strength of Roebling's bridge, which was replaced in 1896 by the present double-deck steel arch. The neighborhood at the east end of this structure, though now a part of the city of Niagara Falls, is still called Suspension Bridge. The replacement of Roebling's span marked the end of the railroad suspension bridge, which lacks the rigidity necessary for the heavy moving loads.[5]

Before the end of the decade Roebling was again invited to build a suspension bridge at Pittsburgh, this time to carry 6th Street over the Allegheny River, where a 40-year-old Burr arch-and-truss had outlived its usefulness. Roebling's bridge (1857–60) was identical in form with the earlier Smithfield Street span, although shorter in length and having only four spans, including the anchor. The towers, on granite piers, were separate cast iron bents with wrought iron diagonal bracing. Two pairs of cables with wire-rope suspenders and radiating stays carried the deck. For the first time the cable was spun on the bridge by traveling sheaves. In the spring of 1858 Washington Roebling, then 21 years old, joined his father on construction of the 6th Street bridge to inaugurate his own career as builder and industrialist.

Compared with the heroic undertaking in which he was already involved at Cincinnati, the Pittsburgh project must have seemed a simple chore to the old master. A group of northern Kentucky business men, with great enthusiasm and little money, met at Covington in 1845 to plan a bridge across the Ohio River between Covington and Cincinnati. In the following year they asked John Roebling to survey the possible sites and to submit proposals for a permanent bridge. He suggested a suspension bridge with a single span of 1,200 feet, a structure whose cost considerably dampened their enthusiasm. Ten years later, after enlisting the aid of Cincinnatians, they formed the Covington and Cincinnati Bridge Company, with a capital of $314,000. Roebling was given the contract, and excavation for the masonry towers began in 1856. He had investigated the soil of the river banks and had discovered a gravel bed not far below the surface of the alluvial sediments which was sufficiently stable for the tower foundations. It was a brave beginning to eleven years of trouble and frustration. Ice and floods stopped the masonry work completely between February and July 1857. Construction was resumed and continued until December 1858. But the panic of the previous year and the subsequent depression bankrupted the company. The possibility of raising more money was seriously hampered by the Civil War. The project languished until 1863, when enough capital had been raised to begin construction once more. Three times wind destroyed the auxiliary footbridges erected for work on the cables and suspenders. The great bridge was at last opened on New Year's Day, 1867, and was finally completed seven months later. It stands in full use today, unaltered from Roebling's original design.

Nothing that John Roebling had previously done approached the magnitude of the Cincinnati bridge. And in length of clear span it outdistanced all other bridges in the world at the time. The masonry towers stand 230 feet above mean low water. Between them the river span stretches 1,057 feet, and the anchor spans on either side together add another 1,000. Roebling reduced the cables to a single pair, each 12½ inches in diameter and containing 5,180 wires helically wrapped with galvanized wire. All suspension members—suspenders, radiating stays, transverse stays between cables—are wire rope. On either side of the roadway two deep Howe trusses of wrought iron extend continuously between anchorages as stiffening members. The deck, bowed upward slightly between the towers, is 100 feet above mean low water at its center point. The cables are anchored by means of a group of wrought iron eye-bars fixed at their outer ends to huge cast iron plates buried in the masonry of the anchorages. Again Roebling had to turn to British manufacturers for his wire, which was spun into cables on the bridge. The total load of the structure is divided almost equally between the cables and the radiating stays, the former taking somewhat more than half. In its strength and durability, and in the finished quality of its design, the magnificent bridge reveals once and for all Roebling's unchallenged pre-eminence in his field.[6]

John Roebling began his last and greatest work in 1869, but he was never to see any of it beyond the stage of design. In 1867 he had been appointed chief engineer of the New York Bridge Company, which had been founded to undertake the enormous project of bridging the East River between Brooklyn and lower Manhattan. The stream was a dangerous obstacle, in the width and depth of the waterway, in the thick mass of alluvial sediments overlying bedrock, but above all in its swift and turbulent tidal currents. The great volume of shipping on it made a high-level single span a necessity. Projects for bridging the river went back more than half a century, beginning with Thomas Pope's proposal in 1811. They reached at least the possibility of realization in 1857, when Roebling made his first suggestion for such a bridge in a letter to Abram Hewitt. Controversy, opposition, economic depression, and the Civil War prevented any further action for eight years. With the end of the war, however, the last obstacle was removed, and the organizers of the New York Bridge Company moved with energy and decision. They appointed Roebling to his position in 1867 and raised the bulk of their capital by the end of 1868. The United States Army Engineers approved the project in June 1869, and the bill authorizing construction was passed by Congress and signed by President Grant before the end of the month. Roebling began the final survey on July 6, 1869, clearing the site was completed in the next few months, and construction of the caisson for the Brooklyn tower began on January 2, 1870.[7] The caisson was launched on March 19 of the same year, and from that date the work went on for thirteen years to its completion on May 24, 1883 (fig. 93).

For masonry towers of such size and weight it was necessary to excavate to bedrock for the foundations. This involved driving the caissons down through the river bed to a depth of 44 feet 6 inches below water on the Brooklyn side, and of 78 feet on the Manhattan.[8] There were dangerous hazards in the caissons, any one of which could have led to catastrophe. Collapse of walls, water and gas leaks, failure of pressure, drastic changes in pressure, fire—all posed constant threats; yet there were no major disasters, even though the Brooklyn caisson caught fire several times. There were, however, a great many injuries, several of which proved fatal. The chief victim of pressure change was Washington Roebling, who was permanently crippled by the "bends," or caisson disease, in the spring of 1872. As a consequence, he was forced to supervise the work from a sickroom, watching activities by telescope from his window. Down in the caissons the grim job of excavation went on until 20,000 cubic yards of material had been removed for the Brooklyn tower, and 22,000 cubic yards for the New York. Laying up of the granite and limestone masonry was carried on continuously as the caisson sank, the weight of masonry thus serving to drive the caisson into the river bed.

The towers and anchor piers were completed in the summer of 1876. The

93  Brooklyn Bridge, East River, New York City, 1869–83. John and Washington Roebling, engineers.

first traveler rope went across in a scow and was hoisted into position between the towers. The second was spliced into the first, and the two together thus formed an endless rope which passed over pulley wheels on the anchorages. High above the water the construction crew built in succession the plank footbridge, storm cradle, and carrier ropes. With these auxiliaries in place the slow but steady process of cable spinning could begin. Two sheaves suspended from the traveler ropes moved back and forth between the anchorages and over the saddles, each carrying a loop of wire on a single round trip. In this way 19 strands of 286 wires each were spun for each of the four cables. The crucible steel wire was drawn close to the site at the mill of the Haigh Iron Works in Brooklyn. The inner seven strands were wrapped together, then the outer twelve around them were wrapped again. As spinning progressed the cable strands were attached to the anchors, which had previously been built up in the anchor piers. The cable attachments were enclosed in open vaults to facilitate inspection. With the cables in place the rest of the work might have seemed routine by comparison. Twisted wire-rope suspenders, radiating stays, steel stiffening trusses, girders, beams, and roadway followed in that order. Finally, the approaches were constructed, a series of brick arches faced with granite and laid on limestone foundations, the outer masonry thus matching that of the towers and anchorages.

For the Brooklyn Bridge Roebling closely followed the design of his Cincinnati span, with two exceptions: one pair of cables is located at the center of the deck, the other two being in the usual positions at the sides, and the walkways are on either side of the center line at a level 3 feet below the top chords of the stiffening trusses.[9] The great bridge needed only routine repairs for the first seventy years of its life, but the weight of motor traffic eventually required extensive additions to the truss and deck structure (1953).

When the structure was at last completed, the crowds who crossed it on opening day hardly needed the statistics to realize that it dwarfed all previous works of the bridge builder's art. But the man whose vision and courage had created this monument was not among the celebrants. His death shortly before construction began fell into the ancient pattern of classical tragedy, for he had been cut down by the immense operation which he himself had conceived and set in motion. The final survey which Roebling began on July 6, 1869, proved to be the final act of his life. While he was standing on a cluster of piles near the site of the future Brooklyn tower, a ferry boat worked against the piling, caught the end of his foot, and crushed the toes. He survived the amputation of the injured members but died from the resulting tetanus infection on July 22, 1869. His death was a calamity to the whole building art and at first seemed the end of the grand project, but the example of his life itself was the energizing force that carried his ultimate monument to completion. The directors of the bridge company paid him the highest tribute when they appointed Washington Roebling chief engineer in August 1869. His own courage was as necessary to seeing the construction through as was his father's genius in creating the design.

The subsequent architectural influence of Brooklyn Bridge nearly matched its technical importance. John Roebling consciously sought to make it a work of civic as well as structural art. A few years after its completion Montgomery Schuyler subjected it to an exhaustive critique in an essay which is a masterpiece of analytical criticism in architecture.[10] While recognizing its greatness as a work of total structural art, he nevertheless found many questionable elements in the details of the towers, approaches, and anchorages:

The utilitarian treatment of our monument is as striking and as characteristic a mark of the period as its utilitarian purpose. It is a noble work of engineering: it is not a work of architecture. . . . Its defects in design are not misdeeds, but short-comings. They are defects of being rudimentary, of not being completely developed. The anatomy of the towers and the anchorages is not brought out in their modelling. Their fingers, so to speak, are all thumbs. Their impressiveness is inherent in their mass, and is what it could not help being. . . . But a far nobler thing than this is the central span of the great bridge itself, its roadway slowly sweeping upward to meet the swift swoop of its cables. . . . What monument of any architecture can speak its story more clearly and more forcibly than this gossamer architecture? . . . This aerial bow, as it hangs between the busy cities, . . . is perfect as an organism of nature. It is an organism of nature. There was no question in the mind of its designer of "good taste" or appearance. He learned the law that struck its curves, the law that fixed the strength and the relation of its parts, and he applied the law. . . . The designer of the Brooklyn Bridge has made a beautiful structure out of an exquisite refinement of utility, in a work in which the lines of force constitute the structure. Where a more massive material forbade him to skeletonize the structure, and the lines of effort and resistance needed to be brought out by modelling, he has failed to bring them out, and his structure is only as impressive as it needs must be. It has not helped his work, as we have seen, to trust his own sense of beauty, and to contradict or to conceal what he was doing in accordance with its dictates. As little would it have helped him to invoke the aid of a commonplace architect to plaster his structure with triglyphs or to indent it with trefoils.[11]

Lewis Mumford later saw Brooklyn Bridge not only as a work of art but as prophetic of a new movement in architecture:

In this structure the architecture of the past, massive and protective, meets the architecture of the future, light, aerial, open to sunlight, an architecture of voids rather than solids. . . . In its absence of ornament, its refusal to permit the steel to be other than its own unadorned reality, the Brooklyn Bridge pointed to the logic and aesthetics of the machine. . . . This was not the first work of engineering to be a work of art; but it was the first product of the age of coal and iron to achieve this completeness of expression. It needed a man of John Roebling's intellectual and philosophic capacities to conceive such a clean, untramelled work; it needed Washington's courage to make it an actuality. . . . If the lesson of the Brooklyn Bridge has been less potent in our engineering and architecture than it should have been, it is perhaps because our engineering schools have had a narrower conception of the engineer's vocation and culture than John Roebling had. . . . The Roeblings perhaps never used the word aesthetics in this relation; but it was their distinction to have made it visible.[12]

The magnitude of Brooklyn Bridge overshadowed subsequent suspension bridges in the nineteenth century. The precedent of Roebling's span made the flexible cable everywhere dominant, although there were a few essays before the end of the century in other types of construction.[13] It was again the need for spanning the Ohio River that led to the last of the large suspension bridges of the past century, but they were much inferior in size to Roebling's major works.

The first, designed by E. K. Morse, crosses the river at Rochester, Pennsylvania (1895–97), less than a mile above the huge cantilever bridge of the Pittsburgh and Lake Erie Railroad, which was to follow it by a few years. The form of the towers may have been derived from Roebling's Pittsburgh bridges: they are steel bents resting on masonry piers, each consisting of four tubular posts with a transverse bracing of horizontal and diagonal members. They represent a refinement in the direction of the simplified tower of the contemporary suspension bridge, which generally consists of a single pair of vertical members joined either by an arch at the top or by a simple system of horizontal and diagonal bracing.[14]

The second of the two Ohio River bridges, designed by Hermann Laub, is the Lincoln Highway crossing at East Liverpool, Ohio, 1897–99 (fig. 94). Of steel construction throughout and virtually identical with its immediate predecessor, it is essentially the modern suspension bridge by virtue of the simplification of the towers and the absence of the radiating stays which distinguish the Roebling bridges. Thus the entire load of the East Liverpool span is carried through the suspenders by the single pair of cables. Each tower consists of two vertical members joined by two transverse girders with a pair of diagonals between them.[15] Except for the masonry anchorages and the wooden flooring, the bridge is of steel construction throughout. It was strengthened and somewhat altered in 1939, by which time its simple form had been used without essential change for ever-increasing spans, until the maximum of 4,200 feet was reached at Golden Gate.

94  Bridge over the Ohio River, East Liverpool, Ohio, 1897–99. Hermann Laub, engineer.

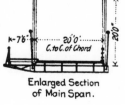

Enlarged Section
of Main Span.

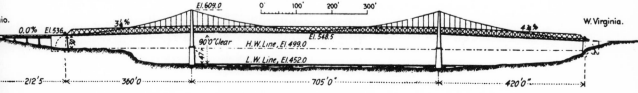

# VI

## THE IRON ARCH BRIDGE

Except for the suspension bridge, the arch is the oldest form in which iron has been exclusively employed for structural members. The first iron arch was built by Darby and Wilkinson over the River Severn at Coalbrookdale, England (1775–79). In America Tom Paine of *Common Sense* fame was the pioneer in proposing the construction of an arch bridge in iron. He began to make sketches of possible designs in 1785, and in the following two years he constructed three models, one of wood, a second of cast iron, and a third of wrought iron and blocks of wood representing cast iron pieces. He intended the bridge to span the Schuylkill River at Philadelphia. According to Cooper, an early historian of railroad bridges, the last model "consisted of wooden blocks representing cast iron voussoirs, spliced together by wrought iron bands fitting into recesses in the blocks and secured by screws." [1]

Paine took this model to Paris and exhibited it before the Académie des Sciences. A committee of mathematicians studied it and reported that an arch constructed on his principle could be built up to a length of 400 feet. The principle, as Paine understood it, could hardly have been conceived and stated more naively. As he put it, "the small segment of a large circle was preferable to the great segment of a small circle." [2] What he meant was that he saw the advantage of a single greatly flattened arch for long spans. There is no question that the bridge was structurally feasible, and it was certainly prophetic, in the shape of the arch, of widespread practice in the United States during the last quarter of the nineteenth century and on. The main problem was construction of sufficiently strong skewbacks to sustain the immense horizontal thrust of a long and very flat arch. But it could be counteracted with a great enough depth of masonry and adequate anchorage.

Paine went to England in 1788 on the advice of Benjamin Franklin to secure a patent on his design and to find a manufacturer for his castings. He had planned on an arch of 400-foot length to clear the Schuylkill in one span. Before the end of the year he entered into contract with the Messrs. Walker of Rotherham Ironworks, who made the castings in 1789 and set them out for public exhibit on a bowling green at Paddington. At this time, however, a far more potent influence began to operate on Paine. The outbreak of the French Revolution called him to Paris, and he left his bridge castings in the hands of his creditors. The castings appear to have remained in that state until about 1793, when Paine's patents were unscrupulously appropriated by Rowland Burdon. Together with the engineer Thomas Wilson, Burdon made some changes in the original design, bought the castings, and in 1793–96 erected a bridge of 236-foot span over the River Wear at Sunderland in England. The success of the Sunderland bridge made it an influential structure in England, and a number like it were built and projected. In the United States, however, the design aroused little interest, mainly because there was no foundry capable of casting on so large a scale. It was forty years after the completion of the Sunderland bridge that an iron arch was built in the United States, and forty-four years before an iron truss appeared.

Yet there was much that was instructive in Paine's bridge. Using cast iron exclusively, he designed all structural parts as compression members. The flat segmental arch consisted of three concentric ribs built up of separate castings in the form of voussoirs. The ribs were braced radially by a closely ranked series of castings set between them. The spandrels contained a number of contiguous iron rings of diminishing radius from abutment to crown. These carried iron stringers and transverse beams which in turn supported the slightly bowed deck. The skewbacks were corbels built out from the river face of the abutment walls. All connections between members were bolted. The breaking up of the ribs into iron voussoirs indicate that Paine was using masonry precedents as a guide for construction in iron, but the use of ribs, the flattened form of the arch, and the open spandrels pointed toward arch forms appropriate to iron and steel.

Until the last third of the century, though, the iron arch was to remain a rarity in the United States. It is difficult to determine exactly why this was the case. There was nothing novel about the form itself, which had been used continuously in masonry construction since the Hellenistic period. Further, since in theory the arch is subjected only to compressive stresses, there should have been less hesitancy about building it in iron than there was in the case of the truss. But the wooden truss was easy to erect, and its practical value was given so many excellent demonstrations that it seemed perfectly logical to retain it in iron. When the arch of iron and steel finally began to compete successfully with other forms, it did so because the builders frequently chose it on aesthetic rather than functional grounds. The form lent itself to these considerations, but there was in addition the peculiar idolatry which for centuries had been paid to the physical remains of classical antiquity, including the Roman bridge. The builders sought, where beauty was of paramount importance, to imitate or to approach the Roman arch in newer materials. Perhaps the chief argument against the iron arch was the relatively large size of its main structural

95    Bridge carrying Pennsylvania Avenue over Rock Creek, Washington, D. C., 1858. Montgomery C. Meigs, engineer.

members, which for a long time taxed the foundries and mills beyond their capacity. Another was the difficulty of computing stresses in fixed and two-hinged arches, which are indeterminate structures.

The first iron-arch bridge in the United States was built to span Dunlap's Creek at Brownsville, Pennsylvania, in 1836. A single-span semicircular arch, it was designed by Richard Delafield of the Army Engineer Corps, and the iron was cast at a local foundry and mill established in 1824 by John Snowden.[3] The Brownsville bridge stood until 1921, at which time samples of the iron were analyzed in the laboratory of the American Rolling Mill Company at Middletown, Ohio. The metallurgist reported that it had deteriorated very little and that it was "nearly as pure as the rust-resistant, commercially pure iron manufactured in open hearth furnaces at the present day."[4]

The iron arch at Brownsville was apparently the only structure of its kind for twenty-two years after its completion. The second one, built in Washington, D. C. (1858), was a curious combination of aqueduct and highway bridge (fig. 95). One of several aqueducts built by General Montgomery C. Meigs for the Washington water supply system (1857–64), the structure carried both water and the roadway of Pennsylvania Avenue over Rock Creek through the novel device of using the water mains as tubular arch ribs. The primary structural members of the bridge were two parallel cast iron water mains which spanned

200 feet between abutments. As important as the tubular arches were the unusual spandrel trusses which carried the load of the deck to the pipes.[5] The bridge was designed to support an extremely heavy load, the total of traffic, superstructure, and water delivering a thrust to each skewback of 940,000 pounds.[6] There was no evidence of failure or excessive leakage in the bridge, which performed its double function satisfactorily until its replacement in 1916.[7]

On the basis of these modest structures James B. Eads, who had never built a bridge before, proposed in 1867 to span the Mississippi River at St. Louis with three enormous tubular arches, each of more than 500-foot clear span (figs. 96, 97). The enterprising townspeople, many of whom had grown wealthy in the river trade, had long been enthusiastic about the idea of connecting their city with the Illinois shore. There had been no lack of engineers and builders ready with projects which they hoped would satisfy the demand. The first proposal was offered in 1839 by Charles Ellet, who suggested a wire-cable suspension bridge of 1,200-foot span. A second and similar proposal came from Josiah Dent in 1855. John Roebling in the following year made the third, for a combination structure of a suspension bridge flanked by parabolic arches. Since the suspension principle appeared to be unpopular, the city engineer, Truman J. Homer, in 1865 offered a fourth proposal, for a tubular span modeled on Stephenson's Britannia Bridge. Eads's project two years later seemed to the St. Louis entrepreneurs to offer the best feasibility of construction while arousing the least opposition from the steamboat interests. Accordingly, when the construction company was established in 1867, Eads was appointed engineer-in-chief. It was hoped that the well-known builder of railroad bridges, Jacob H. Linville, would act as a consultant, but Linville was the first of the reputable engineers to attack the project and to refuse to associate himself with it. But there were others of considerable ability who were willing to work with Eads: C. Shaler Smith as consultant, Henry Flad and Charles Pfeifer as assistant engineers, and William Chauvenet, Chancellor of Washington University at St. Louis, as mathematical adviser.

Eads's life up to the time of his appointment as chief engineer revealed great enterprise, unusual inventive talent, and a thorough knowledge of the Mississippi River, but little to suggest ability as a bridge builder. This extraordinary man was born in Lawrenceburg, Indiana, in 1820. An irregular schooling at Cincinnati, Louisville, and St. Louis ended when he reached the age of 13. In 1838 he realized the dream of Mark Twain's boyhood when he became a purser on a Mississippi River boat, which made it possible for him to travel the river steadily between St. Louis and New Orleans for the next four years. In 1842 he invented a diving bell by means of which he made a fortune salvaging sunken steamers (within six years he paid off a debt of $25,000). In 1845 he established a factory for the manufacture of glass at St. Louis and continued

96  Eads Bridge, Mississippi River, St. Louis, Missouri, 1868–74. James B. Eads, chief engineer.

to make money with both enterprises. His wealth enabled him to build, largely at his own expense, the armored, steam-propelled gunboats which proved effective in the Mississippi campaign of the Union Army during the Civil War.

After completion of the St. Louis bridge Eads distinguished himself further by building the South Pass jetties at the mouth of the Mississippi River (1875–79), a pioneer work of waterway control that effectively prevented the deposition of sediment in the channel.[8] In 1884 the British Society for the Encouragement of Art, Manufacture, and Commerce awarded him the Albert Medal, its first presentation to an American citizen. His own country was slow to pay him a comparable honor: he was elected to the Hall of Fame—the first engineer to achieve this distinction—in 1920, thirty-three years after his death in 1887.

The choice of Eads for the St. Louis project rested in large part on his intimate knowledge of the river. For the builder who proposed to found his piers on the rock far below its bed, it was a formidable obstacle indeed. Its current irregular and turbulent, subject to extreme increases of flow during floods, loaded with sediment, carrying floating debris during all seasons and drifting ice during the winter—this great river, of unmatched beauty in its grander reaches, could be a destructive force of irresistible power. The pilots could read its surface with remarkable skill for the hidden snags and bars that once menaced them, but only Eads knew at first hand its fluid, shifting, treacherous bed. He had seen its depth change from 20 to 100 feet at obstacles in the bottom as the result of the scouring action of currents. In a report issued in 1868 he provided a vivid description of what workers might expect at the indefinable zone where the water passed over the bed:

I had occasion to examine the bottom of the Mississippi, below Cairo, during the flood of 1851, and at sixty-five feet below the surface I found the bed of the river, for at least three feet in depth, a moving mass, and so unstable that, in endeavoring to find a footing on it beneath my bell, my feet penetrated through it until I could feel, although standing erect, the sand rushing past my hands, driven by a current apparently as rapid as that at the surface. I could discover the sand in motion at least two feet below the surface of the bottom, and moving with a velocity diminishing in proportion to its depth.[9]

With the design of his bridge substantially completed and sufficient capital available, Eads began clearing the site and constructing the caissons in the summer of 1867, but difficulties with his iron and steel contractor soon required a suspension of operations. Eads had already decided to substitute steel for the traditional cast iron in the arches and thus became the first to introduce the stronger metal into American building techniques.[10] The Carnegie-Kloman Company at first found it impossible to roll pieces with the physical properties

97 Eads Bridge. Side elevation showing the profile of the river bed and the bedrock on which the piers are founded.

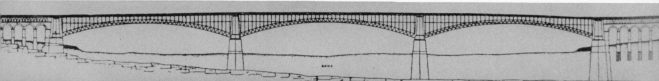

that Eads demanded. The earlier cast steel samples had already failed in the testing machines. At this point Eads insisted on the costly and hitherto unused chrome-steel, an innovation which was to have wide implications for structural and mechanical engineering. With this problem solved, construction was resumed early in 1868.

Eads began with the east, or Illinois, pier, where the maximum depth of bedrock offered the most formidable challenge. The pneumatic caisson was a necessity, and thus Eads became the first to introduce its use in the United State, anticipating Roebling by a year. It had been used in Europe since 1849, when Lewis Cubitt and John Wright developed it for the construction of the piers of a span at Rochester, England. By 1860 the method was common on the Continent as well as the British Isles. Eads built a cylindrical iron-shod caisson of massive timbers heavily reinforced with iron bands. Its diameter was 75 feet, the working chamber 8 feet deep. Within this huge enclosure the masonry pier was built up, the weight of the masonry forcing the cutting edge into the river bed. The Eads's caisson extended continuously up to the water surface, successive rings being added as it sank lower. A so-called sand pump, another of Eads's inventions, drew out the excavated material by suction. Men and supplies moved in and out of the working chamber through a cylindrical opening left in the center of the masonry and later filled when the rest of the pier was completed. The caisson for the Illinois pier reached bedrock at 123 feet below water level at the time of construction.

Five months of excavation and pumping were required to reach the foundation rock. The serious effects of increased air pressure on the construction workers began to appear at the level of 60 feet below the water surface: cases of painful "bends" occurred, but they were not followed by permanent damage. At 76 feet the first cases of paralysis and crippling appeared. At 93 feet the pressure had to be stepped up to 44 pounds per square inch above atmospheric, or to a total of about 59 pounds. At this point Eads and his physician, Jaminet, began to take heroic measures. Air pressure reduction was held to 6 pounds per minute, every worker was required to submit to a daily physical examination, and daily shifts were reduced to two of two hours each separated by a four-hour rest period. The diet of the workers was carefully supervised, and alcoholic liquors were absolutely prohibited. But for all their precautions, the toll was high: of 352 men who worked in the east caisson, 80 required medical treatment, and among these two were crippled for life and twelve died. Since the bedrock rises steadily from the east to the west bank, the caissons for the center and west piers had to be sunk to a progressively smaller depth, reaching a minimum of 86 feet at the St. Louis pier (fig. 97). As a consequence, there were fewer cases of paralysis, and none with permanent effects. Another fatality occurred when the tornado of March 8, 1871, destroyed most of the temporary construction facilities. The river piers and the arches of the west approach were completed in 1873. All masonry work is limestone with granite facing, the limestone having been shipped from Grafton, West Virginia, the granite from Richmond, Virginia, the latter by boat via New Orleans. Steel and iron came from Pittsburgh down the Ohio River.

The construction of the steel arches and the superstructure was a relatively simple matter after the dangerous work on the piers and required only about one-fifth of the time. In this part of the project Eads introduced another of his important innovations. The tubular arches were erected without falsework by the method of cantilevering them out from the piers to the center of the span. All arches were built out simultaneously from their piers so that the weights of the various cantilevers would balance each other and, on completion, the horizontal thrusts of adjacent arches would cancel each other. With the arches in place, the spandrel posts and the two decks were erected upon them. The bridge was completed and opened to traffic in 1874. The finished structure between abutments is divided into three spans, the one at the center 520 feet long, the two at the sides 502 feet each, the rise for all of them 45 feet.[11] Wrought iron spandrel posts with transverse bracing transmit the load of the two decks to the arches. The upper one carries a roadway, the lower a double-track railroad line. The decks are not level but curve upward slightly from the east approach to the center because of the wide, low-lying river flats scarcely above water level on the Illinois side.

The arches of Eads Bridge are the hingeles or fixed-end type and hence are statically indeterminate structures. It is possible that Chauvenet was familiar with the recent work of French theorists in the solution of problems arising from arches of this kind, and certainly he knew of the many carefully designed wrought iron arches which had been built by French engineers before 1865.[12] But for all the mathematical computations of Eads and Chauvenet, they relied to a great extent on empirical approximations and gross overbuilding. Eads calculated that his bridge would be capable of sustaining a total load of 28,972 tons uniformly distributed—about four times the maximum that can be placed upon it—and of withstanding the force of any flood, ice jam, or tornado that the Mississippi valley could level against it. Now in its ninth decade of active service, the bridge carries a heavy traffic of trucks, buses, automobiles, and the freight trains of the Terminal Railroad of St. Louis.

As a work of structural art Eads Bridge remains a classic. In its method of construction and its material, in the testing of full-size samples of all structural members and connections, in the thoroughness and precision of its technical and formal design, and in the close association of manufacturer and builder, it stands as a superb monument to the building art. It is, moreover, an architectural achievement as well as an engineering. Eads was careful to reduce his masonry elements to the simplest possible form, depending on the rich texture of the granite facing to provide the dignity and sense of restrained power that he was consciously striving after. Nowhere does the masonry extend above the line of the parapet to distract the attention from the overall profile, the major parts, and their relation to each other. The tight curve of the arches is the primary visual as well as structural element, and Eads knew that the best he could do was to give full expression to the combination of stability and energy implicit in the form.

As in the case of Roebling and the suspension bridge, the iron and steel arch seems to have passed its heroic age with the completion of Eads Bridge. Certainly there was nothing so dramatic and so great in sheer size; yet there were structural innovations which were not only technically important but which also provided the builder with the means to an elegance and refinement of appearance that make much of the earlier work seem crude by comparison. Foremost among the technical achievements was the introduction in the United States of the three-hinged arch, which was first used by the Philadelphia engineer Joseph M. Wilson. The form, which had been used in Europe for nearly two decades before its American appearance, offered several advantages over the fixed type. Hinged at the two end-points and at the crown, rather than fixed at the abutments and rigid throughout, it is as a consequence a statically determinate structure whose hinge reactions can be exactly calculated by simple algebraic equations. Further, since the points of maximum bending stress are the mid-points of the two segments and since there can be no such stress at the hinges, each segment has the theoretical form of a crescent-shaped figure decreasing from maximum depth at the center to a point at the hinges. Finally, if the situation requires it, the arch may be asymmetrical, the two segments unequal in length and the two springing points set at different elevations. Above all, its determinate character led to its common use in bridges, trainsheds, and other wide-span vaults.

Joseph Wilson, who was at the time an engineer of buildings and bridges with the Pennsylvania Railroad, first proposed the use of the three-hinged arch in 1867 as the primary structural element for the trainshed of the railroad's new Pittsburgh station. The project was rejected at the time as too costly, and it was twenty-five years before Wilson was to have an opportunity to design such a shed for actual construction. In the matter of bridges the company was more tolerant of the new idea. Wilson designed the bridge built in 1869 to carry the tracks of the Pennsylvania main line over 30th Street in Philadelphia (fig. 98).

Since the thoroughfare was at that time one of the principal drives to Fairmount Park, "it became essential to have something neat and artistic in design and finish." [13] The form Wilson chose was that of a wrought iron elliptical braced arch made up of twelve parallel arch ribs hinged at the abutments and the crown. The deck rested on wrought iron I-beams carried to the ribs by

98  Bridge carrying the tracks of the Pennsylvania Railroad over 30th Street, Philadelphia, Pennsylvania, 1869–70. Joseph M. Wilson, engineer.

posts braced with a single diagonal between each pair. An additional rib, acting partly as a tie, extended continuously between abutments above each main rib and was connected to all the posts at their mid-points. The entire structure was pin-connected throughout. Wrought iron was used for all structural members except the hinge blocks at the abutments and crown, which were cast iron. The ornamental cornice was of galvanized sheet iron, and the railing wrought iron. The abutment walls were faced with ashlar masonry. Wilson stated that he chose the three-hinged arch for two reasons: first, its determinate character, and second, its lack of rigidity, which made possible compensation for strains introduced by changes of temperature and settlement of the piers.[14] The bridge over 30th Street was an important pioneer structure, but its type was to remain comparatively rare until the end of the century.

The common form of arch bridges for short spans in the last quarter of the century was one in which the arch structure consisted of two or more parallel arched trusses, fixed at the abutments and rigid throughout, which in turn carried the spandrel posts that supported the level deck. An early and typical example was the wrought iron arch bridge built to carry Forbes Street over a ravine in Pittsburgh, 1874 (fig. 99).[15] Bridges of this kind represented a simple and not very attractive form which was erected in large numbers up to about 1915, when concrete displaced the earlier iron construction.[16]

The three-hinged arch of ribs rather than trusses offered greater possibilities, both structural and aesthetic. Few, if any, appear to have been built in the decade after Wilson's pioneer work at Philadelphia. A much purer form of

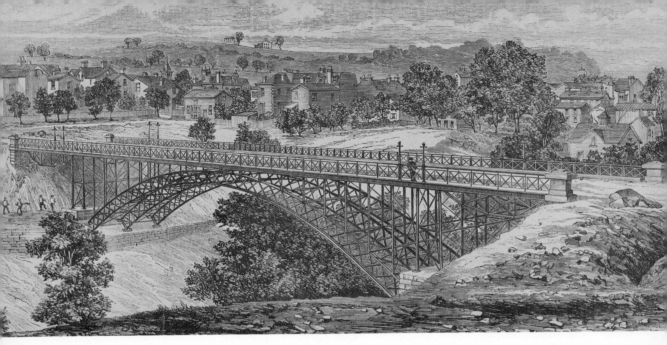

99    Forbes Street Bridge, Pittsburgh, Pennsylvania, 1874.

greatly increased span was built in 1882 to carry a highway over the Salmon
River at Pulaski, New York. The main span, 216 feet long, was made up of
parallel wrought iron arch ribs. There were no spandrel posts, the roadway
resting on a system of single diagonals in the form of the original Warren truss.
The Salmon River bridge was replaced in 1924 by a concrete arch. By 1890
the three-hinged arch was beginning to appear with some frequency in the
eastern cities chiefly to carry street traffic, since it was felt to be insufficiently
rigid for rail service.[17]

The classic work of its kind in steel at the end of the century is the Panther
Hollow Bridge in Schenley Park, Pittsburgh, 1896–97 (fig. 100), designed by
H. B. Rust, chief engineer of the city's Department of Public Works. The
approaches at both ends lie on semicircular masonry arches. Between the abutments, which rise to the level of the deck, is the superb central arch of four
parabolic three-hinged arch ribs.[18] Panther Hollow Bridge stands in a setting
of great natural beauty, a park of rugged topography traversed by a deep
wooded ravine from which the structure takes its name. A bridge at such a
site establishes two primary requirements for the designer: it must be as unob-
trusive as possible, offering no obstruction to the view from the roadway and
a minimum from below the structure, and it must be the most graceful form
available to the builder. In the rich quality of its simple, fine-textured masonry
elements, in the lightness and purity of the arch, and in the sweeping curve
of the parabola, with its 8:1 proportions, Panther Hollow Bridge satisfies these

requirements as fully as it is possible to do so. It represents the culmination of thirty years of progressive development in the arch, and there are few structures of its kind that can match it.

Although Eads Bridge had provided a powerful demonstration of the potentialities of the steel arch, the builders were hesitant about adopting the form for long-span structures. The chief demand for such bridges came from the railroads, but they were inseparably wedded to the truss and saw little merit in the arch for their uses.

There were several factors operating against the ready acceptance of the arch on a large scale. Until the builders developed the technique of suspending the deck from the soffit or underside of the arch rather than carrying it above, the form was often useless for wide-river crossings where the land on either side of the stream is at slight elevation above the water surface. Further, the problem of rigidity was crucial for long spans. Eads Bridge satisfied the requirement perfectly, but it was a fixed arch whose costly materials and indeterminate nature discouraged the engineers and builders. The development of the three-hinged arch solved the problem of indeterminacy, but it was felt that it lacked adequate rigidity for long spans and was expensive to build because of the necessity for elaborate falsework.

What was needed was a compromise which preserved some of the virtues of both types; it was already available in the two-hinged arch. In this form the arch is rigid throughout its length but hinged at the abutments or spring line; as a consequence, the maximum bending stress is at the crown, from which it decreases to a theoretical zero at the hinges. The profile of the truss or rib in a two-hinged arch is crescent-shaped, with maximum depth at the crown and a minimum at the hinges, where it may be drawn to a point. That the two-hinged form was satisfactory for long-span railway bridges had been given a

100   Panther Hollow Bridge, Schenley Park, Pittsburgh, Pennsylvania, 1896–97. H. B. Rust. engineer.

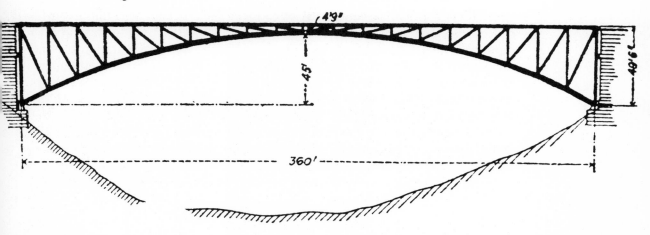

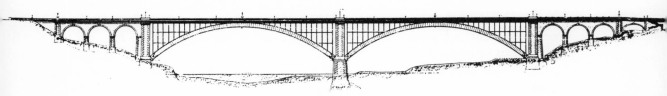

101 Washington Bridge, Harlem River, New York City, 1887–89. William R. Hutton, engineer; Edward H. Kendall, architect.

most striking demonstration by Gustav Eiffel in his Garabit Viaduct in France (1884). If it still seemed unacceptable for American railroad practice, where train loads are much heavier than they are in Europe, there was certainly nothing against its use for highway bridges.

The two-hinged arch suddenly achieved prominence when it was selected for one of the great steel spans of the century, the Washington Bridge over the Harlem River at 181st Street in New York, 1887–89 (fig. 101). The site is exactly the kind for which the arch is best suited. The rocky spine which rises steadily but irregularly up the length of Manhattan Island reaches a high point at Washington Heights, on the narrow tongue between the Hudson and the north end of the Harlem River. The smaller stream at this place lies between high, steep cliffs between which a bridge would have to cross at an elevation of about 110 feet above the water. There were a number of proposals for a span at this point, including one of concrete by Thomas C. Clarke.[19] The design that was ultimately constructed was that of the engineer William R. Hutton and the architect Edward H. Kendall.

Since the east, or Bronx, side of the Harlem River at 181st Street has the gentler slope, Hutton designed a bridge with a long east approach on semicircular masonry arches followed by two great steel arches, of which the western span alone lies over the river. There is another but shorter approach of masonry arches on the Manhattan side. Each of the main arches, separated by a stout masonry pier, consists of six enormous steel arched girders with a span of 508 feet 9 inches and a rise of 83 feet 4 inches. They are built-up girders composed of a succession of riveted plates, with a maximum depth at the crown of 9 feet. The deck of the bridge rests on the usual spandrel posts, but the curious feature is that there is no diagonal bracing whatever, the stiffening members consisting entirely of horizontal struts running both transversely and longitudinally. Washington Bridge is unquestionably an impressive work of structural art, technically and visually, but its designers were handicapped by a site which made a somewhat asymmetrical design inevitable. The main arches are balanced, but the approaches and the height of the abutments between grade and springing are unequal. The structure as a whole was one of the few New York bridges which satisfied Montgomery Schuyler's high if rather narrow standards of civic architecture. He found in it the closest union of the aesthetic and the structural, the ideal that he was always looking for. Washington Bridge today is an important traffic link in the New York arterial system, connecting one Manhattan approach of George Washington Bridge with the Cross-Bronx Expressway.

So far no arch exceeded in length the longest trusses, but before the end of the century the arch was to increase in span well beyond the common form and to retain that superiority up to the present time.[20] The second arch bridge at Niagara Falls (1895–98) was to reach the maximum length for any bridge of its kind in the nineteenth century (fig. 102). Designed by L. L. and R. S. Buck, it was a two-hinged steel arched truss built to take the place of the suspension bridge built in 1868. The river crossing of Buck's bridge consisted of a pair of parallel arched trusses with a span of 840 feet.[21] The masonry skew-backs for the arch carried high steel bents which supported the deck between the main arch and the flanking bowstring trusses. Over the arched truss the deck was carried by spandrel posts without bracing, which was confined to the space between the trusses.

The deep gorge and the swift and turbulent currents of the Niagara River proved no obstacles to the bridge builders, who had spanned it many times since the middle of the century. In the winter, though, when the great falls and the violent currents are enclosed in ice, the river becomes dangerous. Buck's record-breaking arch fell victim to this irresistible force. On January 27, 1938, the ice jam in the gorge reached the level of the tops of the skewbacks. The pressure of the slow-moving mass sheared the arch at the hinges and dropped it with its superstructure onto the surface of the ice, which easily supported

102 Bridge over the Niagara River, Niagara Falls, New York, 1895–98. L. L. and R. S. Buck, engineers.

103    Niagara River bridge, 1895–98. The wreckage after the bridge was cut down by ice, January 27, 1938.

the entire mass of crumpled steelwork (fig. 103). There was ample warning of the disaster, so that the bridge had been closed before it went down and no lives were lost.

The question naturally arose as to whether this accident might have been foreseen and steps taken to avoid it. Buck's bridge was of light construction by present standards, but forty years of service indicated that it was adequate for the loads to which it was subjected. It might have been possible to protect the hinges from ice, but the only sure guarantee of safety lay in locating the skewbacks above the level of the maximum jam. As long as the ends of the arch stood in the path of the ice, it is doubtful that any steel construction could have been devised to withstand the load thrust against them. It was a sad end to a fine work of structural art. The bridge which replaced it, a combination of concrete approaches and a steel girder arch, lacks the unity of the older span, which was of steel truss construction throughout.

# THE RAILWAY TRAINSHED

## 1. THE ORIGINAL FORM OF THE RAILWAY STATION

The railroad so thoroughly dominated bridge construction in the nineteenth century that much of the development of the art was coextensive with the growth of the rail network. In buildings the requirements of the railroad covered every conceivable type and size, but in construction they did not differ from other commercial and industrial structures. It was the station trainshed that was the peculiar contribution of the railroad to the building arts and the prototype for many modern wide-span structures.

In the early decades of rail construction the shed was incorporated within the station building itself, and as long as wood provided the main structural material, the design of the shed differed little from that of any similar enclosure with timber framing. At about the same time that iron began to be substituted for wood as a framing material, the shed was separated from the head house, or station building, and was radically distinguished from it in shape and construction. While the gable form was in use, though—and it persisted until the end of the century—the framing of the shed was very much like that of any building whose roof was carried on iron trusses and columns.

By the last third of the century, however, the shed evolved into a unique form, a huge, wide-span barrel vault known as the balloon shed, which rested on a series of parallel arched trusses. Although the primary structural elements were similar to those of certain bridges and buildings, they were used in novel and ingenious ways. Further, the kind of structural and architectural problem which the station builder had to solve was peculiar to his age, and there were no historical precedents to guide him. The complex association of tracks, platforms, and station facilities, together with the problem of handling large numbers of people in a relatively small space and over intricate lines of movement, placed the railroad station in a special category of building types.

For the first twenty years of its history, however, the railroad station was an extremely simple thing, the construction of which involved nothing more

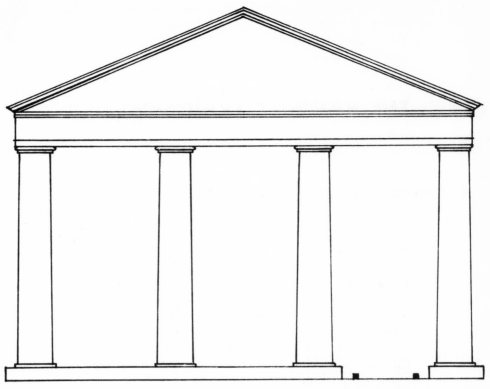

104　Station of the Boston and Lowell Railroad, Lowell, Massachusetts, 1835. Front elevation.

elaborate than traditional column-and-beam and truss framing usually in timber or combinations of wooden members with iron tie rods. The first station which was a combined trainshed and station building—that is, one in which the trains passed into the building on a track extending throughout its length—was that of the Boston and Lowell Railroad at Lowell, Massachusetts, 1835 (fig. 104). The plans of this building also constitute the earliest surviving station drawings. The Lowell station was rectangular in plan, its gable roof supported either by wooden trusses or roof rafters, which in turn were carried on Doric columns of wood extending around the periphery of the building. The single track passed through the station by means of openings set between a pair of columns at one side of each end. In addition to the track the interior contained a platform and a general hallway. The Lowell station was the prototype not only of hundreds of stations whose gable roofs were supported by wooden trusses or beams, but also of the many stations erected up to 1850 in the form of the Greek temple.[1]

While most of the early stations were built with standard roof trusses, usually king-post with a pair of diagonal struts, there was one exception that pointed the way to the types of framing common in the vaulted sheds. The arch-reinforced Howe truss was adapted to use in the gable shed of the Boston and Worcester Railroad station at Boston in 1842.[2]

Among the original group of stations in the Boston area, the one to enjoy the longest life was that of the Boston and Maine Railroad at Salem, Massachusetts (1847). The station building, which included the shed, was constructed of massive granite exterior walls with heavy flattened arches in the ends through which the two tracks passed. These arches sprang from corbels in the walls set at a height of about 10 feet above the tracks. The wooden roof rested on triangular trusses whose top chord consisted of a pair of massive timbers the ends of which rested on the walls and were tied by a horizontal wrought iron rod. There was undoubtedly a vertical member between the apex and the tie and possibly one or more diagonal struts. The interior of the shed was lighted by a row of seven high, narrow windows in the end walls above the arches. The Salem station survived in regular use for 108 years, a life exceeding that of any other railroad building in the United States except for the Baltimore and Ohio's Mount Clare Station in Baltimore, which has been preserved as a museum piece.

By the mid-forties the construction of the station trainshed was fixed, at least on the more prosperous roads, in the form of the gable roof on wood and iron trusses supported by masonry bearing walls. The shed was to remain an integral part of the building for another thirty years, but by that time the incorporated form was rare, for the builders had begun to treat the shed as a separate structure as early as 1850. There were many variations in plan, and a constant increase in the size and number of facilities for passengers and the operation of trains.[3]

The original passenger station in Cleveland, built in 1854 along the lake front near the Cuyahoga River, was a unique variant with two stub-end terminals set at right angles to each other. The one with the open end facing east was used by the Cleveland, Painesville and Ashtabula Railroad, the other, facing south, by the Cincinnati, Columbus and Cleveland.[4] The enclosed gable form of the sheds themselves was completely surrounded by masonry walls, which were spanned by the wooden roof trusses with their iron tie rods. The double station was abandoned when the original Cleveland Union Depot was completed in 1866.[5]

The most elegant station at the time of the timber-framed shed, according to current descriptions, was that of the Atlantic and Great Western Railroad at Meadville, Pennsylvania, 1862 (fig. 105).[6] The building measured about 120 × 300 feet in plan and contained under its high gable roof a trainshed,

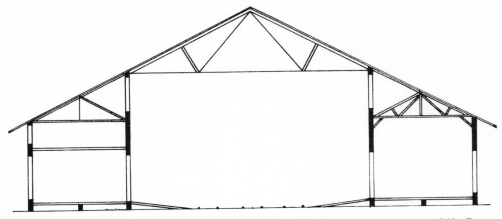

105  Station of the Atlantic and Great Western Railroad, Meadville, Pennsylvania, 1862. Cross section through the building. The waiting room was on the left, the trainshed at the center, and the dining room on the right.

waiting room, dining room, and railroad offices. The interior for most of its length was divided into three parallel enclosures: the central and largest was the trainshed, which spanned 66 feet 6 inches and covered three tracks and two platforms; on one side of the track area, facing the front, was the waiting room; on the other was the dining room. The portions of the roof over the narrower areas were supported by wooden triangular trusses whose ends rested on brick partitions. That over the trainshed was carried on trusses with heavy timber top chord, wrought iron main diagonals and bottom chord, and hollow cast iron struts. It was an unusual form and seems to have stemmed from French precedents. The plan of the Meadville station, with facilities on both sides of the track area, was typical of its time, but it was far from satisfactory chiefly because of the location of waiting and dining rooms on different sides of the track. By the time of its construction the practice of separating the trainshed entirely from the station building was becoming common. This marked a considerable improvement in many respects, but in through stations on a single level it still required that passengers cross the tracks in order to board or leave trains.

## 2. THE SEPARATE GABLE SHED

The trainshed as a separate structure, distinct in internal form and construction from the station building, was an English invention of the 1830's, in good part the achievement of Brunel and the Stephensons. By the early 1840's iron structural members had become fairly common for large terminals in both England and France. Thus the American trainshed, like the iron frame and bridge, followed European precedents. Moreover, in spite of the ingenuity and daring often shown by American engineers in the construction of iron bridges, the structural and architectural quality of the trainshed remained throughout its life inferior to that of its British and Continental counterparts. The chief ground for removing the shed from the station building and treating it as a separate structural entity was the growing size of the shed and the resulting impossibility of constructing the large enclosure by the simple methods of framing and masonry work appropriate to the building. In addition, almost to the end of the century, the shed was surrounded by walls that matched the architectural treatment of the station house, so that it was incorporated architecturally in the whole complex. But sheer cost finally prohibited even this concession to unity.

The first American station with a trainshed separated from the building was the original eastern terminal of the Old Colony Railroad, on Kneeland Street in Boston (1847).[1] The architect was probably Gridley J. F. Bryant. Since the terminal was enlarged and improved in 1867, it is difficult to determine precisely the construction of the earlier shed. It seems likely, however, that no changes were introduced in the main part of the shed. The trusses which supported it were crude and primitive: they were trapezoidal in profile, the three members of the top chord being heavy timbers, the rest wrought iron rods. The web system consisted of a vertical hanger at the center, a horizontal member crossing at the mid-line, and two inclined struts. The truss was neither determinate nor rigid and appears to have been a matter of pure self-expression on the part of the builder. The ends of the trusses were carried on heavy wooden posts. The Kneeland Street station was demolished during construction of the present South Station in Boston (1896–99).[2]

The popularity of the separate shed grew by necessity, especially in large terminal stations where the number of tracks had to be increased to park idle cars as well as trains taking on and discharging passengers.[3] The original group of stations in Chicago after the pioneer structure of 1848 were built with unusually spacious sheds. The largest was that of the first La Salle Street Station (1853), built by the Chicago and Rock Island and the Northern Indiana railroads. It spanned 116 feet and rested on triangular Howe trusses with timber chords and diagonals and wrought iron vertical rods. The ends of the trusses were supported by brick side walls 22 feet high. The shed stood 42 feet above the tracks at the ridge line. The station was replaced by a larger structure in 1868, which had to be replaced again after the fire of 1871. The present La Salle Street Station (1903) is the fourth to be built on this site.[4]

Trusses composed entirely of iron appeared in one forerunner of the balloon shed as early as 1865, but the builders were slow to adopt the material for all structural members until late in the 'seventies. With the rapid substitution of coal for wood as a locomotive fuel after the Civil War, acid-bearing smoke became a serious corrosive agent which exposed iron resisted less well than wood. At the same time, the increasing size of the shed and the hazards of fire presented equally persuasive arguments for the adoption of iron. The introduction of ventilating monitors and raising the height of the shed partially solved the problem of corrosion, but it remained such a destructive agent that shortly after the end of the century construction of the all-covering shed had to be given up. In the thirty years after 1870, however, the railroads built an immense number of gable sheds supported by iron trusses and columns.

The first on the scale of the large metropolitan station was the Washington terminal of the Baltimore and Potomac Railroad (1873–77).[5] Its designer was Joseph M. Wilson, who became before the end of the century the leading engineer of large balloon sheds. The shed of the Washington station, a low-pitched gable, was 510 feet long and 130 feet in span. It was carried without intermediate supports on wrought iron trusses with arched bottom chords resting on brick side walls. This was the first of Wilson's big terminal sheds, but it survived for only thirty years, until the present Washington Union Station was completed.[6]

The original Union Station at Chicago (1879–80) had a trainshed whose length established a record which was not exceeded until well into the twentieth century. Covering eight tracks and four platforms, it stretched for 1,000 feet north and south of Adams between Canal Street and the Chicago River. Although in the form of a through station, it actually functioned as two stub-end terminals with trains entering from north and south.[7] Except for the glass and iron light monitor at the ridge, the shed roof was wooden planking covered with tin and was carried on wrought iron Pratt trusses supported by cast iron columns. The latter were bolted to single blocks of stone, which were in turn bolted to huge monolithic footings of great area to reduce unit pressure on the compressible soil along the river. By the end of the century Chicago Union Station served 250 trains and 30,000 passengers a day. This already large volume of traffic continued to grow at such a rate that within another decade the structure had reached the limit of its capacity. It was demolished during construction of the present Union Station (1916–25), the largest and finest of the Chicago terminals and one with a unique ground plan in which two stub-end terminals abut on a single concourse.

The metropolitan terminals of the 'eighties and 'nineties exhibited in their trainsheds the orthodox form of gable construction: roof of tin-covered planking or sheet iron, central light monitor, wrought iron trusses usually triangular in profile but sometimes with arched bottom chords, and cast iron columns on stone or concrete footings. There were minor variations in detail and from time to time some striking exceptions. The Jersey City terminal of the Central Railroad of New Jersey (1887–88) had a shed of typical construction and record size at the time of its completion. Its central roof, spanning 142 feet 7 inches, rested on Pratt trusses set 32 feet on centers. Wind bracing was pro-

106 Dearborn Station, Polk and Dearborn streets, Chicago, Illinois, 1883–85. Interior of the trainshed.

vided by longitudinal trusses with parallel chords set between the main transverse supports. The gable shed was replaced by a Bush shed in 1914, but the combined station building and ferry terminal are still in use.[8]

The largest of all the single-span gable sheds, and one with a unique system of truss framing, was the second Union Depot at St. Paul, Minnesota. The original station was built in 1879–81. Destroyed by fire in 1884, it was rebuilt and reopened the following year, but the shed was replaced in 1889–90. Designed by Charles F. Loweth, it was 640 feet long and 189 feet wide out to out of the roof, including the cantilevered sheds along the sides. The entire roof was carried by steel and wrought iron trusses supported by two rows of steel columns.[9] The shed was open at the sides except for longitudinal windbracing trusses which spanned between the columns. The whole structure was a strictly utilitarian and undecorated work of engineering whose general form and proportions made it one of the most unattractive gable sheds. St. Paul Union Depot was replaced in 1926 by the present station, and platform canopies, which were standard by that date, took the place of the the shed.[10]

Dearborn Station in Chicago (1883–85) enjoys some kind of special status. A railroad antique by American standards, it still shelters the trains and passengers of seven railroads.[11] The trainshed is a curiosity of the gable form (fig. 106). Spanning eight tracks with its area of 165 × 600 feet, the shed is actually two gables set one above the other, the upper one surmounted by a

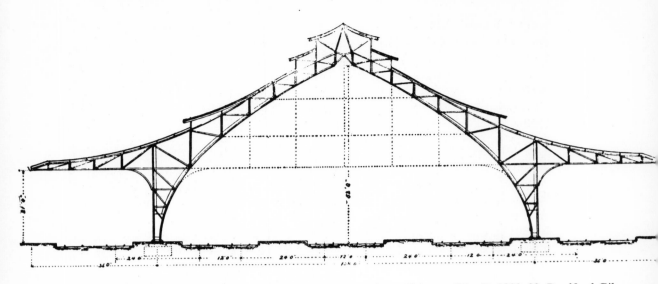

107   Central Station, Michigan Avenue at 11th Place, Chicago, Illinois, 1892–93. Bradford Gilbert, architect; J. F. Wallace, engineer. Cross section of the trainshed.

light monitor along the ridge. The wooden planking of the roof rests on complicated trusses of heavy timbers and groups of wrought iron rods carried on two outer and two intermediate rows of columns. The clear span between the inner rows is only 65 feet. The main feature of the station building, designed by Leopold Eidlitz, is a clock tower which once rose to a height of 166 feet, but the removal of its steeply pitched Flemish Gothic roof cut it down considerably. The interior of the building was modernized in 1946, but the shed was left intact, a museum piece still surviving in its original form.

The second and present station of the Illinois Central Railroad at Chicago (1892–93) had the only gable shed supported on three-hinged arched trusses (fig. 107).[12] The station building has been the subject of controversy since it was opened. Designed by the New York architect Bradford Gilbert, it was hailed as a civic monument by the local press and bitterly condemned as a planning nightmare by Louis Sullivan in his *Kindergarten Chats*. The plan is seriously defective and gives the impression of attempting to squeeze everything into the narrowest possible compass. On the other hand, certain features of the building reveal a genuine architectural distinction. Professor Carroll Meeks, the leading authority on the architecture of railroad stations, has provided the most balanced judgment:

The Chicago station is [Gilbert's] masterpiece. The metropolitan site and an ample budget permitted him to surpass his previous efforts. There are four main elements: train-shed, tower, office building, and waiting room. The latter, in the form of an arched train-shed, is a clear instance of the metamorphosis of the train-shed into another element of the station complex. This noble room is placed on the second floor over the tracks, so that passengers are required to climb up to it and then descend again to the tracks.... The waiting room was elaborately decorated, perhaps partially to compensate for its inconvenience.... At the end toward the lake there was a huge arched window recalling that of the Gare de l'Est but transformed with "cathedral glass set in rich and glowing colors."[13]

The handsome trainshed of Central Station was replaced by an unattractive concrete slab hung from flat trusses in 1931, but the building still remains.[14]

By far the largest multispan trainshed built in the gable form was the first North Station in Boston (1891–94), which provided a single terminal for the various companies which later comprised the Boston and Maine system (fig. 108). The architects were Shepley, Rutan and Coolidge, and the chief designing engineer Edward S. Shaw.[15] The roof of the shed was corrugated iron, as

108  North Station, Causeway and Nashua streets, Boston, Massachusetts, 1891–94. Shepley, Rutan and Cooledge, architects; Edward S. Shaw, engineer. End elevations and longitudinal sections of the trainshed.

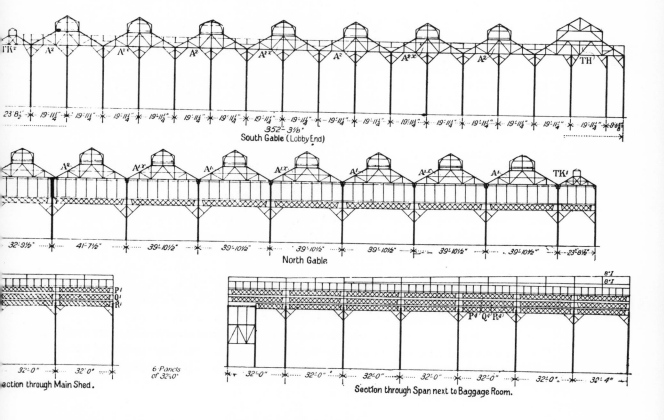

were the curtain wall at the open end and part of the east side wall. All structural members were steel, and the west wall and the remainder of the east were brick.[16] The great size of the trainshed was dictated by the fact that the railroads at the time the station was opened operated 569 trains a day in and out of the Boston terminal. For all its size, however, there was nothing new nor interesting in the construction of the trainshed. Within thirty years this vast and ugly barn of corrugated iron became a costly nuisance to maintain. It was demolished during construction of the present North Station (1928–31). By the time old North Station was completed, the railroad companies had turned to the balloon shed on arched trusses for their big metropolitan terminals; yet the newer and far more striking form was to survive the older by only a few years. The Bush shed of low parallel vaults (1904) and the separate platform canopy (1907) spelled the end of the great single-span sheds.

## 3. THE BALLOON SHED

The trainshed in the form of a barrel vault supported on arched trusses or ribs appeared in England and on the Continent around 1850. The most impressive of the pioneer achievements were the Gare de l'Est, Paris (1847–52), on tied arched trusses of iron, and King's Cross Station, London (1851–52). Not only were these sheds clearly in advance of American practice in structure and appearance, but they were also emancipated from the station building and stood as separate structural entities.

Balloon sheds in the United States continued to be housed in masonry walls until 1870, and full separation from the building was not accomplished until 1893. Wrought iron tension members appeared in the earliest balloon sheds in the United States, but again it was not until 1865 that complete construction in iron was achieved. As a matter of fact, in spite of the immense number of railroad stations built during the nineteenth century, the structural techniques employed in the single-span balloon shed lagged well behind those of the iron and steel bridge until the last decade of the century. This was in part due to the fact that the long-span bridge offered a challenge which demanded all the inventive ingenuity of the builders. At the same time, the volume of passenger traffic on the railroads, although growing rapidly, did not reach until the 1880's the proportions that demanded large-scale vaulted construction for the terminals. Even the multiple-span gable shed, like that of North Station in Boston, would have proved equally satisfactory on functional grounds if methods of smoke-elimination had been improved.

The decision to use the balloon shed for big metropolitan terminals was motivated in good part by aesthetic considerations. The arch and the vault had a long architectural tradition behind them. The engineers felt that the

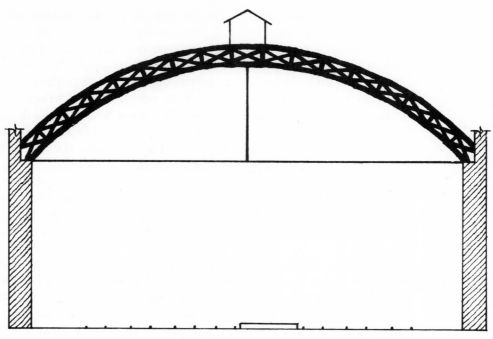

109 Station of the Philadelphia, Wilmington and Baltimore Railroad, Broad and Prime streets, Philadelphia, Pennsylvania, 1851–52. George A. Parker, engineer. Cross section of the trainshed.

curved vault was the appropriate form for a monumental structure, and several of them were seriously concerned with how best to realize its aesthetic potentialities. Further, it was thought that the high vault was superior on functional grounds because it was less exposed to direct blasts of acid-bearing locomotive smoke. In this respect, however, the difference turned out to be slight. The balloon shed went the way of the gable shed at virtually the same time.

The first trainshed in the form of a barrel vault was built for the Philadelphia terminal of the Philadelphia, Wilmington and Baltimore Railroad, 1851–52 (fig. 109).[1] The station was located at Broad and Prime streets, close to the site of the two succeeding Broad Street stations of the Pennsylvania Railroad. Designed by George A. Parker, the shed was probably the largest one in the United States at the time. It spanned seven tracks and one central platform and measured $150 \times 350$ feet in plan.[2] The roof was a somewhat flattened cylindrical vault supported on arched Howe trusses of wood with their ends resting on brick side walls. The arches were tied at their spring line by wrought iron rods, each supported by a single wrought iron hanger descending from the crown of the arch. The side walls thus carried only the vertical load of the roof and arches, the tie rods taking the horizontal thrust. The system of construction was used, with modifications in detail, for every trainshed of similar form for the next twenty years. The pioneer of the Broad Street stations was demolished in 1881, when construction began on its successor.[3]

All American trainsheds were surpassed in size by the original Union Depot at Cleveland, Ohio (1865–66). Built by several roads which in 1869 were merged to form the Lake Shore and Michigan Southern Railroad, it was a through station, one of the few with an arched shed to be constructed on this plan. Spanning eight tracks, it was 600 feet long and 180 feet wide. In most respects the structural character followed that of its predecessors except for the use of iron in the framing members: the shed was completely enclosed by masonry walls; the 49 arched Howe trusses of iron, set 12 feet on centers, sprang from sidewalls at a height of 27 feet; the end walls were pierced by eight arched openings and by a number of high, narrow windows above them (fig. 110).

The unique feature of the Cleveland shed was the curious system of ties and struts under the arch. Not only was this system radically indeterminate, but it would have been impossible to decide exactly what the distribution of tensile and compressive stresses might have been. When the New York Central engineers began to demolish the shed in 1914 and replace it with platform canopies, they had to support the entire system of roof, arches, and framing

110   Union Depot, Cleveland, Ohio, 1865–66. B. F. Morse, engineer. Half-elevation of a roof truss in the trainshed.

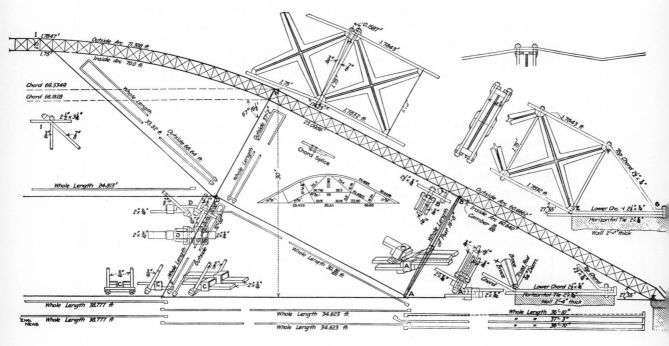

111　Station of the Central Vermont Railway, St. Albans, Vermont, 1869. Interior of the trainshed.

on falsework while the arches and ties were dismantled. The designer of this naively vernacular structure, B. F. Morse, died the day that demolition began. The Cleveland depot continued to function as a union station until the present Union Terminal (1925–30) was nearly completed. At that time the Pennsylvania Railroad leased the property from the New York Central and kept the old structure as its Cleveland station until 1953, when all but a small part of the original building was finally wrecked. The remainder still stands in a shabby and disordered area of tracks, abandoned streets, and weeds, a sad commentary on the civic spirit of the city and the railroads, which have allowed the lake front to lie in this disreputable condition.

A return to the original system of construction with timber Howe trusses characterized the vaulted shed of the St. Albans, Vermont, station of the Central Vermont Railway, 1869 (fig. 111). Surrounded by brick walls on four sides, the roof of planking spans four tracks and platforms under its area of 88 × 351 feet.[4] The end walls of the shed contain the familiar arched openings for the passage of trains, one for each track. The St. Albans station is in active use today, one of the oldest to retain its original form, and an important division point on one of the routes between Boston and Montreal.

112　Grand Central Terminal, Park Avenue at 42nd Street, New York City, 1869–71. John B. Snook, architect; Isaac C. Buckhout, engineer. Interior of the trainshed, looking toward the head house, or station building.

The gulf that separated the vernacular structures of the St. Albans station and its predecessors from the sophisticated engineering of the first Grand Central Terminal in New York was so great that one can account for it only on the basis of foreign precedents. As we have already noted, balloon sheds on shallow arched trusses of iron had been built in England and on the Continent for a period of more than twenty years previous to the construction of the New York terminal. The development of such sheds on fixed arches reached its culmination in St. Pancras Station, London (1863–76), designed by the architect George Gilbert Scott and the engineers W. H. Barlow and R. M. Ordish. In this immense vault the arched trusses spring from the track level and rise in an unbroken and unencumbered curve to the crown.

The problem of design in a large shed such as this was relatively simple. The depth and spacing of the arched trusses had to be calculated for the light static load of the sheet metal or wooden roof and the variable loads induced by wind pressure. Since the roof load acted vertically, with one component always in a direction normal to the truss chords, only wind loads required lateral bracing between trusses to resist twisting or buckling strains in the roof. The chief difficulty in design arose from the use of fixed arches, which are indeterminate structures. These new principles of shed construction were introduced in America by the New York engineer Isaac Buckhout, who first incorporated them in the trainshed of Grand Central Terminal.

By 1869 Cornelius Vanderbilt had acquired control of the New York and Harlem, the Hudson River, and the New York Central railroads and had merged the last two into a new company, the New York Central and Hudson River. Vanderbilt decided in the same year to unify the rail facilities of these companies in New York into a single terminal at Fourth (now Park) Avenue and 42nd Street, the East Side site chosen so that the New York and New Haven could use the new station and retain its trackage rights over the New York and Harlem. But this decision involved the construction of a new line connecting the Hudson River and the Harlem companies. The connection was completed in 1870 along the east bank (the Bronx side) of the Harlem River, joining the Hudson River Railroad at Spuyten Duyvil with the New York and Harlem at what was later 138th Street.

Construction of Grand Central Terminal began in the summer of 1869 after the design of John B. Snook as architect and Isaac C. Buckhout, who had designed the Hudson River Railroad's St. John's Park terminal, as engineer. It was opened two years later, on October 9, 1871. The station building was L-shaped in plan, with a width of 249 feet along 42nd Street and a length of 695 feet along Vanderbilt Place. The trainshed, spanning twelve tracks and five platforms, occupied the inner area of the L (figs. 112, 113). The general planning of the track layout and station facilities contained a number of

113 Grand Central Terminal, New York City, 1869–71. The curtain wall at the rear end of the trainshed.

irrationalities. The head house was divided into three self-contained parts, one for each of the three participating railroads. This division was carried out so thoroughly that a passenger changing trains from one road to another had to leave the building and come in by another door. Having confused the passengers, the designers then decided to include those responsible for the operation of trains. In order to separate the streams of people moving in opposite directions the outbound tracks were located on the west side of the shed and the inbound on the east side. This arrangement required left-hand operation within the station area, but since this is contrary to American railroad practice, the inbound and outbound tracks crossed each other above 45th Street, then continued north through an open cut in Park Avenue. The resulting nuisance was in part corrected by later moving the crossovers to Spuyten Duyvil Junction on the Hudson River Railroad and to Woodlawn on the Harlem. The railroads then followed left-hand operation to these points until the present terminal was under construction. The final error in planning was locating the baggage room in such a way that it opened into the trainshed, with the result that the passenger had to show a railroad ticket in order to claim baggage. A curious feature of track planning, arising from the demands of the New Haven Railroad, was the opening which extended entirely through the station building to allow two tracks of the railroad to continue down Fourth Avenue to the old station at 26th Street. The opening was closed and the tracks removed in 1885 with the abandonment of the New Haven's downtown freight station.

The great trainshed, an approximately cylindrical vault of corrugated sheet iron and glass, was 600 feet long and 200 feet wide. It was carried on thirty arched Howe trusses of wrought iron set 20 feet 8 inches center to center. The arches were tied at their fixed end-bearings by wrought iron rods, which passed under the tracks and platforms in pipes to protect them from corrosion and to resist the impact of passing trains. Although the arches were semi-circular in form, the external profile of the shed did not conform to their shape. Brick walls about 30 feet high extended along the sides throughout the length of the shed. Above them rose a series of flanking monitors on each side which provided light and ventilation, the series culminating in a central monitor under a gable roof. A system of truss framing carried the load of the sloping monitor roofs to the main arches. The open end of the shed was covered by a highly decorated iron curtain wall with ten arched openings at grade level for trains and a number of windows above them of various shapes and sizes (fig. 113). This wall was developed into a false gable whose elaborate outer profile bore no resemblance to the shape of the trainshed.[5] The Architectural Iron Works of New York manufactured and erected the ironwork of the structure.

For all their impressive size, both the head house and the trainshed of

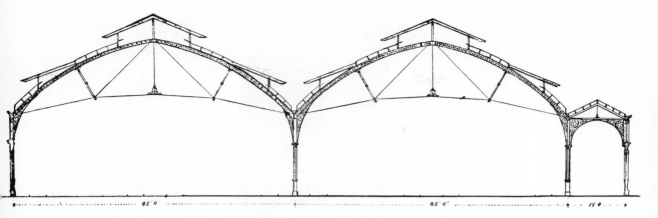

114  Broad Street Station, Philadelphia, Pennsylvania, 1880–82. Joseph M. Wilson, engineer. Cross section of the trainshed.

Grand Central Terminal proved to be inadequate for the expanding traffic within twenty-five years after its opening. Plans for additional facilities were prepared by C. P. R. Gilbert in 1897, and the construction was carried out in 1899–1900. The enlargement was so extensive that the original terminal became a minor part of the new complex of tracks and buildings. Four tracks under a single gable shed were added on the east side, and 21 under seven parallel gable sheds were added on the west. The sheds on the west side lay entirely north of the original structure, and the rail ends were located near the line of 45th Street. This complicated hodge-podge of 37 tracks and four separate buildings, the result of piecemeal additions set down in a crowded urban area, served the three railroads for five years. In 1906 construction began on the new electrified terminal and was completed in 1913. Beside this magnificent achievement—the grandest work of building and civic art ever undertaken by a railroad company—the first Grand Central Terminal and all its contemporaries seemed hopelessly primitive.[6]

The second Broad Street Station in Philadelphia (1880–82), designed by Joseph M. Wilson, marked a return to an older form of truss construction, a consequence of the Pennsylvania Railroad's continuing resistance to Wilson's proposals for sheds on three-hinged arches. The trainshed at Broad Street consisted of two parallel vaults nearly cylindrical but actually having the form of a flattened pointed arch in section (fig. 114). A light monitor under a gable roof extended along the ridge of each vault, which was 85 feet wide and spanned four tracks. In addition to the eight passenger tracks there were two at one side under a 19-foot gable shed for baggage and mail. The roofs were supported by wrought iron trusses carried on wrought iron columns encased in ornamental envelopes of cast iron. The top chord of the truss was a heavy

115 Grand Central Station, Harrison and Wells streets, Chicago, Illinois, 1888–89. Solon S. Beman, architect; W. S. Jones, engineer. Interior of the trainshed, looking toward the head house.

rib curved to match the profile of the roof, while the bottom chord, which was slightly cambered, consisted of four wrought iron rods. The diagonals, struts, and hangers that made up the web system were also of wrought iron.[7] The form of the Broad Street sheds was chosen to harmonize with the Gothic character of the station building. In their design Wilson followed his primary aesthetic principle of giving structure full expression, except for the encasement of the columns. The ornament, however, was spare and in low relief. The graceful curves and good proportions of the vaults made the Broad Street trainsheds unusually pleasing examples of the form, although they lacked the heroic size and dynamic spatial quality of the larger balloon sheds. The second Broad Street Staion survived for only eleven years. It was demolished during construction of the third and last terminal at this site.

The three-hinged arch, which finally became the standard for the fully developed balloon shed, had appeared in exposition buildings in Paris as early as 1850. The engineer who introduced these new structural techniques in the United States was Joseph M. Wilson of Philadelphia. His first proposal for a balloon shed on three-hinged arches was made in 1867 for the Pittsburgh station of the Pennsylvania Railroad. The shed was to span 158 feet. It was turned down on the grounds of its excessive cost. He submitted two more projects to the Pennsylvania in 1872, one of modest size, 110 feet in span, for the Washington terminal, and the other, of 220-foot span, for the Jersey City station. Neither was built, again because the company regarded each as too expensive. Before Wilson had an opportunity to design a shed on the European model, the New York engineer Isaac Buckhout had begun to incorporate the new principles in the trainshed of Grand Central Terminal.

The Pennsylvania Railroad finally accepted the balloon shed on three-hinged arches when it began the building of its second Jersey City terminal (1887–92), but ironically enough its chief engineer was Charles C. Schneider rather than Wilson. The trainshed was by far the largest in the United States at the time of its completion, since the station provided the railroad's terminal facilities for the entire New York area.[8] The station was located at the ferry docks so that passengers could make the train-to-ferry transfer at the site. With the completion of the Pennsylvania's New York station in 1910, traffic at Jersey City was reduced to a few local trains. Eventually the shed became a useless expense and was dismantled in 1922.

The trainshed of Grand Central Station, Chicago (1888–89), was somewhat smaller than the predecessors of its type, since it handled less traffic than the big Eastern terminals (fig. 115). The station was designed by Solon S. Beman and W. S. Jones, respectively architect and engineer, and was built by the Chicago and Northern Pacific Railway, a line originally intended by Henry Villard to connect Chicago with his Northern Pacific Railway at St. Paul.[9] The balloon shed of the station is an exact half-cylinder of circular section supported by fixed arched trusses of steel.[10] The end of the shed through which the trains pass is completely open, while that at the head house is closed by a glass-and-iron curtain wall which is the handsomest feature of the whole structure. A roof of glass spanning the baggage platform adds further to the remarkable light and airy quality of the trainshed. In the restraint and finish of its design and workmanship, Grand Central Station is a classic of its kind. It is still in use, empty most of the day and hence quiet, filled with a soft, diffused light, a most pleasing survivor of nineteenth century building art. Once a busy terminal, its traffic is now reduced to 16 trains a day.

The single-span hinged-arch balloon shed reached its high point in the United States with the simultaneous construction of the Philadelphia terminals of the Reading and Pennsylvania railroads, both the work of Joseph M. Wilson's engineering firm. The Reading Terminal (1891–93), on Market Street at 12th, was the smaller of the two (fig. 116). It is still in use today, little altered from its original design, sharing with Grand Central Station, Chicago, the distinction of being the last American survivors of the balloon shed without intermediate supports.[11] The track level of Reading Terminal was raised

116　Reading Terminal, Market and 12th streets, Philadelphia, Pennsylvania, 1891–93. F. H. Kimball, architect; Joseph M. Wilson and Brothers, engineers. The rear end of the trainshed. The iron framework under the leading pair of arches once supported a glass curtain.

above the street grade to provide space for a market house and cold storage cellar. The shed is enclosed in sidewalls which rise 25 feet above the track level, thus blocking off the view of it from the lower level of the street and merging it with the 8-story head house. At the time of its completion the Reading operated 294 trains a day in and out of the Philadelphia terminal. The extensive suburban service of the railroad was electrified in 1930–32.

The last Broad Street Station of the Pennsylvania Railroad (1892–93) had the largest single-span trainshed in the world (fig. 117), an arched enclosure exceeded in size by only two roofs erected up to that time, those of the Galerie des Machines, Paris Exposition of 1889, and the Manufacturers and Liberal Arts Building, Chicago World's Fair of 1893.[12] Construction of the Broad Street shed involved the novel procedure af erecting the roof over the trainsheds of the 1882 station, which were left in place to provide shelter for the traffic that continued without interruption during the building of the newer structure. The trusses of the larger shed were erected from a wheeled timber traveler whose lowest members cleared all of the older shed except for a narrow portion of the roof and trusses along one side.

Close to the thirtieth anniversary of Broad Street Station, on June 10, 1923, the great roof and the wooden platforms were completely destroyed in one of Philadelphia's most spectacular fires. It was a major disaster for the railroad, since the traffic at the station amounted to 529 trains a day at the time. Normal service was restored before the end of the month, and the trainshed was replaced during the ensuing year. But the cost of maintaining the shed and the nuisance of operating a stub-end terminal in a city which most trains, other than suburban, pass through, led the railroad within a few years after the fire to build a new station of the through type at 30th Street (1927–31). The shed and building at Broad Street, however, were not finally demolished until 1953.

The construction of the two Philadelphia terminals at the same time gave rise to considerable discussion of the architectural as well as the engineering aspects of the large open shed. Wilson was aware of the monumental character of such vaults and turned serious attention to the question of their aesthetic possibilities:

To the architectural engineer the roof is always an interesting study, and when roofs of large span are to be considered, the interest proportionately increases. It is not merely that the space is to be covered with a substantial roof, but the architectural question of an artistic design in harmony with the other parts of the building is of first importance. A handsome roof is the refinement of engineering

117  Broad Street Station, Broad between Market and Filbert streets, Philadelphia, Pennsylvania, 1892–93. Wilson, Truscott, Furness, and Evans, architects; Joseph M. Wilson and Brothers, engineers. Cross section of the trainshed.

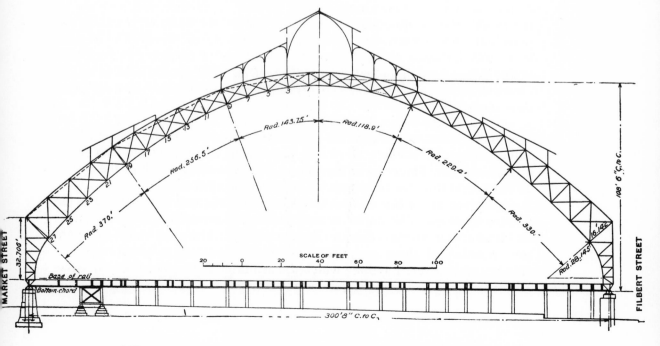

construction. The author, some years ago, designed a number of three-hinged arched roofs of the same general type . . . , but they were not adopted and erected on account of the supposed unwarranted expense. Now it has come to be recognized that this is the proper form of roof for a large railway station, reducing to a minimum the destructive action to the iron or steel construction from the sulphurous vapors emitted by the locomotives, and adding essentially to the comfort and satisfaction of travelers by increased ventilation and improved aesthetic effect. In designing such a roof it is an object to mass the material together as much as possible, avoiding a great number of small pieces and leaving wide open spaces; also to provide ample light and ventilation.[13]

Although Wilson's primary concern was functional, with emphasis on the validity of pure empirical form, he anticipated three cardinal doctrines of modern architectural theory—simplicity, volume rather than mass, and free-flowing space.

A more throughly functionalist or empirical theory of form was that of Walter G. Berg, the author of the foremost American treatise on railroad structures at the end of the century:

Relative to the roof construction of a trainshed it can be said, that the general effect of the interior and its structural efficiency depend largely on the appropriate and artistic design of the roof. The engineering and architectural features of large-span train-sheds are blended to such an extent, that the greatest care should be observed to bring the best talent and experience to bear in every direction in making the plans. The number of tracks and platforms to be spanned determine to a great extent the general design to be adopted for the roof. . . . The curved roofs have the decided advantage of presenting a more graceful appearance, and they can be treated in a more artistic manner. A roof design should, however, primarily impress itself on the observer by its simplicity and the perfect fitness of all its parts in a structural sense, giving at once the appearance of strength combined with utility. Where, in addition to these necessary elements, a graceful contour can be obtained, and details are worked up artistically, the design should certainly prove meritorious.[14]

The major unanswered question in this and in similar analyses is what the author means by working up details artistically, or treating the roof in an artistic manner. The heart of the matter lies here, since much of the rest is, as Wilson calls it, "the refinement of engineering construction."

The curved or vaulted roof on three-hinged arches was not confined to the railway trainshed. The finest examples of such construction were the larger buildings of the World's Fair in Chicago (1893).[15] The glass vaults and light steel framing of these temporary buildings exceeded in refinement and delicacy of structure anything which the armories or trainsheds could show.

118　Union Station, St. Louis, Missouri, 1891–94. Theodore C. Link and Edward D. Cameron, architects; George H. Pegram, engineer. The curtain wall at the rear end of the trainshed and the double wye that connects the approach with the station tracks.

The best examples were Machinery Hall and the Manufactures and Liberal Arts Building. The former consisted essentially of three parallel cylindrical vaults of arched construction.[16] The two central bays across the vaults opened into three domes which were also supported on three-hinged arches, one over each face of the double bay, and on radial ribs extending outward from the center of the dome. The architects of Machinery Hall were Peabody and Stearns, the engineer E. C. Shankland. The Manufacturers Building revealed the most extensive and elaborate system of hinged-arch framing ever undertaken in the United States.[17] The framing of the central part of the roof followed the precedent of the balloon trainshed, while that of the sloping ends was an extraordinarily complex but perfectly articulated array of two- and three-hinged arches. The architect of this masterpiece was George B. Post. Along with the Galerie des Machines at the Paris Exposition (1889), it marked the triumph of steel arched framing in the nineteenth century.[18]

Before the end of the century two companies built single-vault trainsheds of such enormous size that intermediate supports were necessary to carry the roof. As a matter of fact, the size and resulting cost of these structures were important factors in killing off the great vaulted shed. The first of the giants was the trainshed of St. Louis Union Station (1891–94), which has so many unique characteristics that it stands in a class by itself (figs. 118, 119). As the only station in the second-largest railroad center in the United States, it provides terminal facilities for the greatest number of separate railroad companies.[19] Its trainshed exceeds all others in area and linear dimensions and

**219**

PERSPECTIVE OF EXTERIOR OF TRAIN-SHED.

PERSPECTIVE OF INTERIOR OF TRAIN-SHED.

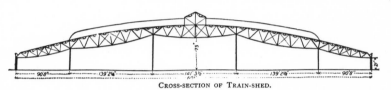

CROSS-SECTION OF TRAIN-SHED.

119   Union Station, St. Louis. Top to bottom: Exterior, interior, and cross section of the train-shed.

spans the largest number of tracks. And finally, the track layout of its approaches forms a system of double wyes which is without parallel for the resulting complexity and inefficiency of train movements. The St. Louis station was built by the Terminal Railroad Association of St. Louis, a transfer and terminal company organized and owned by the participating railroads. The architects of the station building and the adjoining hotel were Theodore C. Link and Edward D. Cameron; the chief designing engineer was George H. Pegram, who had recently achieved distinction through his invention of the Pegram truss.[20]

Since no railroad operates passenger trains through the city, the engineering staff decided to build a stub-end terminal. The decision might have seemed logical enough were it not for the fact that the railroads enter St. Louis from all directions and could not be combined, except at prohibitive expense, into a uni-directional approach. The resulting track plan is a peculiarly awkward one in which the open end of the trainshed faces south, while the approach tracks extend east and west, with entries and departures in both directions. Thus the axis of the shed lies on the stem of a wye through which all trains back into the station. The original wye of two double-track branches was expanded in 1904–5 to one with two pairs of branches, the inner two lines crossing at the station throat. The delays arising from reverse movements and blocking of the crossing could have been avoided by building a through station along the approach tracks.

Pegram's enormous trainshed spans 32 tracks with an over-all width of 601 feet. The great breadth made it impossible to construct a single-span shed on arches. He chose instead to build a low, much flattened vault of five intermediate spans. The tin-covered wooden roof thus rests on a steel framework of transverse Pegram trusses carried on six longitudinal rows of columns.[21] In spite of its 32 tracks—the largest number of any American station at the time —the St. Louis terminal was so congested by the mid-1920's that the company decided to build additional facilities. Ten more tracks with separate platform canopies were added on the west side of the original shed (1929–30). At the time the addition was planned, the station handled 260 trains a day, not a great number compared to the traffic in some of the eastern and Chicago terminals. The extensive trackage at St. Louis was required because the city has always been a major transfer point for passengers, mail, and express.

Pegram's design of the trainshed was based on aesthetic as well as utilitarian ends. He rejected the alternative of separate vaults or gables because he felt that the single shed offered more monumental possibilities. His justification of the truss form and the intermediate supports, however, rested on a questionable analogy:

The natural tendency in designing a building of this great width and small height would be to make what would appear to be more or less a set of parallel buildings. My main aim, architecturally, has been to preserve the unity of design and make its size more impressive, by avoiding, as far as possible, any idea of division which the necessary intermediate lines of supports would cause. The conspicuous part of the interior will, of course, be the roof sheathing, which limits the vision, and this has been made in the form of a single arch. It is believed that the bottom chords [of the trusses], hanging like chains from the columns, will produce an effect of drapery, or at least an effect of continuity something like the sag in a circus tent from the poles, which will tend to neutralize the rigid divisions by intermediate supports.[22]

But the rigid trusses in exact parallel rows do not give this effect of a freely falling curve. They serve only to break up into a multiplicity of angles the otherwise unified space under this vast, dark cavern of a trainshed.

The second-largest continuous trainshed in over-all dimensions was South Station, Boston (1896–99). Designed by Shepley, Rutan and Coolidge and the engineer J. R. Worcester, it was built by the Boston Terminal Company, an organization formed by the five participating railroads.[23] The low vaulted trainshed, which was set in the inner angle of the L-shaped station building, spanned

28 tracks. As in the case of the St. Louis station, the great width of the shed required that it be carried on intermediate supports (fig. 120).[24] At the time of its completion South Station was the busiest terminal in the United States, with an average traffic of 737 trains a day. After the customary life of thirty years the trainshed went the way of most of the rest: it was replaced by separate platform canopies in 1931.

The active life of the balloon trainshed was ended in 1904 when Lincoln Bush, an engineer of the Delaware, Lackawanna and Western Railroad, designed the shed that bears his name for the company's new Hoboken Terminal (1904–6). It was a multispan shed consisting of a series of low parallel vaults on steel girders spanning between rows of columns set on the center lines of the platforms. The advantages of the iron or steel balloon shed were obvious: all-covering protection without intermediate supports and the monumental character of the huge barrel vault. But its defects were so serious that even in its moment of triumph around 1890 there were many engineers who questioned its utility. It was expensive and difficult to erect, it was costly to maintain because of the inaccessibility of its members, and it was subject to continuous corrosion from the exhaust gases of locomotives. Most designing engineers at least insisted on a wooden roof, but many were skeptical of the whole idea of an all-covering vault high above the tracks. The Bush trainshed was not entirely satisfactory for the same reasons. The presence of a smoke slot over each track made it possible to dissipate gases more effectively, but some corrosion always occurred, and soon or late the problem of maintenance came up again. Although the low vault was much more accessible than the balloon shed, painting, cleaning, and replacement of corroded members was a constant necessity. As a consequence, the Bush shed lasted about ten years before it was superseded by the separate platform canopy, which had been introduced early in railroad history for way stations.

The few trainsheds of any kind that remain today stand only because the advent of the diesel-electric locomotive freed the railroad of coal smoke and its attendant evils. But there are some who regret the passing of the great sheds. Blackened with dirt, smelling strongly of smoke and noxious fumes, filled with steam in cold weather to the point where one had to grope blindly among the baggage trucks, they nevertheless had an architectonic power beside which the platform canopy is a mere carpenter's exercise. There was a magic in these huge vaults, fitting shelters for the hissing locomotives and the long lines of cars.

120  South Station, Atlantic Avenue at Dewey Square, Boston, Massachusetts, 1896–99. Shepley, Rutan and Coolidge, architects; J. R. Worcester, engineer. Cross section of the trainshed.

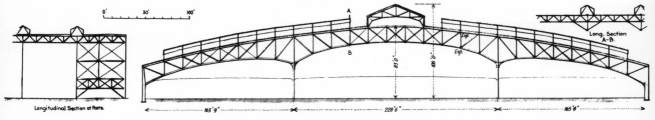

# VIII

## CONCRETE CONSTRUCTION

### 1. PLAIN CONCRETE IN WALLS AND BUILDINGS

Concrete is the oldest building material artificially prepared by man from a variety of natural substances. In view of this fact the long hiatus in the history of its use is surprising. It was unquestionably a Roman invention, yet in spite of the high stage of development which it reached under the Roman builders, there is no evidence that it was used again until the late Middle Ages. Roman concrete was a carefully proportioned mixture of lime, volcanic scoriae, and broken stone aggregate. In its plain form it was common in foundations, walls, and floors; what is most remarkable, however, was its presence in vaults and domes, where it was reinforced with timber, bronze, or brickwork.

The art of building with this most useful material appears to have been lost between the end of the classical period and the latter part of the twelfth century. The late medieval builders began to use it again for the footings of foundation walls in large churches. Composed of rubble and lime mortar, it was poured into a narrow trench, allowed to set, then used as the base for the masonry wall. But this seems to have been the extent of its use until the eighteenth century. The discovery in 1796 of a natural hydraulic cement on the Isle of Sheppy, England, stimulated a renewed interest in the material for a greater variety of structural elements. The age of concrete construction began its vigorous development in England in 1824, when Joseph Aspdin, a bricklayer of Leeds, invented the artificial hydraulic cement known as Portland cement.

The first use of concrete in America appears to be another case of derivation from a medieval precedent. The Spanish builders of the Castillo de San Marcos, St. Augustine, Florida (1672 *et seq.*), made the ground flooring of the fort out of a primitive concrete composed of oyster lime, sand, and shell aggregate, the resulting mixture, when set, sealed and finished with linseed oil. The fort has been preserved as a national monument, but the original concrete flooring remains in only a single chamber within the enclosure. The Spanish continued to be the only users of concrete in the New World during the eighteenth century. A product consisting of lime, sand, and a crude aggregate of stones and pieces of brick and tile was extensively employed in California for walls, domes, and aqueducts. An improvement in the quality of the material and a wider range of applications appeared in the second decade of the nineteenth century.

Modern concrete preparation reached the United States in 1818, when the canal engineer Canvass White discovered a natural hydraulic cement along the line of the Erie Canal near either Fayetteville or Chittenango, New York. He established a mill at Chittenango in the same year and was granted a patent in 1819 for his "water lime," as he called it.[1] During the next decade he made extensive use of it in concrete for facework, docks, abutment walls, culverts, and aqueducts on the Erie Canal. Water lime like that of White's patent continued to be used until about 1890.

A similar discovery was made in 1823 near Rosendale, New York, by the builders of the Delaware and Hudson Canal, who employed it for lock and retaining walls along the waterway. The material was superior to the earlier brand, and, after further improvement by subsequent manufacturing processes, it was used widely in the United States during the remainder of the century. It was calcined in kilns, like lime, to expel volatile gaseous substances (chiefly free carbon dioxide) and to render it friable, and it was then ground to a fine powder. A mill to prepare the Rosendale product was established in that town in 1828. Concrete of this kind continued to be a popular material for canal construction wherever local deposits of natural cement were discovered, but it was limited to small installations such as lock and retaining walls and was always dependent on a supply of the natural binding material (fig. 121).[2] David O. Saylor's invention of artificial cement in 1871 soon made possible concrete construction on a large scale, but until then builders were tied to what they could find in a natural state or to the quantity of Portland cement they could afford to import from England.[3]

121 Miami and Erie Canal, Dayton-Cincinnati Section, 1823–28. Lock walls near Hamilton, Ohio.

In spite of these limitations and the near-total ignorance of correct proportioning and preparation, the advantages of concrete were so great and so immediately apparent as to prove irresistible to builders. First of all, the materials of which it is composed are among the commonest substances in the earth's crust, they are readily available at or near the surface of the ground, and their impurities can be removed at little expense. Once properly prepared and mixed, concrete can be easily cast into any form for which it is possible to make a mold, and it can be poured under water, where it will set and harden as well as in the air. Thus the high cost and cumbersome technical processes of quarrying, cutting, dressing, and transporting stone could be avoided, and the expensive and time-consuming job of laying up stone masonry, even dangerous in deep-water caissons, could become a thing of the past. Finally—though it took a century to realize it—concrete is the only material out of which the builder can fashion a perfectly continuous structure without joints or connections. Difficult problems of reinforcing and stress analysis had to be solved before this technique was feasible. By the early twentieth century it was clear that concrete would soon reach universal dominance in modern construction and that it could be used in every type of structure.

The builders began to appreciate the potentialities of the new material for more complex structures than simple walls shortly after the canal companies first demonstrated its virtues. A New Yorker named Obadiah Parker developed an impure American equivalent of Aspdin's Portland cement about 1830. He calcined and pulverized an association of limestone and alumina and silica clays, then mixed the resulting material with water, sand, and gravel aggregate. Parker began to construct houses with monolithic walls of poured concrete in the 1830's. One of the earliest of these was a small Greek Revival dwelling in New York built in 1835. The side walls, entablature, and cornice were cast as an integral unit, while the columns were cast separately possibly because of the complexity of formwork that complete monolithic construction would require. Two years later a New York merchant, G. A. Ward, built a large house for himself in New Brighton on Staten Island, New York, the exterior walls of which were entirely of concrete. Ward, however, deliberately turned his back on the great advantage of the new material, that of casting entire walls as homogeneous units, and built his walls of precast blocks laid up in mortar to simulate stone masonry. Known locally as the "cement house," it was of massive construction, with extremely thick walls. The house remained in a good state of preservation for at least fifty years.[4]

Joseph Goodrich of Milton, Wisconsin, returned to Parker's technique of pouring monolithic walls when he built his own house in 1844. Wanting a structure proof against incendiary attacks by Indians, he imported Portland cement from England, which he mixed with sand, water, broken stone, and gravel and tamped into wooden forms. He probably used a lean mixture because of the high cost of the long wagon haul from New York. Even so, his house must have been the most expensive in the region for a long time. It was generous in size: the main portion, two stories high, was 42 × 90 feet in plan; at one side stood a three-story hexagonal tower, 24 feet on a side, and at the other there was a one-story wing 200 feet long. The house stood occupied until 1948, when it suddenly collapsed. The structure was described with great enthusiasm by a popular phrenologist, Orson Fowler, who urged concrete construction and the octagonal plan in a book on the subject, *A Home for All, or, The Gravel Wall and Octagon Mode of Building* (1849). The octagonal plan he defended on the ground that it was phrenologically sound.[5]

For the two decades after 1860 the most popular form of concrete construction was that of precast blocks, which could be cast with any kind of surface pattern to simulate rough or dressed stone masonry. The most vigorous development of this type of building occurred in Chicago, where the material was known as artificial stone. The pioneer in the new field was George A. Frear, who was granted a patent in 1868 for his block and who built his first house of it in the same year for H. B. Horton of Chicago. In his published description Frear was careful not to make an explicit statement about how his block was made, but there is no question that his material was concrete cast in molds under pressure. He himself described it as a mixture of sand and gravel "fastened together firmly by chemicals." Frear's original achievement was the introduction of insoluble pigments into the concrete by means of which he could imitate the colors of natural stone. Further, he was prepared to cast it in "any devised pattern or form, such as bricks of various sizes, ashlars, keystones, corner blocks, water tables, door and window caps, sills, cornices, etc."[6] Frear also recommended the material as a wall facing and a fireproofing envelope. He submitted the blocks to tests of freezing and heating and claimed that they were undamaged. Prolonged exposure to weather, he said, served to harden the material. This would be the case if he used a proper mixture of cement and aggregate. Frear's invention rapidly became popular, and by 1873 his Frear Stone Manufacturing Company employed 50 men and sold $100,000 worth of block in a single year. The fire of 1871, of course, proved to be his greatest benefactor. Soon he was providing trim on an extensive scale for large buildings, the best known of which is Burnham and Root's Phoenix Building (1885–86), still standing on Jackson Boulevard near Clark Street in Chicago, but now known as the Austin. His product spread to the West and by 1872 had appeared in San Francisco.[7]

Ernest L. Ransome, who did more to advance the art of reinforced concrete construction than any other American builder, had collaborated in the establishment in 1868 of a company in San Francisco to manufacture concrete block.[8] A Chicago branch, known as the Ransome Artificial Stone Company, was founded in 1872 and in the same year manufactured blocks for the Atlantic

Hotel (1872–73), on Sherman Street near Van Buren. As we have noted, the fire of 1871 gave great impetus to the use of concrete block, especially after one impressive demonstration of the strength and resistance of the new material. The concrete-block front of a store building on Monroe Street (1871) collapsed during the fire as a result of the failure of the interior iron columns. The unbroken blocks were recovered, cleaned, and laid up once more during reconstruction of the store in 1872. The use of concrete as a fireproofing material began in Chicago with the Nixon Building (1871), whose cast iron beams were protected by a 1-inch layer of concrete to make them as fire-resistant as possible.[9] By 1880 concrete was beginning to be regarded as a material with universal possibilities in building. As one commentator wrote, "There is scarcely any limit to the application of this material for building purposes, nor any place where natural stone is employed where it may not be substituted with advantage and economy."[10]

Among the eastern manufacturers of concrete block the New York and Long Island Coignet Stone Company, established about 1870, held the American rights to Francois Coignet's patent of 1867 on the manufacture of concrete. Samples of "Coignet stone," as it was frequently called in the East, were subjected to compression and resistance tests by a Boston manufacturer in 1873 with results which indicated that in most respects the artificial material could compete favorably with stone.[11] What seems to have made it particularly attractive to eastern architects was the ease with which it could be cast into ornamental forms. Among those who welcomed it enthusiastically were some of the leaders in their art, men like Olmsted, Renwick, and Vaux. "I have no hesitation in saying," one builder wrote, "that it is a most valuable invention and addition to our building operations—one that will meet a great architectural need, that of affording the means of the highest ornamentation, joined to great solidity and strength, at a cost far below any other building materials."[12]

Most of the so-called artificial stones which were manufactured around 1870 depended on natural cement for their binding material, or on the importation of Portland cement from England. This limitation was removed in 1871 when David O. Saylor was granted a patent for the manufacture of artificial Portland cement in the United States. Saylor's cement was originally made at Coplay, Pennsylvania, where he built a number of domed kilns of brick in which to calcine the mixture of lime and silicon, aluminum, and iron oxides that formed the major ingredients of his product. After calcination the mixture was ground at his mill to an impalpable powder.

A further impetus to the widening acceptance of concrete around 1875 was the realization that blast-furnace slag could be used as an aggregate and, in some cases, if it were properly ground and sufficiently sharp and hard, in place of sand. The iron and steel manufacturers naturally looked favorably on this development, since they were producing slag in large quantities and found it an ever-growing disposal problem. A typical slag-concrete block usually contained 6 to 8 parts of slag to one of cement. Before the end of the century it was discovered that cinders could also be used as an aggregate.

The federal government stimulated the use of the new invention when it specified Saylor's cement for the South Pass jetties at the delta of the Mississippi River (1875–79). James B. Eads recommended the construction of the jetties and supervised their building. These huge walls, which line the main channel pass of the delta and extend as breakwaters into the Gulf, were designed for a number of purposes, chiefly to maintain clear and stable channels, prevent the deposition of sediment, and obstruct wind and shore currents to retard the formation of bars and spits. A one-mile length of the east jetty and a half-mile length of the west were built of megalithic concrete blocks, the largest of which measured 5 × 13 × 55 feet and weighed 260 tons. Eads proposed concrete on the ground that it was the only material of sufficient density that could be inexpensively formed into blocks large enough to withstand Gulf coast hurricanes.[13]

By the 1880's plain concrete in bearing members under compressive stress only—chiefly walls and footings—was a familiar feature of buildings and waterway and harbor works. Its low cost and fireproof character also made it attractive for floors and beams, but here its inherent weakness imposed severe limitations. Like stone, concrete has a negligible tensile and shearing strength, with the consequence that wherever it is subjected to such strains over any but the shortest spans, it will quickly fail. In spite of this disadvantage, around 1890 several large buildings were constructed with concrete floors built up of separate precast slabs or poured as monolithic units. The advantages, of course, lay in freeing the material from its dependence on the traditional forms of stone masonry and casting it in solid walls and floors.

The decision to use plain concrete in this way on an extensive scale came with the construction of a remarkable building, Henry M. Flagler's Hotel Ponce de Leon in St. Augustine, Florida (1886–88). Most of the structural elements in the building—exterior walls, some partitions, foundations, and footings—are of poured concrete cast in forms on the site. The material has a shell aggregate, like the floors of the old Castillo not far from the hotel. Although apparently without reinforcing, concrete was selected to withstand hurricanes. In this respect the choice was sound, since the hotel stands today in excellent condition. As remarkable as its concrete construction is the hotel's architectural character. Original in treatment, its red brick trim against the gray concrete, elaborately carved wooden beams, palm-trunk columns, and red tile roof give it a playful and exotic quality that suggests the hand of an imaginative architect. The commission went to Carrère and Hastings, but the real author was Bernard Maybeck, then a designer with the New York firm and later one of the pioneers of the modern movement in California. The concrete construction of the hotel aroused much local interest, and before the end of the century at least three other buildings in St. Augustine were built in a similar manner.[14]

But plain concrete construction of this kind was soon to be superseded by reinforced concrete. As builders learned more about the new structural techniques, they came to realize that their possibilities could be most fully exploited in total concrete framing rather than in discontinuous combinations of concrete and steel or timber members.

Since concrete was sooner or later used wherever stone masonry in mass had been the traditional building material, it was inevitable that it would be applied to the construction of bridge piers. The first structure in which concrete formed a part of the pier is the famous Starrucca Viaduct, built by the New York and Erie Railroad (1848) near Susquehanna, Pennsylvania.[15] The footings of its huge stone piers are massive blocks of concrete each 760 square feet in area. The cost of cement at that date was one of the many reasons why Starrucca Viaduct earned the reputation of being the most expensive railroad bridge in the world. This factor was probably the major deterrent to further construction of concrete piers for at least fifteen years.

A builder named W. H. Wood was granted a patent in 1862 for what he claimed was the first concrete bridge pier. His patent design involved a cast iron drum filled with concrete and resting on wooden piles driven into the bed of the stream. The iron cylinder seems to have functioned chiefly for protection rather than as a bearing member. If Wood built any piers of this kind, their location has not been preserved.

The first such drum piers whose location is known were built to support the bridge of the Boston and Providence Railroad over the Seekonk River near Providence, Rhode Island (1867–68). The span replaced an earlier structure, built in 1835. A typical pier consisted of two clusters of 12 piles each, the two groups set 16 feet on centers, one under each side of the bridge on a transverse line. Around each cluster was a cast iron cylinder, the space within which was filled with concrete rammed tight between the piles.[16] The piles were driven to hard pan, but the cylinder only a little way into the river bed. Thus neither the drum nor the concrete had any bearing function but existed wholly for protection against abrasion, ice, and destructive marine organisms. The cylinders were sunk into place by loading them with 15 tons of rails and rocking them back and forth with levers. In the center pile of the draw-span pier an opening was left as a repository for a few memorials—papers containing a description of the bridge, several coins, and a bottle of whiskey. Some fortunate member of a New Haven Railroad bridge crew may have recovered these relics.

Similar drum piers of great size carried the Union Pacific's Missouri River bridge at Omaha, Nebraska (1868–72), but in this case the concrete itself constituted the bearing element.[17] Each pier consisted of a pair of concrete-filled

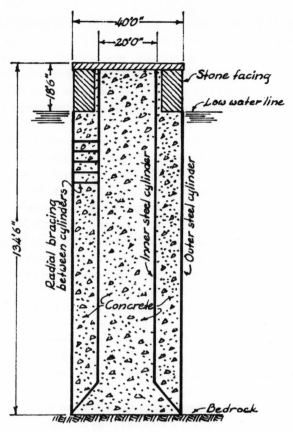

122 Bridge of the Omaha Bridge and Terminal Railroad Company, Missouri River, Omaha, Nebraska, 1892–94. Cross section of the pivot pier under the swing span.

cast iron cylinders about 12 feet in diameter sunk to bedrock 75 to 80 feet below mean low water (fig. 73). Again the cylinders existed chiefly to provide protection against the abrasive action of river sediments.

The foundation and pedestal of the Statue of Liberty (1883–86) constituted a steel and concrete structure of unusual size and complexity. The foundation is concrete throughout, while the pedestal has a concrete core faced with granite block.[18] The concrete was laid up in courses matching those of the granite facing and thoroughly bonded to them. A system of steel girders laid in pairs at right angles and deeply imbedded in the concrete supports the four main posts of the statue frame. The figure is set eccentrically on the pedestal because of the asymmetrical loading resulting from the upraised arm and torch. The designers of the foundation and pedestal faced problems calling for unusual skill and boldness. The engineer in charge was General C. P. Stone, the concrete engineer William Kenish, and the architect Richard Morris Hunt.

The contracting firm of Drake and McGaw built the foundation, and that of D. H. King, Jr., the pedestal.

The Statue of Liberty marked a turning point in concrete construction, chiefly because it was erected at a time when the builders had become sufficiently familiar with the new material to use it on a large scale and in complex ways. Its greatest range of applications came with the development of modern techniques of reinforcing around 1890, but at the same time plain concrete in mass found increasing use in bridge piers and eventually in dams. The huge concrete foundations which were built to support the steel bents of the Poughkeepsie cantilever bridge (1886–88) stimulated interest in the possibility of constructing entire piers of the material.[19] For the remainder of the century, however, the builders generally preferred stone masonry with a concrete core or the drum pier with its iron jacket. What may have been the largest of the latter was the enormous pivot pier which supported the 520-foot swing span in the Missouri River crossing of the Omaha Bridge and Terminal Railroad Company near Omaha, 1892–94 (fig. 122).[20] A total of 5,800 cubic yards of concrete went into the construction of this massive pier, which relied on sheer weight for its strength, like a gravity dam. The largest installation of concrete piers before the end of the century was in the Ferry Terminal at San Francisco (1895). The entire structure was built of reinforced concrete and rested on 111 plain concrete piers supported in turn on wooden piles. It was a large-scale demonstration of the great superiority of concrete for construction in salt water and in tidal estuaries.

## 2. REINFORCED CONCRETE BUILDINGS

The technique of reinforcing concrete is very nearly as old as the material itself. The Roman builders employed it wherever they adopted concrete for wide unsupported spans. They introduced brick arches into concrete domes apparently for the sole purpose of increasing the compressive strength of the material. Their use of metal rods and timbers in the roofs of houses and tombs, however, indicates that they understood the weakness of concrete under bending stresses and the consequent necessity of incorporating materials in the cast masonry which could resist deflection. The revival of concrete construction in the nineteenth century soon led to attempts to develop a system of reinforcing which would extend the range of structural uses of the new material.[1]

The pioneer work in reinforced concrete was done by French builders, who had been the leaders of Europe in masonry construction since the twelfth century. About 1840 there were several attempts at Paris to construct floor slabs of plaster of paris reinforced with iron rods and bars, but the metal rusted rapidly and the floors soon collapsed. The reinforcement of Portland cement mortar and concrete with iron rods or wires was proposed in 1849 by Joseph Lambot, who astonished his contemporaries by building a boat in this way. In 1854 an English plasterer, William B. Wilkinson, obtained the first patent for a structurally practical system of reinforcing concrete floors with iron bars, and in the following year François Coignet obtained the first of his many patents for similar methods of construction. A practical method of wire-mesh reinforcing was developed in 1861 by the Parisian gardener Joseph Monier, who used it to build concrete tubs and tanks. The exhibition of the work of Coignet and Monier at the Paris Exposition of 1867 brought the new structural technique to international attention, but it was another decade before it began to appear in buildings. François Hennebique, who constructed his first reinforced floor slabs in 1879, was the leading French builder of reinforced concrete. Within the following decade English, German, and American work reached a similar level of development.

Reinforced concrete construction in the United States appeared shortly after the Paris Exposition of 1867 and was unquestionably influenced by the French achievements. At the same time, there was a long preliminary period of native experiments, some of which may have been carried out independently of the European work.[2] The first patent for a reinforced concrete wall was granted to S. T. Fowler in 1860. The reinforcing consisted of a grillage of horizontal and vertical timbers bolted together. The introduction of reinforced brickwork about the time of Fowler's patent formed an important step in the direction of reinforced concrete for large structures.[3] Two patents were granted to George H. Johnson (1862, 1869) for a greatly improved system of reinforced brickwork to be used in grain elevators. Continuous annular tension bars were united with vertical rods to form a tightly woven net of reinforcing imbedded in the joints. Charles Williams received a patent in 1868 for an application of Johnson's technique to concrete walls, but he used riveted iron straps rather than bars and rods. The first metal-and-concrete floor slab in the United States, patented by J. Gilbert (1867), consisted of corrugated iron plates covered with concrete to a depth of one inch above the ridges.

Thus by 1870 American builders were familiar with the combination of concrete masonry and internal metal reinforcing. All the inventions were based on the intuitive realization that concrete or stone masonry has a negligible strength in tension and shear, but possesses considerable resistance to compression and great hardness and durability. The preliminary essays, however, were primitive and revealed a defective understanding of the exact method of reinforcing necessary for the construction of beams, columns, and slabs in any position.[4] Considerable experiment, combined with theoretical and empirical investigations, was necessary before the builders could arrive at a mature understanding of the possibilities of reinforced concrete. It was thirty years before the new material threatened the supremacy of iron and steel.

The boldest and most spectacular forward step after the period of the early patents was made by William E. Ward, who built his own house at Port Chester, New York (1871–76), entirely of reinforced concrete.[5] Ward's achievement was one of the most remarkable works of building art in the century. With such native inventions as we have described and the French patents of Coignet and Monier to guide him, he and his architect, Robert Mook of New York, succeeded not only in building a large residence in which every structural element was of reinforced concrete but also in anticipating most of the modern techniques of such construction. He spent $100,000 on his creation but never took out a patent and did little to publicize his success. Its importance, however, did not escape the architectural and engineering press, in which there are detailed contemporary accounts. One of the earliest descriptions reveals a full appreciation of its unusual structural character:

This palatial residence . . . is built entirely of artificial stone—the foundation and the roof inclusive—towers, colonnades, floors, staircases, balustrades, balconies, porches, and all. . . . Its strength may be imagined when we state that when the parlor floor, with a span of eighteen feet, had been laid one year, a weight of twenty-six tons was piled in the middle of it and left there through the winter, the apparatus arranged for determining the deflection showing only one-hundredth of an inch depression. Here is another instance of an elegant private residence standing upon an eminence of unusual exposure, swept by the direct north-easterly gales of Long Island Sound, and thoroughly weather-proof and fire-proof.[6]

Within a year after the completion of the Ward house, the British attorney and engineer Thaddeus Hyatt published his classic *Experiments with Portland Cement Concrete* and thus provided the theoretical counterpart to Ward's practical demonstration. Hyatt developed the crude empiricism of earlier metal and concrete construction into a rational science which formed the basis of all subsequent designs. "It is Ward in America and Hyatt in England . . . to whom credit is due for a scientific combination of these materials." [7]

The sheer quantity of material in the Ward house indicated not only its unusual size but also the structural extravagance of his design, as though a 26-ton weight on the parlor floor were likely to be a common occurrence.[8] Exterior walls and interior partitions were plain slabs and the reinforced floors ribbed slabs, all poured as homogeneous monolithic elements. The plaster of walls and partitions was laid directly on the concrete. The method of constructing the floors in general followed the system patented by François Coignet.[9] The construction of the main roof and of the floors and roofs of the porches followed that of the rest of the house, although in the case of the porches some of the slabs were much larger than those of the interior floors.[10] The house had its own water supply, which was accumulated from rainfall and a nearby spring and pumped to a tank set in a large corner tower. Its construction was similar to that of the rest of the house. The stairways and balustrades were concrete, except for the wooden handrail. The only other combustible materials in the house were the furniture and carpeting. The concrete footings rested on hard-pan clay comparable in strength to that supporting many an early skyscraper. The *American Architect's* correspondent summed it all up in a simple under-statement, "The house is a scientific success." [11]

For all the technical virtuosity that went into it, the Ward house remained for fifteen years an isolated phenomenon, its great cost operating as an effective deterrent to further experiments. Much of the expense which Ward lavished upon it, however, was a consequence of its intricate details and its structural redundancy. Greater simplicity of design and more accurate stress analysis would inevitably lead to a reduction in unit cost, especially for large multi-story buildings. The house revealed two things to the builders: the possibilities of the new technique, and the need for further inquiry into the proper uses of it. The decade of the 1880's was largely a period of learning, in which American engineers became increasingly familiar with the theory and the practice of reinforced concrete construction through such works as Hyatt's *Experiments* and their own essays in actual building.

The period saw a number of patents on various kinds of iron reinforcing: expanded metal sheets, rods bent into the form of arches or joined into trusses, networks and meshes of rods or wires, and corrugated sheets. By the end of the decade the engineers were making the first proposals for reinforced pre-cast beams. Column footings of concrete poured around grillages of iron beams or rails became common in cities with compressible soil, chiefly Chicago and Boston. The technique was introduced for the first time in Burnham and Root's Montauk Block in Chicago (1882).[12] What was probably the first successful concrete sidewalk reinforced with rods was laid in Bowling Green Park, New York, in 1884. Potentially the most important of the innovations of the 'eighties was embodied in a patent granted in 1886 to the San Francisco engi-neer P. H. Jackson for prestressed concrete beams.[13] His method was to bury a grease-coated steel bar in a concrete beam and to tighten end plates fixed to the bar against the end surfaces of the beam in order to compress the con-crete. But the technique failed because, as the concrete set, it shrank, and the bar eventually lost its tension and released the load on the beam.[14] The engi-neers had by this time come to a fairly mature understanding of the correct method of reinforcing and of bonding metal to concrete and had at least recognized the problem of providing adequate jointing for thermal expansion and contraction. The stage was set for the inventive designer who could create a fully developed structural technique out of the innovations that now lay at hand.

The man who did more than anyone else in the United States to make reinforced concrete a common structural material was Ernest L. Ransome of San Francisco. Born in England, he began his career as an apprentice in his father's factory, the Ransome and Sims Iron Works at Ipswich. His father, Frederick, in 1844 had invented a concrete made by heating flint stones to a high temperature in a caustic alkali solution. Various improvements in hardening and weatherproofing this material eventually led him to establish the Patent Concrete Stone Company to manufacture the product. When Ernest Ransome left England for America in the late 1860's, he had already acquired considerable knowledge of the physical properties of concrete. He decided to go directly to California, where iron was expensive and an alternative building material likely to prove popular. He became superintendent of the Pacific Stone Company at San Francisco in 1870, having introduced his father's invention to the California builders two years earlier. It was fifteen years, however, before he had an opportunity to make proper use of his inventive faculty.

Ransome's first patent was granted in 1882 for a system of expansion joints in plain concrete floor slabs poured in shallow arches between and over closely spaced iron beams. His first work of reinforced construction appeared in 1883, when he introduced 2-inch tie rods set transversely to carry tensile stresses in the sidewalks around the Masonic Temple at Stockton, California. Ransome used smooth rods, with the result that the walk failed because of inadequate bonding. He solved the problem in 1884 by substituting uniformly twisted bars of square section, for which he received his second patent. When he proposed this simple and now universal device as a reinforcing element for all parts of a building, he was met with widespread criticism from architects, engineers, and builders. In spite of the exhaustive and successful tests to which he subjected sample slabs, enthusiasm for the new system was slow in coming.

Ransome's earliest commissions for structures built in large proportion of reinforced concrete were the storage buildings of the Arctic Oil Works at San Francisco (1884) and the flour mill of Starr and Company at Wheatport, California (1885). He used his twisted-bar reinforcing. It was confined to walls and chimneys in the oil warehouse, but was used for all structural parts of the mill. The owners of both buildings chose the novel system in order to secure maximum protection against fire and earthquakes. Although both were a success, Ransome's next major commission was confined to only a small part of the total structure. He designed the reinforced concrete main floor of the Bourn and Wise Wine Cellar at St. Helena, California (1888), the rest of the three-story building having been constructed of stone masonry, iron, and timber. The floor, which measured 75 × 400 feet, was cast as a continuous slab in the form of a series of beams joined by shallow arches. There was an expansion joint in each beam and a system of reinforcing which consisted of a pair of 2-inch bars set near the lower, or tension, surface of the beam (fig. 123). The floor rested on cast iron columns. The construction was a success; it marked the turning point, and within a few years Ransome became one of the leading structural engineers in the country in the number and size of his commissions.

Two important structures built in 1889 gave convincing evidence of his ability: one was the first reinforced concrete bridge in the United States, the other the Academy of Sciences at San Francisco.[15] For the Academy he again had the opportunity to use concrete throughout except for the cast iron columns of the interior. Four stories high, it was built in the form of an open rectangle around a skylighted court (fig. 124). The floors were continuous, slabs and beams cast as a unit, with the usual bar reinforcing. There was once more a good deal of adverse criticism. Ransome answered the objections by loading a test section of the second floor with gravel to the extent of 415 pounds per square foot. The resulting deflection was only ⅛ inch and there was no cracking of the concrete. In the addition to the Borax Works at Alameda, California (1889), Ransome included the joists for the first time in the floors, casting slab, beams, and joists as a single homogeneous element (fig. 125). Each beam was reinforced with three bars, and the joists with single bars. The floors were again carried on cast iron columns.

Ransome's third patent was granted in 1891 for a once common method of lighting basements under sidewalks by means of glass discs or cubes set directly in the concrete. The chief difficulty in this kind of construction was the cracking and leaking resulting from the unequal coefficients of thermal expansion of glass and concrete. Ransome solved the problem by an ingenious system of expansion joints and a resilient caulking material. He received another patent in 1894 for further improvements in this method of lighting areas under walks.

123   Bourn and Wise Wine Cellar, St. Helena, California, 1888. Ernest L. Ransome, engineer. Cross section through part of the floor showing the expansion joints and the reinforcing rods.

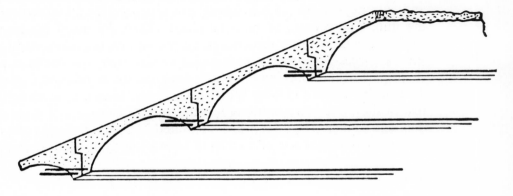

124 California Academy of Sciences, San Francisco, California, 1889. Ernest L. Ransome, engineer. Interior light court.

Meanwhile, he was commissioned as designing engineer for two buildings of some architectural elegance on the campus of Leland Stanford Junior University near Palo Alto, California, one a girls' dormitory known as Roble Hall, the other the University Museum (both 1892). In the dormitory the columns as well as the floors, beams, and joists were of reinforced concrete. The exterior walls were built of precast concrete block laid up in imitation of stone masonry. The architects, Percy and Hamilton, refrained, however, from carrying this imitation to the point of absurdity. The walls were left as smooth planes and the window openings were precise and sharp-edged. The building was erected in 90 days. In the museum the stairways and roof, in addition to the structural elements, were of reinforced concrete (fig. 126). The stair treads and the walls of the hallways were finished with marble slabs. There was no wood or other combustible material in the structure. The sash was steel and all decorative work, including sculpture, was cast in plain concrete. The exterior was finished with a smooth coat of colored cement to imitate brownstone. The building demonstrated what one could do with concrete, even in the service of bad taste.

Ransome's major work of industrial building before the end of the century was the factory of the Pacific Coast Borax Company at Bayonne, New Jersey (1897–98). Although larger in size than his previous structures, it followed an essentially similar method of construction. Ransome regarded it as bringing the pioneer era to its end: "In a measure [this building] marks the  closing of the old-time construction of reinforced concrete buildings, constructed more or less in imitation of brick or stone buildings, with comparatively small windows set in walls."[16] During construction of the Bayonne factory he discovered that the addition of salt to cement, in the proportion of 1 to 5 per cent by weight, materially improved the fire-resistance of the concrete without impairing its strength. Salt had previously been used in mortar to reduce its freezing temperature and thus allow masonry work to progress in periods of cold weather.

125   Borax Works, Alameda, California, 1889. Ernest L. Ransome, engineer. Reinforced concrete floor construction.

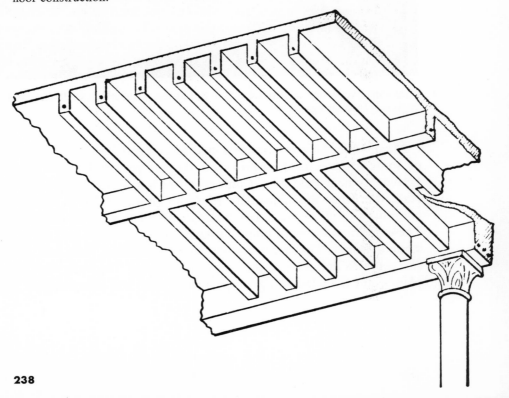

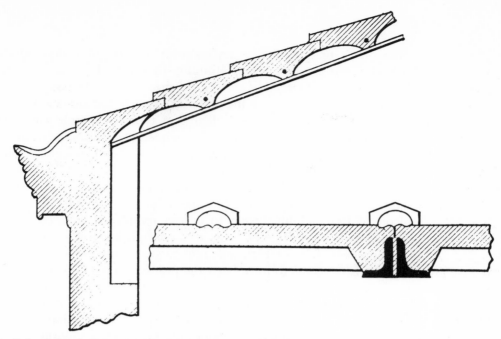

126   Leland Stanford, Junior, Museum, Palo Alto, California, 1892. Ernest L. Ransome, engineer.
Reinforced concrete roof construction.

Ransome's late work, in the first decade of the new century, showed nearly complete emancipation from the earlier masonry precedents of concrete construction. By the mid-nineties he had gained national prominence, and his designing organization, the Ransome Engineering Company, received commissions from the eastern and mid-western cities as well as from the Pacific area. At the same time his inventive genius brought him a number of patents for techniques which now form part of the established practice in concrete construction. Most of them were granted in 1902. The first was for a method of bonding new concrete to old by imbedding half a helically coiled bar in the previous work and leaving it half exposed to form part of the reinforcement of the addition. He first used the technique in the office building of the Foster-Armstrong Company at East Rochester, New York (1904–5). A second patent was issued for extending the floor slabs by cantilevering them beyond the outer wall plane to form belt courses on the exterior of the building. Its initial application appeared in the machine shop for the Kelly and Jones Company of Greensburg, Pennsylvania (1903–4). The method is now standard for buildings whose windows form a continuous band. Still another patent was granted for uniting reinforcing bars in the same line by winding steel cable around their lapped ends. Most famous and useful of his late inventions was the so-called unit system of construction, patented 1902 and 1909, whereby forms are made fairly durable and are used repeatedly for similar structural elements on one or several different jobs.

Ransome's imagination as an inventor and his skill and reliability as a designer acted as a powerful stimulus to the widespread use of concrete which suddenly emerged at the end of the century. As late as 1890 builders were still hesitant, confining the material to a few parts of the whole structure and overbuilding to an extreme degree. A typical example was the City Hall at Scranton, Pennsylvania (1888–89), whose 9½-inch floor slabs, reinforced with ¾-inch rods, rested on 15-inch girders and 7-inch joists, both in the form of wrought iron I-beams. The floors would have carried a locomotive: their breaking point was estimated at 2,000 pounds per square foot, yet the actual maximum load would never have exceeded 200 pounds. When Joseph M. Wilson of Philadelphia began to design reinforced concrete floors around 1890, Ransome's early work was well enough known so that he and a few other engineers felt confident enought to scale down this costly redundancy. Niles Poulson seems to have been the pioneer in New York, his earlier reinforced floors, dating from about 1892, revealing a more scientific approach. In spite of the early and extensive use of concrete block in Chicago, the use of reinforced concrete seems to have lagged behind that in some of the eastern and west coast cities. Floors were becoming common in the 'nineties, but the first complete structure appears to have been the Winton Building (1904).

By the mid-nineties the engineers were willing to try their hands at complex forms. The large Ferry Terminal at San Francisco (1895) consisted of a series of groined vaults cast as a continuous structure in reinforced concrete. Even more advanced was the nave ceiling of the Church of St. Mary the Virgin in New York (1895–96). This was a shell of reinforced concrete cast in imitation of French ribbed vaulting of the fourteenth century. The reinforcing bars were fixed to steel ribs curved to conform to the shape of the vault groins. It is one of the misfortunes of American building art that such essays were not further developed in the twentieth century, as they were so brilliantly in Europe by men like Freyssinet, Maillart, and Nervi. Concrete construction in the United States, in spite of such brave beginnings, has fallen into apparently permanent eclipse, compared to the European and Latin American achievements.

## 3. THE MASONRY ARCH BRIDGE: STONE AND CONCRETE

Behind the concrete arch lay centuries of unbroken experience with arch construction of stone masonry in both buildings and bridges. On the basis of Etruscan and eastern precedents the Roman builders developed the form to great size and refinement in a long series of structures, several of which have survived to the present day. To the medieval builder it was not only long familiar but the only method for permanent bridges. During the eight-

127 Carrollton Viaduct, Baltimore and Ohio Railroad, Baltimore, Maryland, 1829. Jonathan Knight and Caspar Wever, engineers; James Lloyd, architect.

eenth century the French, chiefly through the work of Jean Rodolphe Perronet, carried the arch to the point where many of the essential features of the modern concrete span were clearly anticipated.

The American colonists would gladly have used masonry construction for their major bridges were it not for its prohibitive cost and the scarcity of qualified masons. With moderate skill, however, a patient man could build up a small arch of carefully selected undressed or irregular masonry even without mortar. A few were built in the colonies, but they were confined to a scale sufficient only for pedestrian use. When the National Highway was built during the early years of the Republic, stone arch construction was chosen for several bridges in Pennsylvania, Maryland, and Virginia. The highway was an ambitious project for which the masonry arch seemed most appropriate because of its classical sanction as well as its permanence and dignity.[1]

It was the railroad that provided the means as well as the demand for large masonry bridges of finished construction, and it was again the Baltimore and Ohio that led the way. The first of the company's stone arches is Carrollton Viaduct in Baltimore (1829), the first masonry railroad bridge and easily the oldest railroad span of any kind in the United States, since it survives in full use today (fig. 127). The architect of the Carrollton arch was James Lloyd, and the engineering designers were the members of the B. and O.'s Board of Engineers. The men who played the major role in the design and construction of the bridge were Jonathan Knight and Caspar Wever, the latter of whom acted as chief of construction. Carrollton Viaduct is a single Roman arch of 100-foot span built up of carefully dressed stonework, a handsome and durable example of the stone mason's art. But the bridge belongs to an old and thoroughly developed tradition which looked back to the classical past rather than to the new railroad age with its unprecedented demands.

128  Thomas Viaduct, Baltimore and Ohio Railroad, Patapsco River, Relay, Maryland, 1835. Benjamin Latrobe II, engineer.

The fact that Carrollton Viaduct still serves the railroad indicates that it proved perfectly capable of absorbing the stresses induced by heavy moving loads, but it does so only through sheer mass of masonry, which in a large multispan bridge would have had to be increased to such quantity as to be prohibitive in cost and in time required for construction. New and lighter forms had to be developed, forms which ultimately pointed the way toward the concrete arch at the end of the century.

A few years after completion of the Carrollton arch Benjamin Latrobe's genius found its great opportunity in the design of Thomas Viaduct, built to carry the B. and O. Railroad's line over the Patapsco River at Relay, Maryland, 1835 (fig. 128).[2] The bridge is one of unusual size for its time and may be said to mark the real beginning of masonry construction for railroad service, since it was carefully designed by Latrobe for precisely this role. Located on a curve, Thomas Viaduct has an over-all length of 600 feet on the arc divided into eight full-centered arches with an average span of 60 feet and a total height of 65 feet above mean water level. The chief problem of design arose from construction on a curve, which necessitated variations in span and pier width between opposite sides of the structure. The lateral pier faces were set on radial lines, a mode of construction for which Latrobe found few precedents. Thomas Viaduct is an architectural as well as a functional masterpiece. Uniform in its fine-textured masonry, ornamented only by simple moldings and a shallow wrought iron guard above the parapet, its straightforward treatment emphasizes the mass and dignity of the Roman arch. Named after Philip E. Thomas, the first president of the B. and O., the bridge stands today, carrying the full weight of the railroad's traffic between Baltimore and Washington.

Since the art of masonry construction was so well known, the advancement in the size and structural quality of the stone bridge was extraordinarily rapid in the first half of the century. The truss bridge of wood or iron seemed all the more primitive by comparison. No structure of the time demonstrated this more powerfully than the bridge built to carry New York City's Croton Aqueduct over the Harlem River near what is now 174th Street (1839–42, 1848). Designed by John B. Jervis, the chief engineer of the project, it replaced a much lower vehicular span and hence came to be called High Bridge, a name which it retained throughout its life rather than the official Aqueduct Bridge (fig. 129). In its total size there were few structures of any kind which could approach it at the time. By 1840 the population of New York had reached 360,000 and an adequate water supply had become a desperate necessity. With the completion of Croton Dam in 1842 the city had a storage reservoir capable of meeting its current needs. An aqueduct of brick and stone carried the water to the palisades along the east side of the Harlem River. To maintain a level at the hydraulic gradient required a bridge of great length, since the river occupies a relatively narrow portion of the valley width. The structure which Jervis designed was a series of full-centered arches nearly 1,200 feet long.[3]

129　Aqueduct (High) Bridge, Harlem River, New York City, 1839–42. James B. Jervis, engineer.

The problem of distributing the water load uniformly to the arch barrels Jervis met with an ingenious system of interior walls and struts. Longitudinal walls carried the load directly from the deck of the attic to the back, or extrados, of the arch barrel, while lateral walls braced by stone struts set diagonally in the horizontal plane provided additional rigidity to the spandrel walls. This extraordinary system of interior walls in the hollow volume between arch and deck marked a long advance over traditional solid masonry construction and pointed clearly toward the open and articulated structure of the concrete arch, in which the main structural elements—ribs, posts, deck—stand clear and separate. Aqueduct Bridge was an elaborate and expensive construction which cost the city $963,400 by the time of its completion. The bridge survived in its original form until 1937, when five of the arches, spanning the river and the New York Central tracks, were replaced by a single steel arch of plate-girder construction. (By this time the aqueduct system had been placed underground and the old distributing reservoir at the site of the Public Library, Fifth Avenue and 42nd Street, had long ago disappeared).

Construction of the initial line of the New York and Erie Railroad began in 1847. With the lavish backing of British capital, the company was willing to spare no expense to build a first-class railroad. Accordingly, when the tracks reached the wide valley of Starrucca Creek near Susquehanna, Pennsylvania, the builders determined to take it at one jump to avoid the grades and curves that would have been the alternative. John P. Kirkwood, at that time assistant to George W. Whistler, chief engineer of the Western Railroad of Massachusetts, was invited to design and supervise construction of a masonry bridge, after three contractors failed and gave up on the job.[4] Kirkwood, with a gang of 800 men at his disposal, completed construction of Starrucca Viaduct within a year, before the end of 1848. The resulting structure is remarkable not only for its size and articulated construction, but also for the slender proportions of the high piers, which are unique for bridges of its type and material (fig. 130).[5] Arches, spandrels, and deck are built of local bluestone (an argillaceous sandstone), but the pier footings and deck finishing are concrete. Starrucca Viaduct is another example of open interior construction: three longitudinal brick walls, set between the spandrel walls, carry the load from the deck to the arches. Its cost of $320,000 earned it the reputation of being the most expensive railroad bridge in the world at the time of its completion, although it is a piece of straightforward empirical building, without moldings or decorative courses of any kind. Starrucca Viaduct continues to carry all the traffic of the Erie's eastern main line.

The span length and the proportions of the single stone arch in the United States changed markedly when Montgomery C. Meigs built the Cabin John Aqueduct over Cabin John Creek in Washington, D. C., as part of the city's

130  Starrucca Viaduct, New York and Erie Railroad, near Susquehanna, Pennsylvania, 1848. John P. Kirkwood, engineer.

new water supply system (1857–64). Meigs was undoubtedly guided by European precedents, since no masonry arch in America at the time approached it in size or shape. The 220-foot span of its single arch made it the longest of masonry construction until the concrete arches of the twentieth century. With a rise of 57 feet, it was a segmental arch of unusually flattened form, recalling Perronet's once daring structures of the eighteenth century and foreshadowing the concrete arch that was still to come. The spring line of the Cabin John arch is well above the water level, giving it an over-all height of 101 feet above the surface of Cabin John Creek. The arch ring, 4 feet deep at the crown and 6 feet at the springing, is of granite, while the spandrels are of sandstone. The backing or infilling for some distance beyond the arch is carefully laid with radial joints to increase the strength. Cabin John Aqueduct is a carefully designed work throughout, its bold form set off by two horizontal moldings at the parapet, which provide the only relief to its otherwise uninterrupted surfaces. The fine bridge still stands, now used as a highway span rather than as an aqueduct.

The long railway viaduct on masonry arches formed a small proportion of the total number of spans erected during the great age of bridge building following the Civil War, and the proportion decreased as the century progressed. The chief reason for its scarcity was (and continues to be) the relatively high cost of stone masonry construction, which requires skilled handwork not only in the laying up of the blocks but also in the quarrying, cutting, and dressing of the stone. Further, there are two serious disadvantages in the use of masonry for bridges over wide streams. One is the multiplicity of piers, which usually form the most expensive part of the total structure, and the other is that over navigable waterways a series of stone arches offers as effective a barrier to shipping as a dam. At the same time, of course, there are the great advantages of superior strength, durability, and beauty, but in the face of the capital investment required, they lost much of their attractiveness to the railroad companies. Thus the few that appeared did so because of the combination of appropriate setting and willingness on the part of the railroads to make the necessary expenditure. The fact that most of these bridges remain in service today and have been used continuously without major repairs or strengthening indicates their superiority to bridges of girders or trusswork.[6]

The plain concrete arch was a natural outgrowth of the stone masonry form, but its brief history in the United States during the past century proved to be without structural or architectural interest. Several factors contributed to this state of affairs. First of all, concrete was substituted for stone in bridges for the same reason that it was in buildings: it offered the means to a great reduction in cost and in time of construction while at the same time providing a material equally satisfactory in its performance. But by the time American builders began to use concrete, European engineers and experimenters had understood the precise nature of arch action under heavy moving loads and hence the necessity for metal reinforcing if the builder were to take advantage of the full potentialities of the new material.[7]

The pioneer work of construction was done in France during the 1830's. What was probably the first successful concrete span for highway traffic was built over the Garonne Canal at Grisoles in 1840. It was a modest structure but remarkably flat in the proportions of the arch, which had a rise of 5 feet 3 inches for a span of 39 feet 4 inches. It was thirty years before the American builders used the new material for bridges. The first one, limited to pedestrian use, was built in 1871 in Prospect Park, Brooklyn, New York. Designed by John C. Goodridge, its span of 31 feet made it a timid initial essay. In the following year a second was built to carry a walkway in the Cemetery of the Evergreens at East New York, New York. Its span was the same as that of its predecessor, and the rise 5 feet. The flat proportions already indicated a considerable emancipation from stone masonry construction. A work comparable to the concrete vault and certainly a stimulus to the further development of bridge construction was the introduction of concrete for the lining of railroad tunnels. The first such use of the material in the United States was made by the Erie Railroad in 1874, when it covered the bare rock of its 28-foot tunnel at Bergen, New Jersey, with concrete.

Many of the few plain concrete bridges built during the succeeding two decades included generous amounts of stone masonry, usually for voussoirs and spandrel facing. Thus the total load was distributed in varying proportions between the two materials. The span of the arches was severely limited either because of the proportions of the semicircular arch or because of the relatively high horizontal thrust exerted by the flatter form, a thrust which increases with the degree of flatness. The Nashua Aqueduct, constructed by the Metropolitan Water Board of Boston (1895–97), was a structure of some size in its over-all dimensions, 389 feet long and 31 feet high above mean water level, but the span of its seven arches was a modest 29 feet 6 inches. The voussoirs and spandrel facing were of cut stone, which thus carried some of the load.[8] The combination of plain concrete in mass and stone facing was so nearly like traditional masonry construction that the engineers decided by the end of the century that it could be used in railroad bridges of great size and traffic load. The largest of all such structures is the long viaduct that carries the Pennsylvania Railroad tracks over the Susquehanna River at Rockville, a few miles above Harrisburg, Pennsylvania (1900–02). The bridge supports a heavily traveled four-track line and extends almost four-fifths of a mile in length.[9] The small arch span and the orthodox construction, however, reveal the limitations imposed on bridges of this kind. Further, the use of concrete in conjunction with stone facing and voussoirs again meant that the stone masonry carried a considerable part of the load. To progress beyond the point reached by the Susquehanna bridge and to free the arch once and for all from its dependence on the older masonry forms required the addition of iron reinforcing, which in turn made possible a radically new approach to the design of arched structures.

## 4. THE REINFORCED CONCRETE ARCH

The arch of reinforced concrete was mainly the achievement of French theorists and inventors and of Swiss engineers. By 1885 the French had built small reinforced arches on the Monier system, in which wire mesh reinforcing was embedded in the concrete and bent in a curved surface approximately matching that of the soffit, or undersurface, of the arch. By 1890, using the

131　Alvord Lake Bridge, Golden Gate Park, San Francisco, California, 1889. Ernest L. Ransome, engineer.

same basis, the Swiss had built at least three bridges of more than 120-foot span. The last decade of the century saw an extraordinarily vigorous development of theory, invention, and practical construction in many European countries. Most of the American work, as a matter of fact, was carried out under European patents.[1]

The American origin of arch reinforcing was a patent issued in 1881 to S. Bissell for a method which was questionable in the light of his primary purpose. The system involved a double set of iron rods, one group laid longitudinally in horizontal planes, the other diagonally in vertical planes. By anchoring the horizontal rods in the abutments, it was his intention to construct an arch of small span which would exert only a vertical thrust on the abutments, the horizontal presumably sustained by the longitudinal reinforcing. It is doubtful, however, that he would have achieved this exact separation of components between the metal and the concrete. There is no record that any bridges were built according to the Bissell patent. The first proposal for the use of reinforced concrete in a specific bridge was submitted by Thomas C. Clarke in 1885, when he offered a plan for Washington Bridge over the Harlem River in New York.[2] He proposed a bridge of three arches, each of 285-foot span, built of concrete with stone facing for voussoirs and spandrels and with reinforcing in the form of wrought iron I-beams at the crown and the haunches.[3] The design was rejected on the ground of its novelty.

It was Ernest L. Ransome who built the first reinforced concrete arch shortly after he initiated the American use of the technique for buildings. The Alvord Lake Bridge, designed to carry one roadway over another in Olmsted's Golden Gate Park, San Francisco, was constructed in 1889 (fig. 131). It was a modest beginning, but it met the requirements satisfactorily and has been in continuous use since its completion. The bridge is almost a vault rather than an arch: its span is 20 feet and rise 4 feet 3 inches, but its over-all width is 64 feet. The reinforcing consists of a series of twisted iron bars imbedded longitudinally in the concrete near the soffit and bent in approximately the same curve. The surfaces of the span were finished in imitation of rough-faced stone masonry. Although the Golden Gate represents essentially the modern method of reinforcing, it had no immediate successor which involved the same technique.

The first reinforced arch in the East, and very likely the second in the United States, was built to carry Pine Road over Pennypack Creek in Philadelphia (1893–94). It consisted of two arches, each with a span of 25 feet 5 inches, a rise of 6 feet 6 inches, and a depth of 27 inches at the crown. The reinforcing was a variation on the Monier system: sheets of 1½-inch wire mesh were distributed in horizontal and vertical planes through the concrete at intervals of 2 feet. The primary intention of its designer appears to have been to use the mesh as a binding element rather than as reinforcing. The vertical surfaces of the bridge were finished in imitation of rough-textured stone masonry.

The vigorous life of the reinforced bridge began suddenly in the United States with the introduction of the method of reinforcement invented by the Viennese engineer Joseph Melan, who was granted an American patent for the invention in 1894. The technique was simple but functionally sound, for it involved the combination of two well-tested but widely different systems of arch construction. The reinforcing consisted of a series of parallel iron or steel I-beams curved to the profile of the soffit and having a depth very nearly equal to that of the curving slab or vault of concrete (fig. 132). Thus Melan effectively combined the iron arch rib with the masonry arch. As a matter of fact, if the beams were of sufficient size and number, his bridge might be considered as an iron arch span covered with concrete. The familiarity of such

132  Franklin Bridge, Forest Park, St. Louis, Missouri, 1898. Longitudinal section.

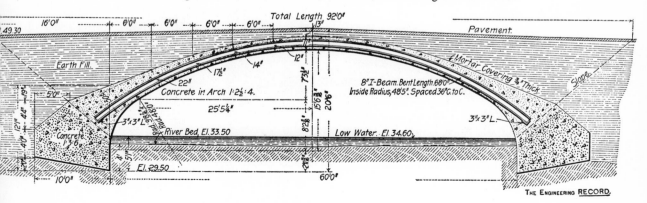

construction to American builders led to immediate and widespread adoption of the Melan system. The major figure in establishing its popularity was the German-born engineer Fritz von Emperger. For six years after its introduction it had no serious competitor in the construction of reinforced concrete bridges.

Emperger's first bridge was built to carry a street over a small stream in Rock Rapids, Iowa, 1894 (fig. 133). Its span and rise, respectively 30 feet and 6 feet 6 inches, conformed to the common dimensions for such bridges at the time. In the following year, however, the length of span increased sharply with the construction of Emperger's foot bridge over the Housatonic River at Stockbridge, Massachusetts (fig. 134). In its lightness and delicacy as well as its strength it would be a fine representative of the best contemporary design.[4] The bridge is a straightforward work of functionalism, its ornament reduced to a narrow double molding to emphasize the gentle upward curve of the deck. Although the Melan system has been superseded to a large extent by methods of bar reinforcement, the Housatonic bridge is in every respect the progenitor of the modern form.

Emperger's last bridge in the original form was built to carry a park drive over a through street in Eden Park, Cincinnati (1895). It was considerably larger than any of its predecessors in total volume of material.[5] Set in one of Cincinnati's superb hilltop parks, it was felt that the bridge ought to have a

133  Vehicular bridge, Rock Rapids, Iowa, 1894. Fritz von Emperger, engineer.

134  Pedestrian bridge, Housatonic River, Stockbridge, Massachusetts, 1895. Fritz von Emperger, engineer.

monumental character. As a consequence, it was heavily ornamented in the manner of the new Renaissance revival, with moldings and panels on the spandrels and abutments, elaborate balustrades, and soffit paneling. For all its ornamental detail, it cost the city only $7,130. In the commissions immediately following the Eden Park bridge, Emperger made two additions to the Melan system and was granted a patent for these changes in 1897. The resulting design required nearly as much steel as a bridge built entirely of that material. He added a set of horizontal I-beams in the deck, then joined the deck and arch beams by means of bars set on radial lines. The deck reinforcing was essentially similar to that used in the previous decade for concrete floor slabs, but the combination of it with the soffit ribs involved so much steel as to offset the economy of construction in concrete. Emperger's patent, however, did point the way toward the deck girder bridge of reinforced concrete, which was to appear about 1900.

The first Melan arch in the United States to be built for rail traffic embodied a further modification of the original system, introduced by the designers of the structure, W. H. Ashwell and Company. The bridge was built to carry the tracks of the Michigan Central Railroad over a park boulevard in Detroit (1895). The arch barrel, heaviest of its kind at the time, was reinforced with steel arched trusses rather than I-beams.[6] The facing, voussoirs, and the parapet were ashlar masonry, felt to be appropriate to a park setting, but the remainder of the structural material was reinforced concrete.[7]

Near the end of the century the federal government planned the construction of Memorial Bridge over the Potomac River between Washington and Arlington, Virginia, and invited designs in a national competition. Two projects, submitted by the engineer W. H. Burr and the architect Edward P. Casey (1899–1900), involved Melan arches of unprecedented span. The first proposed a central steel movable span of 159 feet flanked on either side by three granite-faced Melan arches of 192-foot span. The second reduced the draw to 125 feet and the number of arches to two on each side, with an individual span of 283 feet. Famous engineers, among them L. L. Buck and George S. Morison, submitted alternatives, but Burr and Casey's first design was ultimately accepted and built in the early years of the new century. The engineering problems arising from the construction of arches of this size could be readily solved by competent men. What required special attention and was to prove a more difficult problem was the question of architectural design in a monumental bridge for the national capital. Steel and concrete were required by structural necessity. How was one to deal artistically with these new materials, for which Rome and Florence offered questionable solutions?

It was again the indefatigable Montgomery Schuyler who brought the matter to public attention. He wrote a long critical essay on the architectural merits of the various entries, with the winning design being subjected to the most thorough examination. Schuyler was unusually cautious in his approach, yet it is clear that the central problem to him was that of presenting concrete arches with stone facing, as though they were constructed throughout of stone masonry. He pointed out the split or disharmony that exists when the engineer, concerned with structure, is at odds with the architect, who is concerned ultimately with aesthetic form. Beyond this point, however, he is ambiguous and makes no attempt to suggest how steel and concrete ought to be dealt with architecturally:

Upon the whole it will be argued that the adopted design . . . promises a satisfactory result. The only question that remains is . . . whether in a monumental work, and national work, the United States could not and should not afford the actual structure of masonry which the adopted design simulates. In this case, however, it would remain true that the bridge would be an example of historical architecture rather than of modern engineering. Of course that would be nothing against it. But it would deprive the structure of the particular interest which has induced us to give so much space and study to the competition, the interest of an essay in what can be done towards raising works of modern building in metal to the ranks of works of architectural art.[8]

It was well into the new century before concrete was always allowed to stand unadorned in a monumental span.[9]

The treatment of concrete in ways appropriate to its continuity and plasticity began to appear around the turn of the century in small rail and highway spans in inconspicuous places. A series of inventions in the late 'nineties were important factors in forcing builders and designers to realize that the material could no longer be equated with stone masonry. In 1898 F. W. Patterson, engineer for the Department of Public Roads of Allegheny County, Pennsylvania, began to design small highway bridges in which he introduced several decisive modifications in the Melan system. One was to replace the single arch slab or barrel with two or more separate parallel concrete ribs, each with its steel reinforcing beam. Another was a variation on Emperger's deck reinforcing, in which the deck was formed into a series of small arches between the steel beams, much like the tile or concrete floor construction of a steel-framed building. Finally, Patterson appears to have been the American pioneer of true deck-girder construction in concrete. Starting from the system of deck reinforcing, he added two deep I-beams, one at each side of the deck, poured heavy concrete girders around them, and dropped the arch entirely. The result was a bridge of concrete which functioned like the iron or steel girder spans so common on American railroads.

In the same year David A. Molitor, who was familiar with the new work of the French, German, and Swiss engineers, designed the first three-hinged arch in concrete, with a span of 236 feet and a rise of 32 (fig. 135). The simplicity and emphasis on continuity of his second design strongly suggested the advanced work of such European engineers as Freyssinet. The first three-hinged arch of concrete in the United States was built at Mansfield, Ohio, in 1903–4 after the design of the city's chief engineer.

The Melan system of reinforcing has never been wholly abandoned, but for most bridges its reliance on heavy steel ribs or beams proved to be unnecessary. Ransome's method of reinforcing with bars was revived for concrete bridges, but in many cases the arch barrel was divided into separate ribs, a practice which has now become universal for large bridges. At the same time, a few engineers abandoned reinforcing entirely as unnecessary in arches whose ribs are sufficiently massive to absorb potential deforming stresses that might subject any part of them to tension.

**253**

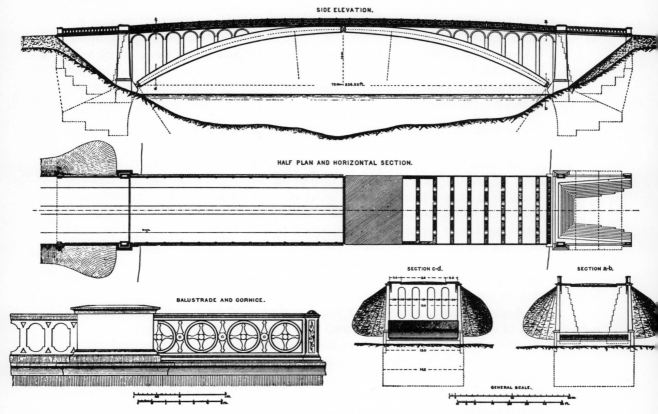

SIDE ELEVATION.

HALF PLAN AND HORIZONTAL SECTION.

BALUSTRADE AND CORNICE.

SECTION c-d.

SECTION a-b.

GENERAL SCALE.

135    Project for a three-hinged arch of reinforced concrete, 1898. David O. Molitor, engineer.

The main tendency in the twentieth century, however, has been to aim at ever-increasing attenuation of ribs, to the point where some are virtually solid steel with a concrete covering. Construction in slabs, introduced by the Swiss engineer Robert Maillart in 1900, has never been used with such thoroughness in American bridges. The main structural elements have nearly always been arch ribs and separate spandrel columns or bents. As a matter of fact, the concrete bridge, like other forms of concrete construction, has never reached the level of sophistication in the United States that it reveals in Europe and Latin America. Where labor is costly and material is cheap, as in this country, the natural tendency is to reduce formwork to a minimum and to rely on quantity of material rather than nicety of design to do the job. Moreover, working stresses on rail and highway structures in the United States are much below what they are in Europe, where the weight of trains, trucks, and automobiles is considerably lower. As a consequence, the extreme attenuation of Maillart's bridges, for example, is simply not possible in American practice.

# 5. THE MASONRY DAM: STONE AND CONCRETE

Among the earliest structural techniques of a strictly utilitarian nature were those associated with the control of water. The absolute dependence of the ancient Egyptians on the Nile River, whose annual summer floods provided them with all the fertile soil they possessed, required an extensive system of water control. Their first task was to drain the unbroken marshes along the river's banks. Eventually they learned to contain the flood waters within designated areas, and finally to distribute them as widely as possible by means of a system of irrigation canals. All such operations involved the construction of dikes and levees of earth, which thus formed the first steps in the direction of true dam construction.

The peoples of the Mesopotamian valleys initially faced the same task of draining the immense marshes that once covered most of the lower shores of the Tigris and Euphrates rivers and their numerous secondary channels. The Babylonians, early in the second millenium, began the extensive system of irrigation and drainage canals for which they were famous. These were not only contained within their courses by earth dikes but were also impounded by earth dams with clay cores to form irrigation reservoirs. The dam constructed of earth and loose rubble masonry seems to have been originated by the Sabaeans, a Semitic people along the eastern short of the Red Sea, where rock is plentiful and water scarce. There has been little archaelogical investigation of the area, but there is no question that some of the remains are those of true dams built as early as the tenth century B.C. The largest, known as Marib Dam, has been described as anywhere from a half mile to two miles long and as having been constructed with a rubble masonry core.

Hellenistic and Roman engineers must have learned the technique of dam building from their eastern predecessors. By the late classical period they had carried the art of dam construction in masonry to a level it was not to reach again until the beginning of the Industrial Revolution. Most remarkable of the classical achievements was the construction of the first arch dam, the work of Chryses of Alexandria, one of Justinian's engineers, who built the structure at the Byzantine town of Daras near the Persian frontier.

Medieval Europe did not face the problem of irrigation, but it was deeply involved with the problem of generating mechanical power. The Middle Ages initiated and completed one of the greatest of technical revolutions, the substitution of wind and water power for the labor of human slaves, and as a consequence their control of streams aimed most often at providing a head of water to turn a wheel. The associated dams were either of earth and rubble masonry or clay, or were built up of timber cribbing filled with rubble. Medieval dikes for shore protection were more elaborately constructed. The main mass of packed clay with battered faces was protected on its seaward face by a double crib. The inner extended to the height of the dike, the space between the crib and the clay being filled with seaweed. The outer crib was much lower and was used to retain the rubble stone which protected the foot of the heavy timbers. The masonry dam had a continuous history in Islam, from which it passed to Christian Spain in the fourteenth century.

Thus there were medieval precedents for all the types of dams known to the American colonists—rubble and cut stone, earth and clay, and timber crib. All kinds were built in the eastern colonies, chiefly for power generation at mills, but the earth and timber forms predominated. The first masonry dam was built in 1743 at New Brunswick, New Jersey, for the local water supply, but no details of its construction seem to have been preserved. The first such dam for irrigation was built sometime between 1770 and 1790 by the priests and workers of the San Diego Mission in California. About 5 feet high, it was constructed of rubble stone set in mortar, with a wooden control gate or sluiceway in the center. The little dam stood, largely in ruins, at least until 1916, but seems to have disappeared since that date.

The history of dam construction in the United States during the nineteenth century was extremely irregular and hardly shows a clear line of development in a particular direction. But this is to be expected in view of the large number of variables that determine the size and construction of works of waterway control. In the first place, dams are built to satisfy a wide range of requirements. The most common purpose is to impound water for the basic needs of the community—drinking, bathing, washing, sewage disposal, and industrial uses. Both canal and rail transportation depend on the storage and distribution of water. In arid regions the primary need is irrigation for crops. As the nineteenth century passed, installations of ever-increasing size were built for flood control, navigation on natural waterways, mechanical and electrical power, drainage, recreation, and hydraulic mining.

Nineteenth-century dams exhibit extreme variation in size, depending on the function, the nature of the waterway, and the local topography. The mode of construction may vary not only with these factors but with the economic resources of the builders and the availability of building materials. In addition to all this, there is the fact that each mode of construction has its own functional validity, with the result that timber forms, earh fill, and rubble masonry were used throughout the nineteenth century and continue to be today, along with the more advanced but still ancient method of laying up masonry blocks in mortar.

What complicated the situation further during the last century was the simultaneous application, in a number of dams, of all the techniques appropriate to their construction. Concrete by itself came late in the century, and even then was seldom used until the great period of reclamation and hydro-electric generation in the present century. Thus systematic history of dam construction does not exist, and one does not see in it the developing pattern of problem and increasingly scientific solution that one finds in bridge design, for example.

Up to 1850 many of the dams were built to provide a head of water for the generation of mechanical power. On the smaller streams they were often solid timber walls braced by diagonal struts on the downstream face and protected on the upstream, or sometimes on both, by a heap of rubble stone. A flume or a narrow canal at one end of the dam carried the water to the one or more wheels that rotated the drive shaft of the milling or spinning machinery. The entire canal is known as the millrace; the portion above the dam is the head-race, that below the tailrace. One of the largest of the early timber dams was built in 1822 to provide power for mills along the Merrimack River at Lowell, Massachusetts. The installation was said to be capable of delivering a maximum total of 12,000 horsepower to the drive shafts of the various mills. The manufacture of cotton textiles and paper expanded rapidly in New England, with the result that nearly every stream that passed through a town had at least one dam across it. Many of the later structures of masonry still survive, but if they are used to generate power, it is electrical rather than mechanical.

The dam of the Holyoke Water Power Company in the Connecticut River at Holyoke, Massachusetts, built to serve paper mills, was probably the largest rubble-and-timber structure of its kind. In its original form (1848) it was simply a braced timber weir, but it was insufficient in strength and was swept away before the water reached its full head. The second structure was a double-walled timber crib filled with broken rock and gravel. It was built up in 170 sections from a timber foundation bolted to bedrock, one section at a time, by means of a cofferdam, which made possible the exposure of the rock underlying the river bed. Extensive rock formations at or near the surface of the ground formed one of the many factors that made possible the rapid growth of the paper and textile industry of New England. Dams in streams with deep beds of river sediments would have been prohibitive in cost because of the difficulties of excavation, disposal, and cofferdam construction.

The first big masonry dam in the United States was Croton Dam of the New York water supply system (1837–42), the initial structure in the city's never-ending and sometimes desperate struggle to provide itself with an adequate quantity of water. By 1835 the needs of the population had outgrown the springs and wells of Manhattan Island and, without a natural body of fresh water in the vicinity, it was necessary to impound an artificial one. John B. Jervis, appointed chief engineer of the project in 1836, selected a site on the Croton River about 40 miles north of the city hall. The construction of a cofferdam made possible excavation to bedrock, above which a gravity dam with a rubble core and granite ashlar facing was raised to a height of 50 feet.[1] A wide central spillway controlled by gates provided the means to impound an additional head of water at times of maximum use, or to release the excess during floods. The trapezoidal cross section of old Croton Dam has been characteristic of dams from the beginning of their history. The first builders intuitively grasped the stability of the form, and although proportions changed with newer materials and more advanced techniques, the essential profile remained unchanged.[2] Croton Dam, one of the largest and most massive of its day, served New York City adequately for about forty years.[3]

Masonry construction often proved too costly for dams the size of Croton. The only alternative was the earth-fill variety, which is perfectly satisfactory if the fill is properly shaped and protected and surrounds an impermeable core. It is highly unstable if it can be penetrated by water under pressure and if it is subject to erosion by the turbulence of the stream or the run-off of rainfall. One of the largest earth-fill dams of the early period was completed in 1839 to impound a reservoir for the Pennsylvania State Canal system. Designed by the canal engineer William E. Morris, it was located on the South Fork of the Conemaugh River near Johnstown, Pennsylvania (fig. 136). The citizens of the town were later to learn about the proper construction of dams in one of the greatest disasters of the age. South Fork Dam was a model of its kind when originally built, a carefully designed combination of earth, rubble masonry, and slate.[4] It was abandoned in 1857 when the canal system could no longer meet the competition of the railroads. The state, unfortunately, neglected to drain the reservoir, a most tempting little lake in the mountains of southern Pennsylvania.

A local hunting and fishing club acquired the dam and water in 1859 and spent much of the next three years repairing minor breaks and erosional damage. Several additional breaks occurred in 1862, at which time the Pennsylvania Railroad took possession of it to provide a source of locomotive boiler water. In 1875 the dam, reservoir, and about 500 acres of neighboring land passed to the South Fork Hunting and Fishing Club of Pittsburgh, which organization repaired all breaks, strengthened the fill, and raised it to a height of 75 feet. On May 30 and 31, 1889, a total of 6.65 inches of rain fell intermittently over a period of 16 hours on the Conemaugh watershed. The entire fill of South Fork Dam broke through in two places and a 400-foot center section was swept away like a heap of sand. Behind it the water level dropped 65.5 feet in a few minutes. The enormous wave swept down the narrow valley and caught the helpless townspeople in a trap: on either side of the river rose high, steep hills; before them, lying across the stream, was the masonry arch bridge of the Pennsylvania Railroad. The bridge, acting like a dam, held a mass of floating debris which quickly caught fire. Those who were not drowned outright or crushed

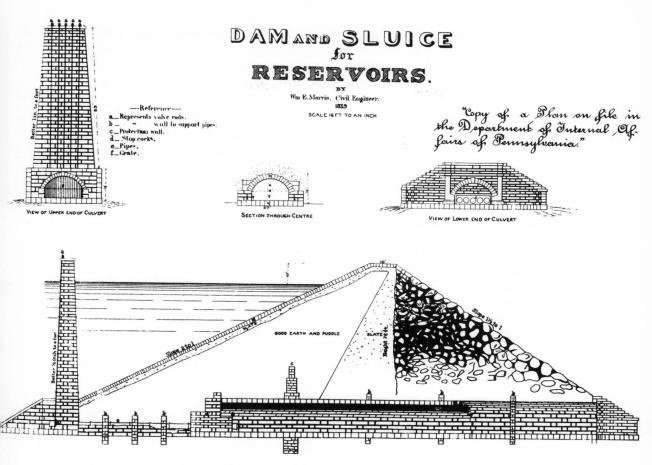

136 South Fork Dam, South Fork of the Conemaugh River, near Johnstown, Pennsylvania, 1839. William E. Morris, engineer. Cross section of the dam and details of the sluiceway and gatehouse.

in collapsing buildings died on this pyre. An accurate count of the dead was impossible, but the estimated total came to about 2,000 lives lost.

There was little left on which to base an investigation, but it was possible to put together enough evidence to establish the fact that although Johnstown would undoubtedly have been subjected to a damaging flood because of the heavy rain, the dam failed because the interior sluiceway was closed by sediment and the spillway was largely obstructed by vegetation. As a result of these conditions South Fork Dam was overtopped, and the fatal consequences inevitably followed. The best-constructed dam may fail if the water behind it cannot be released through controlled passageways designed for that purpose.

Nearly all dams built during the remainder of the century were either earth-fill, stone masonry, or combinations thereof. Those of masonry construction followed the precedent of Croton Dam, depending entirely on their mass and the tightness of mortar joints to hold the water behind them. As in the case of the masonry arch bridge, however, the cost of quarrying, dressing, and laying up stone blocks eventually led to its abandonment for large projects. Folsom Dam, in the American River near Sacramento, California (1888–89), was a typical early western structure and was almost identical with old Croton Dam. Its width varied from 60 to 25 feet for a height of 69 feet and a length of 218. Ashlar facing on both sides covered the usual rubble core.

Before the end of the century the need for water in the inter-mountain and Pacific coastal regions grew to such proportions that it was necessary to think of waterway control on a vastly greater scale than had ever been attempted previously. With the establishment of the Bureau of Reclamation in 1902 the means for such a development was available. In the great age of dam construction stone masonry had to give way to concrete. It survived only through the completion in 1911 of Roosevelt Dam in the Salt River about 60 miles above Phoenix, Arizona.

In spite of the Johnstown disaster, the earth-fill dam fared better. It remained a common type for low-head installations and has been used in recent years for projects of great size, the largest of all being Fort Peck and Garrison dams in the upper Missouri River. Spillways and other control works for the passage of water, of course, are built of concrete. The faces of the dam are almost always protected by loose rubble masonry.

The development of the concrete dam was a gradual transition from stone masonry to monolithic construction in which the proportion of the new material steadily increased. At first it was used as a binding material to impart rigidity and impermeability to the core wall. One of the earliest of this kind was Lynde Brook Dam, built to impound a reservoir for the water supply system of Worcester, Massachusetts (1870–71). An earth-fill dam about 700 feet long, it had a core wall of cobble stones and concrete 3 feet thick. The cobbles were laid up in mortar to form two parallel walls, the space between which was filled with concrete. A sluiceway in the form of a box culvert with an arched or vaulted cover ran through the dam in the former stream bed. The side walls of the culvert, 5 feet thick, were built in the same way as the core except that granite blocks took the place of the cobbles. Combination walls such as that at Lynde Brook were generally of more irregular construction.[5]

The first of the dams in western canyons, a type for which the United States eventually gained a world-wide pre-eminence, was built in the Sweetwater River near San Diego, California, for irrigation, 1886–88 (fig. 137). It also came close to being the first dam to be constructed entirely of concrete. The original plan called for a plain concrete arch structure with a height of 50 feet and a

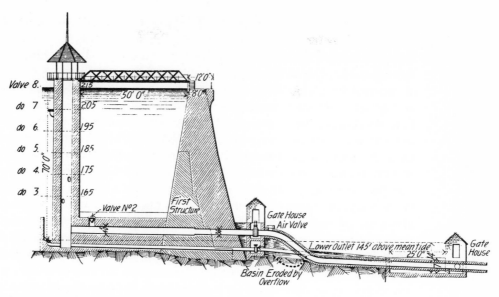

Valve 8.
do 7
do 6.
do 5.
do 4.
do 3

Valve Nº2

First Structure

Gate House
Air Valve

Gate House

Lower Outlet 145' above mean tide
25'0"

Basin Eroded by Overflow

137   Sweetwater Dam, Sweetwater River, near San Diego, California, 1886–88. James D. Schuyler, engineer. Cross section through the gate house, dam, and interior sluiceway.

width varying from 10 to 3 feet. An embankment of loose earth was to be filled in against the upstream face—a highly questionable practice. After two months of excavation, cofferdam work, and concrete pouring the plans were changed in favor of a larger and more traditional structure. Designed by James D. Schuyler, the dam as built was 90 feet high from foundation to top of parapet and 30 feet long on the curve, the base and top widths being 46 and 12 feet, respectively. In construction it was the familiar combination of stone masonry and rubble in concrete. The most interesting feature was the concrete intake tower built as a separate structure well above the upstream face of the dam. Overflow water passed from the tower through a tunnel to the outlet works below the downstream face. A similar method for the intake of turbine water was later used on an enormous scale at Hoover Dam.

The first dam of concrete throughout and the first to embody all the essential features of modern design and construction was built in San Mateo Canyon, California, by the Spring Valley Water Company for the water supply system of San Francisco. Begun in 1887, it was completed according to initial plans in 1889, then enlarged in 1894. Its chief engineer, Hermann Schussler, could rely only to a very limited extent on masonry precedents. Concrete poured in so large a mass involved problems for the solution of which there was no previous guide, while stress analysis in the arched structure proved to be of unparalleled complexity.[6]

An arch-gravity dam, San Mateo was of record size at the time of its construction: 700 feet long on the arc, 170 feet high, and 175 to 20 feet wide. Excavation was carried to bedrock between cofferdams. The concrete was mixed on the site and poured in separate 9-ton blocks, each of which had to set seven to ten days before the next was poured. The blocks were described as having "uniformly irregular" dimensions—that is, matching irregularities that made it possible to key the blocks together for maximum solidity. (The present technique is to build forms with matching keys and grooves and to grout the joints after the concrete has set.) Because of the great spillway height at San Mateo Dam—nearly equal to that of Niagara Falls—Schussler built out the toe in the form of a curving apron laid over the stream bed as a protection against erosion of both the dam and the bed. The water thus flowed down the plane surface of the spillway and out over a concave surface which ended approximately tangent to the stream bed. Both faces of the dam sloped inward toward the top to provide maximum stability against overturning. The total mass of concrete was greater than would now be used in an arch dam, but it was a precaution that Schussler took to offset the substandard quality of the material. He built well, for the dam survived the San Francisco earthquake of 1906, with 32 billion gallons of water in the reservoir behind it.

The use of concrete for the construction of entire dams spread slowly in the last decade of the nineteenth century. The topographic and climatic features peculiar to the Pacific coastal region led to its immediate pre-eminence in the building of concrete dams. Because of the work of the Bureau of Reclamation, it maintained this position up to the time of the large tributary projects of the Tennessee Valley Authority. In the East traditional masonry construction remained standard until very nearly the end of the century. Small mill and water supply dams of concrete began to appear in the 'nineties. A typical one, perhaps the first in the region composed entirely of concrete, was built near Coxsackie, New York, for the town water supply (1894–95). It was small by the standards that were becoming common in the West: its length was 162 feet, height 33, and its width varied from 24 to 5 feet.

A few years later the West pioneered again by inaugurating the reinforced concrete dam. Known as Upper Otay Dam, after the stream in which it was located, it was built by the Southern California Mountain Water Company for San Diego's water supply (1899–1900). An arch dam 84 feet high, it was another designed to impound water in a deep, narrow canyon. The dam, which was unusually narrow in cross section, was 14 feet wide at the base and 4 at the top, and depended on its arched form to withstand the water pressure. The builders reinforced the concrete near the base with several beds of 1¼-inch wire cables set on 2-foot centers and anchored near the ends of the arch by fixing them to steel plates imbedded in the concrete.

Before the end of the century a wholly new area of technology was to have a decisive influence on the design and construction of dams after 1900. The method of generating electric power by means of falling water was a new use of an ancient technique, which depended directly on discoveries in physical science that could not have been made before 1830. Scarcely a century separates the experiments of Henry and Faraday from the enormous projects of the Tennessee Valley Authority and the Bureau of Reclamation. The development that took place within that period is without parallel in the history of technology. Its most striking feature is the symbiotic union of the many branches of science and engineering that had to come together to make such an evolution possible. Discoveries in physics, geology, and geography had to be combined with new structural techniques and with inventions for the generation and transmission of electric power. Finally, this complex synthesis was integrated with the concept of regional planning, a twentieth-century contribution whose roots lie in the nineteenth.

Behind the invention of hydroelectric generation was the long history of the water wheel as a source of mechanical power. It was initially a matter of combining three relatively simple devices: the dam to raise a head of water, the wheel, and the generator. But as the demand and hence the size of the installation grew, the wheel was transformed into a battery of turbines, the generators grew to gigantic proportions, and the dam became an intricate complex of internal passages and mechanisms of control.

The first hydroelectric plant in the United States which involved impounding water to maintain a head was built on the Fox River at Appleton, Wisconsin, in 1882.[7] The water was carried by a flume from the river to a small timber weir that admitted the water into the lower chamber of a small wooden structure housing the turbine and the generator, which were connected by a vertical shaft. Needle valves controlled the flow of water at the discharge end of the flume. It was crude enough, but it worked, and for some years it generated sufficient power for the few electric lights that existed in the town at the time. The installation was abandoned in the early years of the new century and by 1918 it had pretty well fallen into ruins.

The next hydroelectric generator involved more substantial construction. The plant was built at a falls in the Wilamette River near Oregon City, Oregon, to provide power for the city of Portland (1889). In 1894 a dam in the form of a rock-filled timber crib was built to provide a more stable head than was available at the falls, and thus became the first dam in the United States constructed exclusively for the generation of hydroelectric power. The old powerhouse was at the same time replaced by a concrete structure, the initial use of the material in a hydroelectric project.

The rivers of the West were the first to be considered as sites for hydroelectric developments requiring the construction of permanent and relatively large dams. There were two primary reasons for this: the need for irrigation provided an additional use for the stored water, and the rapid fall of streams in or near mountainous regions offered the best locations for impounding a high head.

The first large masonry dam for power generation and water storage was built on the Colorado River near Austin, Texas (1889–93), by the city itself to provide a water supply and power for pumps, electric lights, and streetcars. In construction the dam was the familiar combination of granite ashlar facing around a concrete and rubble core. It was 65 feet in over-all height and 1,150 feet long, its volume requiring 88,000 cubic yards of masonry. Its capacity of 14,636 horsepower was astonishingly high in view of the limited size of its predecessors. But its life was short: it was badly damaged by a flood on April 7, 1900, and was abandoned a few years later. It was subsequently reconstructed and restored to service (1937–40) by the Public Works Administration of the federal government. The dam was completely encased in a massive envelope of concrete to increase its total mass and hence its stability and to prevent leakage through the old masonry. It has been in continuous service since its reconstruction.

The hydroelectric dam of concrete appeared at the very end of the century. One such project, designed by George H. Pegram, then chief engineer of the Union Pacific Railroad, was a curious structure that appears to have been the forerunner of the dam of buttresses holding movable gates. It was built near Ogden, Utah, by the Pioneer Electric Power Company sometime between 1897 and 1900. The dam consisted of six massive piers set between abutments and joined at the top by a series of full-centered arches. The upstream faces and the level deck were encased in iron plates. The concrete piers were reinforced with layers of iron rods set at one-foot intervals throughout the depth of the dam. Constructed for irrigation as well as power, it was 400 feet long and 60 feet high.

The largest hydroelectric development in the United States at the end of the century was the elaborate project at Massena, New York (1897–1902). The whole complex embraced a canal connecting the St. Lawrence with the Grasse River, a dam at the junction of the canal and the latter stream, powerhouse, spillway, and control works. The unusual feature was the casting of the dam and powerhouse as a homogeneous unit. The dam was 350 feet long and about 45 feet high, and the installed capacity in 1902 was 35,000 horsepower. All structures of waterway control in the vicinity of Masenna have been replaced by much larger installations in connection with the construction of the St. Lawrence Seaway.

The final preparation for the new century was the initial discussion in 1899 by the Committee of Congress on Rivers and Harbors on the subject of water control for navigation and power in the Tennessee River. It was thirty-four years before the Congress acted on these preliminary explorations, but eventually they were to lead to the Tennessee Valley Authority, one of the twentieth century's major works of creative engineering and social planning.

# AN ARCHITECTURAL APPRAISAL

American architecture in the nineteenth century paralleled the European developments. The age began with the Greek Revival, largely a product of the earlier English movement and dominated to a great extent by Latrobe, Mills, and Strickland. In the hands of skilled designers it was nicely adapted to the building needs of the young Republic. Along with it there continued the legacies of Jefferson's Roman enthusiasm and the minor variations on eighteenth century classicism which are usually placed under the general designation of the Federal style. As long as the Republic remained small, homogeneous, and essentially agrarian, the simple harmonies and easy repose of the classical forms provided an admirable architectural expression of American culture.

By 1820, however, the Romantic Movement affected architecture, and classicism gave way to the Gothic Revival, which had begun in England a half-century earlier. For about twenty years the two movements overlapped, with Gothic finally winning an unchallenged triumph at mid-century, most notably in the work of Renwick and Upjohn in New York. On the homely and sober level of commercial building the introduction of cast iron on a large scale in the 1850's resulted in a marked addiction to Venetian Renaissance forms. When H. H. Richardson began his career at the end of the Civil War, the restless age was ready for another change. Richardson himself determined its direction almost single-handedly by the compelling power of his major works. As a consequence, a Romanesque revival rose rapidly to flourish briefly but vigorously from about 1870 to 1890.

A second classicism, derived mainly from the Renaissance, took its place under the influence of the Chicago World's Fair, Daniel Burnham, and McKim, Mead and White. Simultaneously the Chicago school emerged to offer the century's first non-derivative architectural style. The state of sophisticated architecture at the end of the century was probably best represented by two buildings radically different in character—the Boston Public Library of Mc-Kim, Mead and White, and Sullivan's Prudential Building in Buffalo.

Throughout this succession of stylistic changes the world of purely structural techniques was expanding and diversifying into forms, materials, and methods of construction that seemed increasingly at odds with the technical basis and symbolic character of the historical styles. Because of this proliferation of utilitarian demands and inventions it was the fashion, during the doctrinaire phase of the modern movement, to condemn the eclecticism of the nineteenth century as at best a sentimental escape, and at worst a mental aberration with psychopathic characteristics. The dogma was repeated so often and so vehemently that finally even the enthusiast began to suspect its validity. A careful inquiry into the architecture of the past century, free of the bias imposed by the over-simplified theories that have been so common in recent years, reveals that it was a valid and sometimes highly imaginative artistic expression of its age.

In the first place, eclecticism during the past century was never, in the hands of competent architects, a matter of an absolute imitation of previous forms. Wherever the forms were applied in the light of the new requirements of urban building, they were creatively molded to fit the demands of the age. The best designers and builders eventually accepted the technical inventions that came rapidly and used them with increasing ingenuity and boldness. They did not make the mistake of supposing that structural techniques constitute the whole art of architecture. Although the experience of architecture is always in part derived from the appearance and function of its structural members, its total effect is the product of a far richer and more complex association of elements. The best architects of the nineteenth century would have regarded as absurd such reductionist simplicities as the notion that architecture is only space or that it is only structure.

The question whether the building art of the past century expressed the spirit of the age is not a matter of deciding what form the art ought to have taken but rather of discovering why it took the form that it did. A reconsideration of the main cultural developments of the time must precede any attempt to answer the question, and we would do well to remind ourselves once more of what they were.

The intellectual life of the century was to a great extent dominated by scientific and technological interests. The professionalization of science, the systematic training of scientists in the universities, the multiplication and improvement of instruments, the symbiotic relation between science and technology, and the growing understanding of the method of scientific investigation and theorizing—these, and the social factors on which they rested, made possible an accumulation of exact knowledge probably equal to the total product of all previous centuries of rational inquiry. This achievement alone had the profoundest impact on the mind of the nineteenth century, manifested not only in the empirical and positivistic systems of philosophy that characterized the time, but more strikingly in social and political theory, history, scholarship, and religion. The tendency of the time was to look upon science in a Baconian light, as though it were a matter of accumulating empirical knowledge and organizing it into a body of general inductive laws. Actually it had become a complex, organic association of systematic discovery and creative theory which produced a structure of ideas symbolically representing the inner relations of natural processes. The most convincing example of this characteristic may be found in the most exact of sciences: in Clerk-Maxwell's *Treatise on Electricity and Magnetism,* the classic of its century in mathematical physics. Even the great experimenters—men like Faraday, Mendel, and Helmholz—could have carried on their investigations only because a body of scientific and philosophic theory existed to give direction and meaning to their researches.

The area of intellectual culture in the nineteenth century that most nearly approached science in its scope and influence was historiography. It might be said, indeed, that the century was the first one to grasp in all its dimensions the full meaning of the historical point of view and to devote to historical investigations the rational energy that it brought to bear on science. The spectrum ranged from the positivism of Taine and Marx to the imaginative recreation of the ancient mind that one finds in Fustel de Coulanges. The beginnings of this interest in the recovery of the past may be traced to the Italian Renaissance, when an idolatry of classical antiquity first evoked the consciousness of a previous age, which was to be studied, cherished, and if possible perpetuated. From that time on, the interest in history widened and deepened until, by the end of the nineteenth century, historical speculation ideally embraced the whole domain of human experience and activity. The growth of a critical science of history, together with the rise of the German idea of *Kulturgeschichte,* strongly suggests that the historian was seeking to emulate the scientist in method and in the universality of the scientific field.

The history of structural techniques in the nineteenth century corresponded with the progress of theoretical and applied science. The serious concern with the potentially monumental character of engineering works was a reflection of the extent to which the imagination was absorbed by such achievements. It is in the design of buildings beyond utility and function, however, that the structural art responded most fully to the numerous and often contradictory currents of the century. An age so prolific and gifted in the arts of music and literature could never have been satisfied with functionalism and empiricism as the basis of adequate design. Faced with the need to express feeling as well as reason, unconscious response as well as conscious reflection, deeply imbued with the romantic idea of the picturesque and all its moral and literary associations, the architect of the nineteenth century turned to history, as his age repeatedly taught him to do. History to him was the vital fourth dimension in the continuum of man's existence. He used it not as an escape into the past but as a source of forms that could be creatively molded to give symbolic expression to the life of his time. The architecture that he left might seem on the surface to be an ever-shifting body of transient details, like automobile design or women's fashions. Actually it had its own unity and its own inner development. The foremost architects, working on the basis of past styles, repeatedly produced architectural works comparable to representative works in the other arts. If eclecticism ultimately failed, it did so in part because of the failure to achieve a stable system of values that could retain the inheritance of the past without doing violence to the achievements of the present.

Details drawn from the previous architectural styles constituted the surface dress of nineteenth-century buildings. Beneath this, however, there were technical and formal elements that defined the true character of the building art and reflected the inner spirit of the time. The succession of revivals—Greek, Gothic, Romanesque, Renaissance—provided details for doors, windows, moldings, and decorative elements, but beneath them the new techniques made possible an unparalleled expansion of the vocabulary of major building elements. Wings, roofs, vaults, buttresses and columns, arcades, wall openings, flat and curving walls, projecting bays, stairways, and towers (the last constituted a major passion of nineteenth-century architects) multiplied in number and diversity beyond anything that historical sources could have provided. The oriel or projecting bay of late Gothic architecture, for example, was a simple construction, but the nineteenth-century architect gave it a dozen new shapes and carried it up through a multistoried office block or hotel. Wide-span vaults were a commonplace of Roman building and its numerous derivatives, but to expand one into a theater seating 4,000 people and to surround it with a vast hive of offices and hotel rooms required an architectural and engineering imagination of a high order.

As significant as the new forms that were developed out of traditional elements was the freedom with which they were associated. On the basis of formal concepts first explored in the eighteenth century, the architects of the nineteenth freed the building art once and for all from its dependence on the standards of symmetry and gradation that underlay classical and Baroque forms. The influence of vernacular building reinforced the uneven but growing tendency to emphasize simple masses and surface texture rather than ornamental detail.

The majority of nineteenth-century buildings, other than purely utilitarian structures, were dominated by the romantic idea of the picturesque. Within the liberal confines of the picturesque, the great diversity of architectural forms exhibits certain basic characteristics that appear in varying emphasis throughout the century. Historians who have looked beneath the surface dress of borrowed details have generally reduced these characteristics to five—variety, movement, irregularity, intricacy, and textural roughness. These qualities reveal themselves in a double context, historical and contemporary. In terms of the past they stand in opposition to the classical and Baroque legacy of concatenation, gradation, and regularity, and hence represent a deliberate intention to break out of the older program. Beside the vernacular and engineering works of their own century, they reveal a tension that expresses the underlying conflict between the worlds of science and technology on one hand and of art and the non-rational aspects of life on the other. The metropolitan railroad terminal, which formed a microcosm of the whole structural art, expressed this division within the confines of a single building-complex. The arched trusses of the iron-and-glass shed stood at one pole, opposing the exuberant monumentality of quasi-Renaissance or Gothic masonry in the station building.

Yet the very existence of such tension meant that eventually the tangential forces and the restless exploration of formal possibilities would have to be composed into a less exhausting harmony. If there was an over-all evolution in nineteenth-century architecture, it might be described as a movement from the first essays into the romantic picturesque, through the elaborations and redundancies of the Gothic and Romanesque revivals, to the sobriety of the final classical revival, which in the United States was dominated by the architectural firm of McKim, Mead and White. At the same time, around 1880, new movements appeared which in a decade were to lead to an architecture whose forms were radically emanicipated from those of the past. In Europe it was Art Nouveau, in America the Chicago shool under the leadership of Jenney, Root, and Sullivan.

The emergence of a new civic architecture in Chicago was a response to certain constituent facts of nineteenth-century building art, chiefly economic and utilitarian demands and structural innovations. What this body of work clearly reveals is that, although many cultural factors shaped the details of architecture in the past century, by the end of the period technical elements were playing a decisive role. Why they did not seem to do so earlier was due to the ironic fact that eclecticism itsetlf was partly a product of technical development. The architect of the nineteenth century was repeatedly faced with unheard of utilitarian and structural requirements which he was expected to cope with and to master. He had no recourse but to look for those precedents in the past that come closest to satisfying the immediate need. Carroll Meeks, the historian of the railroad station, summed up the matter precisely. "Unless we assume," he wrote, "that there is an unlimited amount of creative energy available to any generation, we must recognize that much of the architectural talent available must have been absorbed in the practical aspects of the new problems."[1]

The structural technology of the age presented the architect with extremely difficult problems of formal expression. But soon or late he felt compelled to meet them on their own terms, so to speak, especially in view of the fact that many purely functional structures, like bridges and trainsheds, were taking on in the popular mind the character of a symbolic art. If the architect attempted to create a genuine architecture out of the empirical forms of structural techniques, several possible avenues were open to him. At worst, he could bow before the new technology, but that melancholy fate he was long determined to resist. The question returned again and again: How was one to deal architecturally with steel and concrete structures? Providing an answer to this question proved to be a complex process, and what ultimately emerged was in good part shaped not only by technical requirements but also by a body of aethetic theory which was developed in the latter half of the century.

This theory was strongly marked by a functionalist and structuralist viewpoint, but before the end of the century it was extended and deepened into a more organic philosophy of building. The high priest of the movement was Viollet-le-Duc, whose doctrine of the structural basis of architectural form closely paralleled the new positivism of the philosophers and historians. For all its shortcomings, it was a provocative and original idea that was destined ultimately to have a revolutionary effect. The new theory reached the United States with Andrew Jackson Downing's insistence in his *Landscape Architecture* (1844) on adaptation to site and on fitness to end. By the next decade Ralph Waldo Emerson had worked out a fairly comprehensible organic theory. He was influenced by his contemporary Horatio Greenough, who was so impressed by clipper ships and tools that his aesthetic speculations tended toward a strict functionalism. Perhaps the embryo of a new style lay here, but it could come to maturity only when architects could detect the confusion in such thought between empirical and aesthetic form. Interestingly enough, it was the physicist Joseph Henry, writing in 1854, who understood somewhat better the number of factors involved in an organic art of building:

Architecture should be looked upon more as a *useful* than a *fine* art. It is degrading the fine arts to make them entirely subservient to utility. . . . But our houses are for *use,* and architecture is substantially one of the useful arts. In building we should plan the inside first, and then plan the outside to cover it. Buildings should have an ethnological character. They should express to other ages the wants, customs and habits of the age of their construction. A Grecian temple was intended for external worship. An old Greek would laugh to see us construct a Grecian temple for a treasury building or a meeting house. It should have no windows in it, and should be entirely too dark for such uses. But it is easier to copy than to originate, and hence our servility.[2]

The functionalist viewpoint would naturally be congenial to the engineering mind. Yet it was characteristic of the nineteenth century that many of the most creative engineers, while committed to a structuralist theory, realized that strict functionalism was insufficient for the creation of a genuine work of building art. An early statement of this doctrine appeared in the engineering press in 1869:

It may be stated, as a general rule, that whatever in construction—in engineering construction even—is true and suitable and proportional to strains and service, is also beautiful; or if this statement is too broad, it will not be denied that those structures in which material is utilized and power is applied to the best advantage, are the most beautiful and pleasing. This is as true of a connecting rod as of a cathedral. The art element should therefore be considered in engineering, on professional grounds as well as in the general interests of civilization and refinement. In architectural construction, and in all great or conspicuous engineering works, the want of farther ornamentation and balance of parts may often appear after the strains and functions are all provided for, but it will nevertheless be found, when "artistic effect" is *stuck on* by an afterthought, that both truth and taste have been violated. The artistic element must be associated with the design from the beginning.[3]

The combination of structural integrity and its aesthetic expression was the deliberate and announced intention of the great engineers of the last third of the century, men like Roebling, Eads, Wilson, Pegram, and Morison. In their work and their writings the doctrine was steadily elaborated. By the 1890's this legacy passed to Adler and Sullivan, the leaders of the Chicago movement. The theoretical foundation of their achievement in the final decade of the century was first succinctly stated by Adler, then later extended and deepened by Sullivan into a comprehensive if somewhat disorganized aesthetic theory:

Let us then welcome [Adler wrote in 1896] the prosaic output of furnace and mill, and even the unpromising and garish sheet of plate glass. If they are always used where they are wanted and as they are wanted . . . , we shall have taken the first step toward the transmutation of these utterances of scientific prose into the language of poetry and art.[4]

That Adler and Sullivan regarded the task as one of transmutation indicates that they properly conceived of architecture as a symbolic rather than a technical art.

In the process of organically transmuting the new demands and techniques, the architects and engineers followed one or another of three avenues of approach. The simplest might be called an untrammeled structuralism, in which works of sheer empirical form, like bridges and trainsheds, were treated so that their size and buoyancy would carry the maximum visual impact. Engineers like Roebling and Wilson knew that certain structural elements are inherently pleasing or stimulating by virtue of the strong empathic response they immediately evoke. The dynamic curve of the suspension cable, the poise of the steel arch rib, the huge vault of the trainshed on its thin trusses—these are naturally exciting forms that are best left to themselves. The primary elements of a great building art may lie in such works, but the pure expression of structure is not a mature architecture. The big bridges of the past century took on a symbolic character in the public mind because their size and boldness came closest to expressing the enormous energies of iron-and-coal technology.

A more sophisticated approach was to adapt the new techniques to the older stylistic forms without sacrificing the visual integrity of structure. The foremost example of such adaptation in America was the interior design of the steel-framed buildings at the Chicago World's Fair, in which immense vaults and domes of glass were carried on highly refined systems of hinged-arch framing. They represented the culmination of the long tradition of glass-and-iron vaulting that so delighted the nineteenth-century designer and often called forth his best talents. In work of this kind the structural elements are made subservient to formal considerations, which in turn can come into existence only because the structural means are available to make them possible. It is true, of course, that the overriding and soundly chosen determinant at the World's Fair was the classicism that served as its theme, but the interior vaulting of the larger buildings went beyond the frontiers of the original forms.

The final approach was the conscious attempt to create a mature civic architecture out of the technical means and utilitarian demands of the age. There is no question that Sullivan is the representative figure of this movement, for his work reveals the most thorough attempt to reach the expressiveness of traditional architectural forms. His doctrine was pretty well developed by the last decade of the century. It is necessary to determine what his work symbolizes and how well it stands comparison with the achievements of past ages. If we set aside the pronounced ethical and political element in his theory, we can find in various passages of his writings the possible key to the inner meaning of his accomplishment.

Most illuminating are the passages of *The Autobiography* on bridges. The first records a childhood experience in which he saw a chain suspension bridge (possibly Finley's) on the Merrimack River. The description is loaded with the most extreme expressions of feeling—at first the structure is something dark, ominous, and sinister, then it is associated with giants, and finally with heroic effort on the part of human beings.[5] Later he tells of his idolatry of Eads and Shaler Smith following completion within two years of the St. Louis and Dixville bridges. To Sullivan these engineers were not only "powerful men who did things," but "Imaginative Dreamers" who literally transformed the earth.[6] Finally, there is the famous passage on the skyscraper. "The lofty steel frame makes a powerful appeal to the architectural imagination where there is any. . . . The appeal and the inspiration lie, of course, in the element of loftiness, in the suggestion of slenderness and aspiration, the soaring quality of a thing rising from the earth as a unitary utterance, Dionysian in beauty."[7]

The heart of the matter seems clearly revealed in these and similar passages. Sullivan's big commercial buildings are characterized in their immediate visual elements either by an extreme vertical emphasis, as in the Prudential Building in Buffalo, or by a powerful statement of structure, as in the Carson Pirie Scott Store in Chicago. Along with these features goes a vigorous sense of movement, an empathic quality developed in linear patterns, in the implied expression of forces, and in the flow of space itself. What he was trying to articulate was some kind of complex psychological reaction to the new structural techniques. As symbols the buildings are celebrations of the new technical virtuosity that Eads and Shaler commanded, and, more subjectively, celebrations of such virtuosity as the expression of masculine potency. There is nothing facile nor histrionic about Sullivan's art; it is a confused but honest expression of the awareness of a new kind of power. The essential thing is, however, that it began and ended with the scientific technology that swept nearly everything before it by the end of the nineteenth century. Behind it one can detect a vague and inchoate sense of the world-view that the scientists were developing.

It is instructive to compare the Prudential Building with McKim's Boston library. The latter is unquestionably superior in its formal elegance and its superbly composed visual details. Sullivan was right in his belief that architecture would one day have to free itself from its dependence on the past. But what his own age and ours seem to have lost is what lay behind the source of McKim's ideas. Every great building art is the symbolic image of a cosmos, an encompassing order, whether civic, natural, or divine. When architecture is reduced to the celebration of technique, it may ultimately degenerate into a sterile geometry for the very reason that it loses itself in the material culture that it ought to transcend. The engineers of the past century did their work only too well. When they were finally asked to serve the architect, they found that he wanted chiefly to make a public memorial to what they had done. The scientific basis of their work had to be broadened into a concept of the natural and the human world for which architecture might provide a comprehensive representation.

**273**

# NOTES

## INTRODUCTION

1. A continuous beam is one which extends continuously over more than two supports. A simple beam is supported only at its ends. When a beam of any kind is subjected to a load, it is bent or deflected, and consequently a number of forces are called into play to meet or sustain the load. These forces are the reactions in the supports and the internal stresses within the material of the beam. In an elastic material, such as wood or iron, all these forces must balance the load if the beam is to regain its original form after deflection and to remain in place on its supports. A balanced system of this kind is in equilibrium, the mathematical condition of which is that the sum of all the external and internal forces must equal zero. The reactions in the supports and the tendency of the beam to bend under load can be readily calculated for a simple member. In a continuous beam, however, the number of reactions is redundant—that is, greater than necessary to provide equilibrium—and as a consequence the reactions and internal stresses exceed the number of conditions necessary for equilibrium. The whole structure is said to be indeterminate because the number of unknown quantities exceeds the number of equations that can be written to determine them. The mathematical solution of the problems of stress distribution and deflection is then much more difficult. All this applies to structural elements such as trusses which play the part of beams.

2. On the American bridges considered in Navier's work, see pp. 163–5.

3. A truss is a system of individual members which ordinarily form a series of triangles and which act together as a single rigid element, usually in the same way that a beam functions. The repetitive triangular pattern of the truss arises from the fact that the triangle is the only structurally useful rigid figure—that is, the only one whose shape cannot be altered without deforming at least one of its three sides. (The circle or any closed curve is also a rigid figure, but its structural uses are severely limited.) A truss which extends over more than two supports is an indeterminate structure for the same reason that a continuous beam is indeterminate. In addition, a truss may be indeterminate because it contains redundant members—that is, more members than are necessary for rigidity. A continuous arch with fixed or hinged end-points is indeterminate because, as in the case of a continuous beam, the deflecting forces, the internal stresses, and the reactions at the ends contain more unknown quantities than the number of equations one can write to represent the conditions of equilibrium.

4. Any load will set up deflection or bending stresses in a beam or truss. The bending force varies directly with the distance of the load from the nearest support, the greater the distance, the greater being the bending force. The bending moment is the product of the force and its distance from the support, measured along a line at right angles to the line of the force. A bending-moment diagram is an abstract geometrical representation of the changing moment along a beam or truss.

5. The leading figures in this program of stress analysis and the structural forms they investigated were the following: Jourawski, Howe truss (1844); Whipple, Pratt truss (1847); Fairbairn, Blood, and Doyne, Warren truss (1850); Karl Culmann, Burr truss (1851) and graphical analysis of continuous beams (1866); Mohr, graphical analysis of fixed and two-hinged arches (1870); Thaddeus Hyatt, reinforced concrete structures (1877); August Föppl, three-dimensional, or space, trusses (1892). The Howe, Whipple, and Burr trusses were American inventions, though some had European counterparts. The Warren truss was an English innovation. For details of these forms and the particular problems associated with the analysis of stresses in their members, see the following passages: Burr truss, pp. 82–5, 293–4; Howe truss, pp. 94–6; Whipple truss, pp. 114–15, 117; Warren truss, pp. 117–18, 304; reinforced concrete construction, pp. 231–3, 336–7. The space truss, whose members may lie in several planes, did not appear in the United States until the twentieth century.

The action of a truss cannot be described in detail for all types because the action differs with different forms and under varying conditions of load. Certain fundamental generalizations, however, can be set down. A truss acts in its totality like a beam. When a simple beam is deflected downward, its lower part (approximately half) is subject to tension and its upper part to compression. The center line of the plane between the two zones is called the neutral axis. Since a simple truss behaves in the same way, its lowest line of members, or bottom chord, is under tension and its topmost line of members, or top chord (which may sometimes be inclined), is under compression. The vertical members, or posts, if they exist, are ordinarily under compression, and at least one diagonal between each pair of posts—that is, one diagonal in each panel—is ordinarily subject to tension. Additional diagonals may be subject to compression. It is possible, however, to design a truss in which this distribution is reversed. Moving, eccentric, and wind loads greatly complicate the pattern of stresses and often add shearing forces, which set up still another kind of stress within the members. Continuous trusses are even more complicated. For these, see pp. 137, 275, 306–7.

6. A tubular bridge is one in which extremely deep girders are laced together at top and bottom to form a continuous tube in the shape of a box tunnel. For the American counterparts of the type, see p. 301.

7. For Eads Bridge, see pp. 185–90, 321. The original native model for American testing machines was a device for testing boiler plate built by the Franklin Institute *c.* 1830.

8. For details on the profound difference between the European and American attitudes around the mid-century, see p. 93.

# Chapter 1—WOOD FRAMING

## I, 1. THE COLONIAL BACKGROUND

1. Minoan civilization appears to have been the source of many elements of structural art. Its builders used brick nogging, or infilling, in the wall bays of the wooden frame. They were the first to use structural character as the means to architectural expression: in several rooms of the Palace at Knossos the plaster covering over the structural wall of timber and brick was painted to represent the posts and beams underneath, even to the extent of reproducing the grain of the wood. Their downward-tapering columns with spreading capitals suggest an anticipation of the contemporary rigid frame. Immense discontinuities seem to separate the Minoan from later European culture; yet as archaeologists piece together the history of the pre-classical world, the dependence of Western civilization upon it emerges with ever-greater clarity.

2. The framing timbers of the standard New England house consisted of a variety of forms whose shape and size were determined by their respective functions. The sills were stout beams laid on top of the foundation walls to carry the posts. The latter, which constituted the main vertical supports, extended throughout the height of the structure on its periphery. There were usually eight, one in each corner and two in each of the long elevations. The girts, mortised into the posts, were the main beams or horizontal supports carrying the second floor. Depending on their position, they were known as front, rear, end, and chimney girts. Their extension outward beyond the line of the posts supported the overhang of the second floor. The summer beam was a heavy timber spanning a large room at the midline, usually from end to chimney girt, to which it was joined by a shouldered dovetailed joint. The summer beam served as an intermediate support for the floor joists. Because of its long unsupported span it was usually the heaviest beam in the house, as much as 12 inches deep. The large house generally had four summer beams, one for each first-floor room. The joists were small beams, usually 3 × 4 inches, closely ranked at about 20 inches on centers to support the floor boards. Set in notches, they spanned from front and rear girt to summer beam. Where the house had a cellar, ground floor joists were sometimes small logs. The plates, extending along the tops of the posts, were horizontal timbers on which the roof rafters rested. They were comparable to the sill at the base of the wall but usually smaller because of the lighter load to which they were subjected. The rafters were the sloping beams supporting the planes of the pitched roof. The principal rafters rose from the tops of the posts; the common, set between them, were lighter members rising from the unsupported portions of the plates. The purlins were the horizontal beams, parallel to the ridge line, set between the rafters at various levels from plate to ridgepole. The latter, the longitudinal timber at the ridgeline, was rare in colonial houses, where the rafters usually met each other in lapped joints. The braces were diagonal timbers set at 45 degrees in the wall planes at the corners between sills and posts. They served to give the structure some rigidity and to pro-

vide bracing against wind loads. The collar was a special kind of small brace set diagonally between a pair of rafters to keep them in a vertical plane and to provide rigidity for the roof construction. All of these members are still in common use in residential building, either in similar systems of framing, or in variations on the now nearly universal balloon frame. And elaborations on them formed the main structural elements of later iron and steel framing.

3. The king post is the simplest kind of truss. In profile it is an isosceles triangle made up of a single horizontal member, two inclined members meeting at the apex, and a vertical tie extending from the apex to the center of the horizontal piece. In any truss the members lying in a horizontal line which form the base of the figure constitute the bottom chord, while those which form the upper part of the profile constitute the top chord. The members between the chords comprise the web of the truss. They are usually posts and diagonals.

4. The bottom chord of the Hingham church trusses is a tie beam 45 feet long with a heavy king post at the center. The diagonal members are slightly curved, concave on the underside, and meet just below the top of the post. There are additional diagonal members serving as braces and a short beam near the top which supports the roof deck. The roof rafters slope downward from the ends of this beam to rest upon the ends of the bottom chord. Purlins span horizontally between the rafters.

5. I have omitted any discussion of Spanish colonial architecture because it offers little in framed construction. Roofs of adobe buildings were supported on simple beams which differed from Eastern counterparts only in that they were round and rested on decorated corbels or brackets at the walls.

6. Oliver Larkin, *Art and Life in America* (New York, Rinehart and Co., 1949), p. 16.


I, 2. WOOD FRAMING IN THE EARLY NINETEENTH CENTURY

1. The two outer of the three rows of columns in the Slater Mill constitute the wall framing, and the central one provides a line of intermediate supports. The transverse span from wall to central column is about 13 feet; column spacing along the line of the long dimension is 6 feet 6 inches on centers. Heavy transverse beams span from the central columns to the wall posts. Columns and beams are of square section and not less than $12 \times 12$ inches in cross section. Between the beams, parallel to the long axis, are the joists that support the plank floor. The planes of the gable roof are carried on sloping beams, or rafters, that extend from the tops of the wall posts to the ridge beam. Their spacing and size are similar to those of the floor beams, in spite of the fact that they carry a much smaller load. A series of small dormer windows in the roof admit light to the third, or attic, floor. The framing of these dormer extensions is curious: their sides are wedge-shaped boards whose shape corresponds exactly to the angle between the main roof plane and the little dormer roof.

2. The essential dimensions of Pemberton Mill were the following: 60 × 300 feet overall in plan; height of the five stories, 63 feet above foundations; bay span, 10 feet on the long axis, 26 feet 10 inches on the transverse; cross section of beam, 14 × 16 inches, built up of two 7 × 16-inch pine timbers.

3. The great development of the truss came in connection with bridge construction. From here forms in both wood and iron found their way into every type of building.

4. This method was used in the Senate Chamber of the Capitol at Little Rock, Arkansas (1835), one of the few capital buildings to spring from the vernacular tradition. The chamber, which measured 42 × 50 feet in plan, was covered by a gable roof. Three trusses spanned the length (which was the shorter dimension), parallel to the ridge, the center one taking the place of the ridge beam. Thus the respective depths of the trusses varied from 8 feet for the one at the center to 4 feet 9 inches for those at the sides. The truss construction was homely guesswork. Each was a rectangle divided into three panels by two end and two intermediate posts. Each end panel contained a single diagonal brace, while the center panel had only an additional horizontal piece placed immediately below the top chord. Individual members were hand-hewn cypress, the top and bottom chords being single timbers 42 feet long. There was no iron; all joints were mortise-and-tenon secured with wooden pins.

5. The building walls of the Illinois Central freight station, extending 572 feet 6 inches on the long dimension, are of irregular limestone masonry (the familiar Niagara limestone that was available in great quantities during the excavation of the Illinois and Michigan Canal). The roof is supported on a series of triangular trusses with bottom chord and verticals made up of groups of parallel wrought iron rods. The diagonals and top chord are of wood, the latter composed of two 6 × 12-inch timbers bolted together. A pair of joists lie along the sloping top chords of each truss and carry the purlins, which in turn support the roof planking. All connections are bolted.

Wooden trusses reinforced with auxiliary iron members were used in St. Peter's Church, Clark and Polk streets, Chicago (1865). The inclined timbers of the top chord were reinforced on their under surfaces with wrought iron rods, two in tandem to each member, joined at their free ends by turnbuckles to maintain constant tension.


I, 3. THE BALLOON FRAME

1. The balloon frame, as it was generally constructed, rested on sills fixed to stone or brick foundations. If there was no foundation, the sill rested on a row of contiguous wooden posts, usually cedar, with a diameter equal to the breadth of the sill. The posts were generally 4 to 6 feet in length and were set below the frost line on a series of rafts or platforms of planks, each platform about 2 feet square and composed of a double thickness of 2-inch planks, one set laid at right angles to the other. The sills were joined at their ends, usually by nailing through lap joints, and

the posts in turn were framed into the sills by spiking. The posts, or studs, were generally $2 \times 4$ inches in cross-sectional dimensions and were closely spaced, usually at 16 inches on centers. The joists of the first floor were nailed to the sills and the studs. Spiked to the top of the studs was a horizontal plate of two boards to support the lower end of the roof rafters, which were spiked to the plates and framed to bear laterally on them. Joists and roof rafters were set on the same spacing as the studs. Short boards laid double acted as lintels at door and window openings. Two or three studs were generally spiked together for additional strength at points of maximum stress, such as the corners. If there was a second story, the studding was continuous to the full height of the walls. A horizontal $1 \times 4$-inch board, called a ribbon, was framed into notches in the studs to carry the second-floor joists, which were spiked to both the ribbon and the studs. Floors were laid upon the joists and were nailed down directly through the face. The outside of the entire structure was covered with common boards nailed to the studding and finished with siding. For the roof, sheathing boards were nailed to the rafters and at first covered with shingles, later with roofing paper or other synthetic materials. Except for the use of concrete foundation walls, the present technique of constructing the residential balloon frame differs in no essential way from the original.

2. Quoted in "Prefabs for the Prairies," *Journal of the Society of Architectural Historians,* 11:1 (March 1952), pp. 28–30.

Although prefabrication in the United States was probably developed independently of European precedents, the technique was employed in England as early as 1855, when I. K. Brunel built prefabricated hospitals for the British government to be used in the Crimean War.

## Chapter II—IRON FRAMING

### II, 1. THE BEGINNINGS OF IRON CONSTRUCTION IN THE UNITED STATES

1. Except for the fact that all three are ferrous metals, there is a considerable difference between cast and wrought iron and steel with respect to their chemical and hence physical properties. As a consequence, they are called upon to perform entirely different structural roles. Cast iron was first produced in Europe in the fourteenth century, although it had been used in China as early as the tenth. The metal is made by directly remelting without purification the pig iron that flows from the blast furnace. Cast iron is thus high in carbon, about 3.5% maximum in the structural metal, and high in impurities, which may total another 3.5%. Cast iron is cheap, easy to pour in molds of any shape that can be made from founder's sand, fairly hard and resistant to abrasion, and relatively high in compressive strength. With these advantages, it was the natural choice for early iron construction. But it has serious weaknesses: the presence of the carbon as separate flakes of graphite makes it excessively brittle and relatively low in tensile strength. At the middle of the nineteenth century the best structural cast iron had a tensile strength of 15,000

to 30,000 pounds per square inch, but a compressive strength of 80,000 to 140,000 pounds. But these figures represent the elastic limit and are thus well above what the metal can be safely exposed to in actual practice. Further, the quality of the metal varied extremely and could never be predicted exactly. It was seldom used in tension to sustain a load greater than 4,000 pounds per square inch.

Wrought iron is the earlier form of the metal because of the difficulty of constructing a furnace and producing a temperature sufficiently high to melt iron for casting. Oddly enough, however, wrought iron followed cast as a material for primary structural elements. Wrought iron is made from highly refined iron in which the carbon forms less than 0.1% and the total proportion of impurities no more than 0.4%. It is produced by working slag into a pasty mass of solidifying iron particles, the slag running to about 3.0% maximum. By systematic working the slag is distributed through the iron as an enormous number of microscopic threads, which give the metal its fibrous structure. This structure, together with the mechanical working, gives wrought iron a relatively high tensile strength and elasticity, and hence good resistance to impact. In addition, wrought iron has the highest resistance to corrosion of all ferrous metals other than special steel alloys. The process of purification of the iron and the extensive hand working made the cost of wrought iron prohibitive for heavy structural elements until large-scale methods of manufacture could be developed. Mechanical methods of rolling structural shapes were developed in the United States about 1850. At that time the general run of wrought iron had a tensile strength of 60,000 pounds per square inch and a compressive strength of 70,000 to 80,000 pounds per square inch.

For the chemical and physical properties of steel, see pp. 286–7.

2. Mills, who was an engineer as well as an architect, carefully studied earthquakes and their effects and wrote a treatise on them (now lost) for the guidance of architects and builders.

3. Wrought iron tie-rods had been used as early as 1760 in the colonies, when they were placed in the walls of blast furnaces in the region of Salisbury, Connecticut.

4. John Haviland, *An Improved and Enlarged Edition of Biddle's Young Carpenter's Assistant* (Philadelphia, 1833), p. 45.

5. The choice of wrought iron for the lighthouse frame was dictated by the necessity to resist bending and vibration induced by lateral wind loads.

6. Mott was also the inventor of the now universal method of depositing sand on railway track to prevent the slipping of locomotive driving wheels. He received a patent for the device in 1841.

7. A complete record of the construction, dimensions, and cost of this important but little known building has been preserved. It was a small two-story structure, 20 feet high and 18 × 24 feet overall in plan. The 12-inch walls were brick, and the first floor was composed of stone slabs 2½ inches thick. The second floor, of 1¼-inch planks, rested on the walls and on three iron beams spanning the short dimension and thus spaced about 6 feet on centers. The roof was a series of brick arches of

19-inch span and 2½-inch rise which rested on parallel iron beams of the alternating shapes. There was no functional basis for this alternation, and neither form was adapted to the action of a beam. The lateral arms would have been largely redundant. The total cost of the library was $751.00, divided as follows: structural iron, 6,360 pounds at 3½ cents a pound, $222.60; wrought iron doors, two at $27.00 each, $54.00; masonry, wood, and fittings, $474.40.

## II, 2. THE IRON BUILDINGS OF DANIEL BADGER AND JAMES BOGARDUS

1. The full title of Pickett's work is *A New System of Architecture, Founded on the Forms of Nature, and Developing the Properties of Metals* (London, 1845). It is mainly concerned with the functional and aesthetic possibilities of iron as a building material.

2. James Bogardus, *Cast Iron Buildings: Their Construction and Advantages* (New York, J. W. Harrison, Printer, 1856), p. 4.

3. Most of the buildings for which Bogardus cast the iron members were constructed with wooden beams and brick partitions to carry interior floor and roof loads. Few had complete systems of interior iron framing. Bogardus probably did more than any other builder to make the I-section standard for beams. European investigators had previously determined that the form represented the most efficient distribution of metal, and experiment confirmed their theory. This discovery was probably one of the many things that Bogardus learned on his profitable European tour. For further discussion of the action of beams, see pp. 275, 283, 336.

4. Bogardus, op. cit., p. 7.

5. Quoted in *History of Architecture and the Building Trades of Greater New York* (New York, Real Estate Record Association, 1899), vol. 2, p. 169.

6. Main dimensions of the Harper Printing House were as follows: over-all length of the curved cast iron façade, 130 feet; bay span in the façade, 6 feet 6 inches; maximum interior span, 19 feet 6 inches; maximum depth of arched girder, 18 inches, of joists, 7 inches. A precedent for the use of iron in a large publishing plant was the Bible House (1853), a six-story building which stood until 1956 in the block bounded by Astor Place, 9th Street, and Third and Fourth avenues in New York. The floors were carried on timber beams supported by cast iron columns. The outer walls were brick bearing masonry.

7. The precedent for Bogardus's towers was undoubtedly the iron-framed lighthouse, one of which had been built in the United States as early as 1843. See pp. 28, 281.

8. The height of the McCullough tower was 175 feet; outside diameter at the base, 25 feet 6 inches; at the top, 15 feet 6 inches; thickness of brick curtain wall, 12 inches; depth of foundation, 18 feet; thickness, 4 feet 6 inches. The Tatham shot tower, at 82 Beekman Street (1856), New York, differed from its predecessor only in its height of 217 feet and in the fact that its cast iron columns rested on separate brick footings.

9. Richard Llewellyn Davis, quoted in W. Knight Sturges, "Cast Iron in New York," *Architectural Review,* 114:682 (October 1953), pp. 233–7.

10. William Fogarty, F. R. I. B. A., "The Conditions and Prospects of Architecture in the United States," *Van Nostrand's Engineering Magazine,* 14:85 (January 1876), p. 70.

## II, 3. FROM IRON BUILDINGS TO THE NEW YORK SKYSCRAPER

1. The precedent for these daring proposals was undoubtedly the suspension bridge, the long spans of which were beginning to attract wide attention. Charles Ellet had completed his first cable span in 1842, and John Roebling was already at work on the famous Niagara bridge. To adapt the suspension system to a building was in essence a sound idea, but eighty years had to pass before it was realized in an actual construction. The first such structure in the United States was the Transportation Building at the Century of Progress Exposition, Chicago, 1933–34. The architects were Edward Bennett, Hubert Burnham, and John Holabird.

2. General dimensions of the Crystal Palace were as follows: distance between faces of the octagon, 350 feet; diameter of dome, 100 feet; height of dome above spring line, 150 feet (the largest in the United States at the time); total area of glass, 55,000 square feet. The 190 cast iron columns and the wrought iron roof and dome framing together weighed 1,800 tons.

3. The meridional trusses of the Crystal Palace dome would have been in compression, while those of the polygon at the springing would together act as a tension ring to oppose the horizontal components of the spreading force of the dome. The semicircular ribs of the vault were concentrically paired, the two ribs held in place by means of posts set on radial lines. The absence of diagonals meant that such construction was not a rigid form.

4. Hugh Morrison, *Early American Architecture* (New York, Oxford University Press, 1952), p. 578; inner quotation from B. Silliman and C. R. Goodrich, *The World of Science, Art and Industry in the New York Exhibition* (New York, 1854), p. 4.

5. An early example of rib framing for a dome appeared in the German Winter Garden, on Bowery Street, New York (*c.* 1855). Around its skylighted, elliptical rotunda thin cast iron columns carried cantilevered iron brackets which in turn supported a balcony. Above it a second series of columns rose to take the load of an oval clerestory with a small dome at its center. Clerestory and dome were of glass set in a framework of light radial beams.

6. The first lot of wrought iron beams (1853) had gone to the new plant of Harper and Brothers, the second (1854) to the New York Assay Office. The dates indicate the slowness with which wrought iron beams were at first accepted. It was another decade before they became standard building elements. Wrought iron is much stronger in tension than cast iron and hence more satisfactory for beams, which, being subject to bending, are thus under tension in the lower portion of the member.

7. The story heights of the building are as follows: basement, 22 feet; first story, 16; second, 14; third, 16; fourth, 15; fifth, 18. Column spacing is 17 feet on centers throughout except in the auditorium, where it is 18 feet on the north-south line (the long axis of the building) and 18 feet 9 inches on the east-west. Depth of the wrought iron beams is 9 inches. Footings were originally 4 feet 6 inches square; they were later altered in size and shape.

8. The footing carried a maximum load of 400,000 pounds, which, though not excessive, proved to be too high for the compressive strength of the material used. In addition, certain of the arches used to distribute the load to the basement level of the auditorium columns produced a thrust whose line of action fell outside the outermost column footings. The consequence was that the stone footings tipped, with a resultant failure in both the iron columns and the masonry wall piers.

9. The stone arch girders of The Cooper Union are unnecessarily heavy and awkward. The built-up girder of iron is much superior, but the earliest forms were clumsy and difficult to fabricate. In a store at William Street and Exchange Place, New York (1855–56), floor loads were carried over a 35-foot span by girders each of which consisted of two web plates between flanges and a number of vertical stiffening bars set between the web plates and fixed to the flanges. To connect the bars with the flanges small rectangular slots were cut in the latter, and the ends of the stiffeners, reduced and shaped into tenons, were inserted into the mortise slots and hammered out fast while hot. The two web plates were 18 inches deep and were set 3 inches apart; flange plates were 8 inches wide; stiffening bars measured 3 inches × ¾ inch in section. A similar composite girder, 20 inches deep, was used in the National Bank of Commerce, Cedar and Nassau streets, New York (*c.* 1860). Since a girder of this kind is not a homogeneous member, it is difficult to determine how it might have acted under load. The reinforcing bars were probably wholly redundant. The strength of the girder depended chiefly on the resistance to flexure of the deep web plates, with the flanges providing lateral stiffening and taking some of the tensile and compressive stresses if the web were sufficiently deflected to transmit such stresses to them.

10. The Wanamaker building measured 200 × 328 feet in plan, its five stories rising to a height of 85 feet. Its wall-bay span was about 8 feet. Interior columns, hollow cylinders in form, were cast iron, as were the exterior wall columns, which were hollow rectangles in section. The wooden floors were carried on timber joists supported in turn by wrought iron I-beams spanning between columns. A central rectangular light court was covered by a truss-framed glass-and-iron skylight. The ends of the floor joists at the periphery of the court were carried on deep wrought iron girders of I-section which extended around the four sides of the opening at each floor. The columns at the corners of the court were, like those in the exterior wall, of rectangular section with richly decorated faces. All joints in the frame were made by resting the end of the beam flange on a shoulder cast integral with the body of the column and bolting the beam web to a flange which was also part of the main casting. The decorative elements of the interior columns—base, torus, fluting, and capital—appear to have been cast separately from the structural shaft.

11. Steady improvement in the techniques of iron framing made this constant increase in building height possible, but the technical progress depended in turn on increasing use of scientific discoveries made by European investigators. By the 1860's some of the new theoretical and experimental work became increasingly available to American builders through publication in books and technical journals. The results of Eaton Hodgkinson's experiments were the first to be published in the United States. His classic monograph, *Theoretical and Experimental Researches to Ascertain the Strength and Best Form for Iron Beams,* was published serially in *The Journal of the Franklin Institute* as early as 1832 (it had been published in Manchester in 1830). For a number of years it remained a scientific curiosity in the United States. In the next two decades other important works began to be studied, chiefly the following: Hodgkinson, *Experimental Researches on the Strength and other Properties of Cast Iron* (London, 1846); William Fairbairn, *Useful Information for Engineers,* and *On the Application of Cast and Wrought Iron to Building Purposes* (both London, 1856). A widely studied German work, Julius Weisbach's *Mechanics of Machinery and Engineering,* was translated into English and published in Philadelphia in 1848. The advanced mathematics of the French theorists effectively discouraged most American engineers until the end of the century. As a matter of fact, it also discouraged French engineers until Saint-Venant translated it into more readily usable terms. The publication of European work, as much as practical necessity, stimulated American research into structural mechanics. Testing machines, for example, were installed by the iron manufacturers in 1865. Much of the scientific work was initiated in connection with the construction of long-span iron bridge trusses, which date from the mid-sixties.

12. The Western Union (Broadway and Dey Street, New York) relied on exterior masonry bearing walls, cast iron columns, and wrought iron beams. The Tribune retained the familiar brick partitions to support the iron floor beams. In both buildings it was possible to see clearly the great handicap imposed by the massive walls of stone and brick, which made it impossible to use window openings large enough to admit an adequate amount of natural light. There was no wind bracing in these buildings, which relied on sheer mass of masonry and interior brick partitions to sustain wind loads.

A curious proposal to lighten wall construction was a patent granted to W. J. Fryer, Jr., in 1869 for a wall which consisted of a rectangular latticework of iron bars from which plates of iron were to be hung. If the bars were supported by the outermost beams and columns of the interior frame. Fryer's system might be regarded as a forerunner of skeleton construction. There is no record of buildings erected on this patent.

13. The banking room of the Exchange was 144 × 220 feet in area and 47 feet 6 inches in height to the ceiling. The skylight measured 44 × 167 feet in plan, its periphery being surrounded by the shell of offices. The ridge line of the skylight stood 12 feet 6 inches above the trading room ceiling. Maximum span of the arched trusses over the trading room was 55 feet; maximum bay span in the office block, 20 feet.

A comparatively primitive example of truss framing over a large interior opening was employed in the Seamen's Bank for Savings, on Wall Street, New York (1871), designed by Robert G. Hatfield. To carry the third and fourth floors over the two-story banking room, iron trusses about 40 feet long were introduced between the brick side walls. Each truss was trapezoidal in profile, the sloping end posts, treated as compression members, being cast iron tubes and the verticals, regarded as subjected only to tension, being slender wrought iron rods. Above the top chord running along its entire length, was a wrought iron I-beam which carried the ends of the floor joists. All connections were bolted. The truss framing of the Seamen's Bank shows how rapidly construction progressed in the decades of the 'seventies and 'eighties.

The novel and profitable technique of surrounding an open interior with offices was an invention of the Chicago school. See pp. 56–8, 290–91.

14. "Iron in Architecture," *Carpentry and Building*, 7:7 (July 1885), p. 123.

15. The initial uses of steel for structural purposes in the United States came with the construction of Eads Bridge at St. Louis (1868–74) and Brooklyn Bridge in New York (1869–83). The metal was first used for building framing in the Home Insurance Building in Chicago (1884–85; see pp. 52–5).

Steel embraces such a wide range of ferrous metals, developed for so many purposes, that it is impossible to give more than a superficial description of the properties characterizing the structural metal. In the proportion of carbon which it contains, it is intermediate between wrought and cast iron. Ordinary structural steels contain from 0.08% to 0.50% carbon, those with the higher quantity having the higher strength. The addition of varying proportions of one or more alloying elements increases the strength and the range of desirable physical properties. Chromium, for example, was introduced for the first time into the steel of Eads Bridge. The chemistry of the metal is complex and depends not only on the initial ingredients but on the process by which it is produced. In ordinary structural steels the carbon is present in three forms: as an element dissolved in the iron crystals, as ferric carbide (called cementite), and as a mechanical mixture of the two with a special structure of its own (pearlite). This complex distribution imparts a definite but intricate internal structure to the metal which is the basis of its wide range of superior physical properties. It is much stronger than cast and wrought iron in all respects—tension, compression, resistance to impact and fatigue. Its only defect is its susceptibility to corrosion, which necessitates regular painting of exposed surfaces. The high cost of steel prohibited its use for structural purposes until Bessemer invented the method of refining the metal by blowing air through the molten pig iron that flowed from the blast furnace (1856). But the capacity of the Bessemer process was limited and the price of the metal thus produced remained beyond the reach of many builders. The Siemens-Martin open-hearth process (1865), in which the pig iron is mixed with steel scrap, made possible a much greater volume of production. By 1875 the price fell to a point where the new metal could be used on a large scale in building, but even then it was fifteen years before it was common in structural frames. The Bessemer process was introduced into the United States by Alexander Holley, the Siemens-Martin by Abram Hewitt, both shortly after the Civil War.

16. The over-all height of the statue is 151 feet 5 inches. The copper sheets of the envelope are $\frac{3}{32}$ inch thick; the wrought iron straps over which the envelope is laid are $\frac{3}{4} \times 2$ inches in section. The maximum length of steel posts (from foot to neck) is 93 feet 11⅝ inches. The posts are the chief compression members of the frame. The other members are steel angles of various sizes. The frame was calculated to withstand a wind load of 58 pounds per square foot. Total load of statue and interior framing transmitted to the wrought iron girders in the pedestal is 520,000 pounds. The loading is eccentric because of the upraised arm.

    The external envelope of the figure consists of copper sheets separated into pieces of a size convenient for shipping and handling. The various sections were riveted together on the site, the rivet holes being countersunk and the joints either lap or flush. Immediately inside the copper sheath is a system of horizontal and vertical stiffening ribs of wrought iron strap riveted to the copper. Strips of asbestos were inserted at the contact points between the straps and the envelope to prevent the generation of an electric current arising from the association of the two different metals.

    The steel pyramid formed by the posts is divided into eight bents by a series of horizontal struts lacing the posts together. From the neck to the top of the head four smaller posts continue on the line of the larger, their height being divided similarly into four bents. The system of posts and struts is made rigid by double-diagonal bracing in all panels. Outside the posts there is a light steel frame of trusswork whose outer "vertical" members roughly follow the profile of the body, head, and upraised arm. The horizontal struts of this system are extensions of those in the main bents. Each panel of the outer system of trusswork is braced with a single diagonal. The weight of the copper envelope is carried to the outer members of the frame by means of flat iron straps which extend upward and outward at an angle of about 60 degrees to the vertical members at the points of intersection with the horizontal struts. These straps are attached to the stiffening network of the envelope by means of threaded bolts. (On the concrete work of the pedestal, see pp. 230–31, 335.)

17. The over-all height of the 11-story building was 129 feet. Column-spacing varied, the maximum being 18 feet. Thickness of the brick curtain wall was 12 inches; thickness of the bearing wall above the seventh story was 20 inches for three stories, or 32 feet, and 16 inches for the balance of the height, about 25 feet. Diagonal bracing was calculated for a total wind load of 232,000 pounds, which would have resulted from a gale of 70 miles per hour.

18. John A. Kouwenhoven, *The Columbia Historical Portrait of New York* (Garden City, Doubleday and Company, 1953), p. 396.

19. Ibid. p. 396.

20. When George B. Post designed the grandest skyscraper of them all, he returned to the masonry bearing wall. The Pulitzer, or New York World, Building (1890–91) rose 13 stories above the street, with an over-all height of 375 feet. Floor loads were supported by an interior iron and steel frame, but the whole thing was conceived in terms of masonry construction, and its stone walls spread to a thickness of 9 feet at the base.

   The Jackson Building, on Union Square (1891–92), followed the construction of the Tower Building exactly. Again it was the absurd lot dimensions—28 feet 7 inches × 200 feet—that dictated the choice of upside-down iron-and-masonry construction. The iron frame extended through six of the Jackson's eleven stories. The 26 rectangular cast iron columns rested in cast iron blocks on stone piers carried to bedrock. They measured 12 × 16 inches on the outside faces. The main transverse girders, spanning the full interior breadth of 26 feet 7 inches, were wrought iron I-beams 20 inches deep, weighing 64 pounds per foot. The joists, 9-inch, 21-pound wrought iron I-beams, were connected to the girders by means of wrought iron knees and bolts. The 12-inch brick curtain wall from the basement to the top of the sixth story was supported at each floor by a pair of spandrel I-beams. At the top of the sixth story the columns terminated. Three I-beams in each bay, set parallel and contiguous to each other, rested on top of the columns and were anchored to the seventh-story floor girders. These beams carried a brick bearing wall which was 20 inches thick to the ninth story and 16 inches beyond.

21. The unusual structural feature of the Manhattan Life and American Surety buildings was the system of cantilevered members which supported the columns along the side walls. In the Manhattan the cantilevers were trusses which extended across the full width of the bay. In the American Surety they were 72-inch girders the unloaded ends of which were tied down by a double chain of steel eye-bars anchored in the brickwork of the footings. Loading on the girders varied from 663 to 746 tons. This unusual structural device, which was introduced by William Le Baron Jenney to carry the party walls of his Manhattan Building, Chicago (1890), was employed in the New York buildings to avoid eccentric loading of footings.

22. As the structural system of the contemporary skyscraper was being established in New York, the engineers were developing methods of framing for special kinds of building for which the straightforward steel cage could not be used. Francis H. Kimball's Fifth Avenue Theatre, near Broadway and 28th Street (1892–93), was built with very nearly complete steel and iron framing. The load of the two balconies was transmitted to cast iron columns by means of steel brackets, each rolled in one piece, and transverse steel girders. The domed roof rested on riveted steel trusses set along the rib lines and tied together at the top by a wrought iron compression ring. Wrought iron purlins spanned between trusses in the horizontal plane to support the terra cotta webbing of the dome.

   Three years later the architects N. Le Brun and Sons designed the first church to be constructed on a steel frame, the Church of St. Mary the Virgin (1895–96) in New York. The reinforced concrete ceiling of the nave, 46 × 180 feet in plan, rests on steel ribs curved to conform to the groins of the vault. The ribs spring from a double row of 90-foot high columns. Simple triangular trusses support the gable roof above the nave vault. It was straight Gothic construction done in steel and reinforced concrete.

## II, 4. THE CHICAGO SCHOOL

1. Floor and roof loads of the Leiter (which is now seven stories high) are carried on rectangular 8 × 12-inch cast iron columns set immediately inside the brick piers in the main, or south, elevation and in the solid brick party wall of the north elevation. The timber beams span transversely (east to west), and the 3 × 12-inch timber joists are set between them on 9-inch centers. At the south wall part of the floor load is transmitted to the brick piers by resting the ends of the joists on two 7-inch iron beams that bear on the piers and through a bolted connection on the cast iron mullions, which are continuous and function as bearing members. Cast iron lintels, bolted to the columns, carry the brick spandrels.

2. See Turpin C. Bannister, "Bogardus Revisited," *Journal of the Society of Architectural Historians,* 15:4 (December 1956), pp. 12–22. Professor Bannister kindly allowed me to read this paper in manuscript form before publication.

   As far as his use of steel is concerned, Jenney was undoubtedly influenced by bridge construction. Steel was used for the first time in Eads Bridge at St. Louis (1868–74), a structure which made a profound impression on Chicago architects and engineers. Another possible source of Jenney's system of construction was a project for a system of internal framing proposed by the Minneapolis architect Leroy Buffington in 1882. Buffington was granted a patent in 1888 for skeleton construction in which the masonry of the external walls was to be carried, bay by bay, on shelf angles fixed to the spandrel beams of the frame. He had embodied this idea in three projects submitted in 1882 for skyscrapers respectively 425, 600, and 1,320 feet high. In the same year he had used the system to carry the brickwork of the lobby piers in the West Hotel, Minneapolis, although there seems to have been no functional basis for it. Buffington said that he had derived the idea of iron skeletal construction from the second volume of Viollet-le-Duc's *Lectures on Architecture,* which was published in the United States in 1881. There is no question about the fact that Buffington developed a true system of complete internal framing. His great mistake was waiting six years to take out a patent.

3. Originally by Henry-Russell Hitchcock in his *The Architecture of H. H. Richardson and his Times* (New York, Museum of Modern Art, 1936), p. 275, where the phrase appears in an analysis of the Home Insurance.

4. In the absence of caissons or piling, the "raft" footing was necessary to spread the load of the column as widely as possible on Chicago's compressible soil. It was first used by Burnham and Root in the Montauk Building (1882). After the Home Insurance Building most large buildings in Chicago and other cities with similar soil conditions (notably Boston and Detroit) were and continue to be supported on wooden piles under the column footings. The same technique is used for bridge

piers wherever the weight of the structure and the character of the stream bed require it. To load inaccessible wooden members with the great weight of a masonry footing and a loaded iron column might at first sight seem absurd, but the practice is perfectly sound, has been used for centuries, and continues to be at the present time. The piles under the footings are spaced as closely as it is possible to drive them, so that the load is spread over a large area of wood and the unit compressive stress is held to a minimum. They are driven to a solid base, usually bedrock, and are thus held rigidly in position between the load of the structure above and the unbreakable floor beneath them. Finally, since the piles are completely submerged in water-bearing soil, they are immune to decay.

Very large buildings located where the driving of piles is for some reason impossible are supported on caissons, which were first used under Adler and Sullivan's Stock Exchange Building in Chicago (1893–94). Here the proximity of newspaper presses made pile driving undesirable. The caisson is a massive concrete column which extends from the footing downward to bedrock. In Chicago the bearing rock stratum (Niagara limestone) may lie as much as 125 feet below grade level near the lake. The necessity of digging the narrow caisson wells by hand makes such construction far more expensive than piling.

5. Quoted in Frank A. Randall, *History of the Development of Building Construction in Chicago* (Urbana, University of Illinois Press, 1949), p. 105.

6. William B. Mundie, *Skeleton Construction* (1932), an unpublished ms.; quoted in Randall, op. cit., p. 106.

7. The report of this committee was published in the *Journal of the Western Society of Engineers,* February 1932; quoted in part in Randall, op. cit., p. 107.

8. The contradiction between appearance and published descriptions of The Rookery is not resolved by the only extant framing plan, which was published in *Engineering Record.* The plan shows masonry piers of identical cross section in all four exterior elevations, iron columns only in the interior walls. Yet the first two stories of the rear elevations differ so radically in appearance from the main elevations that one is forced to conclude that the pier or column construction is entirely different. There is now, however, no question that the columns in the rear elevations are hollow cast iron members of rectangular section, similar to those in the court walls. I am indebted to Professor Alec W. Skempton of Imperial College, University of London, for this information.

9. The former hotel rooms of the Auditorium's east block have been transformed into classrooms and other facilities of Roosevelt University, the present owner of the building, including the now abandoned theater.

The immediate predecessor of the Auditorium was the Chicago Opera House (1884–85), designed by Cobb and Frost. The theater, buried in its interior, was surrounded by a ten-story shell of offices and stores. The outer walls were divided into a succession of deep, narrow piers which were covered by iron mullions at the base and by a closely ranked set of shallow false piers above the second floor. The false piers were carried on wrought iron spandrel beams at the second-floor line. The interior framing consisted of iron columns and beams in the office space and iron trusses over the theater. The American origin of this type of construction was apparently Dankmar Adler's Central Music Hall in Chicago (1879), which was the first building to contain a theater surrounded by offices. Little is known about the construction of the Music Hall, which was demolished in 1901.

10. The roof trusses over the orchestra floor of the Auditorium range in span from a minimum of 100 feet to a miximum of 117 feet. The depth of 25 feet 7½ inches is uniform for the six. The arched trusses vary in size from a minimum span of 100 feet 1 inch and rise of 26 feet ½ inch to a maximum span of 116 feet 11 inches and rise of 34 feet 4½ inches. The trusses over the balconies span 46 feet between either side wall and a central line of columns, making the over-all span between walls 92 feet.

11. On the Bollman truss, see pp. 120–21, 304–5.

12. Atwood deserves more attention in the history of American architecture than he has hitherto received. His most widely known work was the special terminal of the Illinois Central Railroad at the World's Fair of 1893. The temporary structure came to have an extraordinary influence on the design of many of the classical terminals built during the early years of the twentieth century, chief among them Grand Central Terminal in New York.

13. For Grand Central Station and The World's Fair buildings, see pp. 215, 218–19, 329, 330.

14. "Chicago Architecture," *Carpentry and Building*, vol. 13 (March 1891), p. 79.


## II, 5. SPECIAL FORMS OF IRON FRAMING IN OTHER CITIES

1. The iron-framed dome of the New York Crystal Palace anticipated that of the Capitol, but having been built of glass solely for exhibition purposes, it was not a reliable guide.

2. For the Howe truss, see pp. 94–5.

3. These crescent-shaped trusses bear the main compressive load of the dome, the form being determined by the fact that if they were subject to deflection, it would be a maximum at the mid-point of the truss. The inner trusses were apparently thought of chiefly as stiffening members which would serve to resist deflections that might occur in the inner chords of the crescent trusses. The over-all height from ground to top of dome is 287 feet 5 inches, of which about half includes the dome proper.

4. The square of the tabernacle measured 78 feet on a side, which was the breadth of the octagon across flats. The ribs rose vertically to a height of 28 feet 4 inches, from which point they continued upward at an angle of 45 degrees to a total height of 42 feet above the tabernacle floor. The vertical portion of the rib was 30 inches deep, the sloping portion 24 inches.

5. The simplest form of rigid frame consists of two columns and a horizontal beam between them, the system being made continuous and rigid by welding or riveting the joints and enlarging their depth so that they resist bending moments. A rigid frame may be composed of any number of vertical, horizontal, and sloping elements.

6. "An Iron Synagogue Roof and Dome," *Engineering Record,* 34:3 (June 20, 1896), pp. 49–50.

7. "Fantasia in Glass and Iron," *Architectural Forum,* 103:2 (August 1955), p. 121.

8. For Pratt and Fink trusses, see pp. 110–11, 122–3; trainsheds, pp. 197–222.

9. For the Pemberton Mill collapse, see pp. 19–20.

10. Theoretically a column is subject only to compression, but a moving load or wind load may also subject it to lateral forces which cause bending, and this in turn will give rise to tensile stresses in that portion of the member under flexure which becomes convex. Further, if a column is actually deformed by compression, its outer surface may in places be subject to tension or shear or both.

## Chapter III—THE WOODEN BRIDGE TRUSS

### III, 1. WOODEN BRIDGE CONSTRUCTION IN THE COLONIES

1. An arched truss is one in which both the top and bottom chords (if both are present) are arched, the entire structure, taken as a unit, being subject to compression. Individual members of the web, however, may be subject either to tension or compression. It is essential to distinguish an arched truss from an ordinary truss combined with auxiliary arches and from an ordinary truss with an arched or polygonal top chord. An arched truss, like the arch itself, exerts a thrust at the abutments which has both horizontal and vertical components, while an ordinary truss exerts only a vertical thrust. These characteristics are further discussed in connection with the trusses invented by Burr, Wernwag, and Town. See pp. 82–5, 87–9, 90–92.

2. Samuel Sewall of New England built the largest of the pile-and-beam spans at the time that they were beginning to give way to sturdier forms. His bridge over the York River at York Village, Maine (1761), enjoyed an astonishingly long life. Its total length of 270 feet rested on 13 transverse rows of piles, each row tied together with horizontal beams bolted to the piling. (Such a connected system of vertical and horizontal members functioning as a pier, abutment, or bearing wall is called a bent.) A crude diagonal bracing was added from time to time during the numerous repairs, which were made in 1794, 1849, and 1873. The bridge was finally replaced in 1934, the original piling still in place and in a fair state of preservation. The longest of Sewall's bridges was one over the Charles River at Boston (1786). Its 1,503-foot deck was carried on 75 pile bents (the 20-foot span was typical).

## III, 2. EARLY FORMS OF THE WOODEN TRUSS: THE WORK OF PALMER, BURR, AND WERNWAG

1. For Finley's bridges, see pp. 163–6.

2. The exact length of the Portsmouth bridge was 2,362 feet between end abutments. The span of the truss was 244 feet 6 inches, the rise 27 feet 4 inches, and the depth, uniform throughout, 18 feet 3 inches.

3. Quoted in Theodore Cooper, *American Railroad Bridges* (New York, Engineering News Publishing Company, no date), p. 6. This work was reprinted from the *Transactions of the American Society of Civil Engineers,* vol. 21. Cooper, as usual, gives no source, but the accurate knowledge of details suggests that the passage is Palmer's own description. The term *concentric* in the first sentence should be *parallel,* to make proper sense of the description.

4. The total length of the deck of the Permanent Bridge was 1,300 feet. The arched spans had the following over-all dimensions: center, length 195 feet, rise 12 feet; each side span, length 150 feet, rise 10 feet. Truss depth was 35 feet at the springing and 20 feet at the crown.

5. Quoted in Cooper, op. cit., p. 7.

6. Ibid. p. 7.

7. The span which followed the Permanent Bridge was built over the Delaware River at Easton, Pennsylvania (1807), and lasted until 1895, when the weight of traffic required its replacement, although it was in sound condition. It was much like the Philadelphia structure except for two innovations: the level deck and, as a consequence, the horizontal top chord of the truss, and wrought iron bolts as fasteners for Palmer's key-and-wedge joints (fig. 25).

8. The bridges of both Palmer and Burr were statically indeterminate structures since they involved arches fixed at their ends (fixed, that is, in the sense that they were not hinged). In such structures the number of internal stresses and reactions exceeds the number of independent conditions of equilibrium necessary to determine the stresses and reactions. This means, at the very least, that the sum of all forces produced by the loading must equal zero and the sum of all bending moments must equal zero. The Burr bridge offered a further difficulty. Since he designed them on the principle of a simple truss strengthened by fixed arches, it was impossible to subject either part to an accurate stress analysis for the reason that there was no precise way of determining where the action of the truss ended and that of the arches began. In the Burr bridge, however, the dead load of the structure greatly exceeded the live, or traffic, load; consequently, a practical way of arriving at a fairly accurate estimate of stresses would have been to analyze it on the basis that the dead load was carried by the arches and the live by the truss. In this way the two parts of the bridge would be treated as separate structures. Burr, of course, relied on intuition and practice rather than on theory, which was

then in a primitive state. An accurate scientific analysis of stresses in the Burr arch-and-truss was developed in 1851 by the German engineer Carl Kulmann.

9. The span lengths of the Trenton bridge were as follows: two at 203 feet, and three at 198, 186, and 161 feet, respectively. The arch ribs were all 32 inches deep, built up of eight 4-inch white pine planks in lengths of 35 to 50 feet laid with staggered joints. The lower chord of the truss was a massive piece composed of two 6½ × 13½-inch timbers. The span of the wing arches was 50 feet.

10. The roadway of the Schenectady bridge was suspended from the ribs by wooden members which acted as hangers where the rib stood above the deck and as posts where it fell below. The piers were diagonally braced wooden bents resting on footings of loose stone in timber cribbing. Around 1830 additional piers were added at the middle of the spans to correct sagging, and in 1873 the entire bridge was replaced by an iron structure. Span lengths of the Schenectady bridge were, in order from end to end, 157, 180, 190, and 160 feet. The arch ribs were built up of eight 4 × 14-inch white pine planks spiked and bolted together.

    The over-all length of the Stockton bridge was about 750 feet, divided into six spans varying in length from a minimum of 104 feet 6 inches to a maximum of 163 feet. Ribs, bottom chord of truss, and transverse beams under the plank decking were built-up timbers of 32-inch depth. The bridge was used continuously for 110 years before its destruction by fire in July 1923. For the lattice truss, see pp. 90–92.

11. Richard Kirby, Sidney Withington, Arthur Darling, Frederick Kilgour, *Engineering in History* (New York, McGraw-Hill Book Company, 1956), p. 224. Their account is condensed from Theodore Burr, "McCall's Ferry Bridge," *Niles' Weekly Register,* vol. 9 (November 18, 1815), pp. 200–202.

12. Among those destroyed by fire was the original Smithfield Street Bridge over the Monongahela River at Pittsburgh, Pennsylvania (1816). It was the longest of his structures, the river crossing being divided into eight covered spans each 188 feet in length. It burned down in 1845 and was replaced by one of Roebling's suspension bridges. (For the replacement, see p. 174.)

13. Among the notable Burr bridges in the Virginias were several built to carry the Northwestern Turnpike over the numerous streams along its route. The one across the Cheat River near Rowlesburg, West Virginia (1834), was built by Colonel Claudius Crozet, who had been a military engineer with Napoleon's army during the Russian campaign. This bridge differed from the standard form in that the posts were inclined in a direction normal to the arch rib—that is, set along radial lines—as in Palmer's truss.

    The first of the Burr type with a double arch rib, one above the other, was the bridge of the Boston and Maine Railroad over the White River at White River Junction, Vermont (1848). Another of the standard form which enjoyed an unusually long life was built to span the Tygart River at Philippi, West Virginia (1852). Its builder, Lemuel Chenoweth, got the contract by placing his model on two chairs and standing on it to impress the Richmond legislators with its strength

(West Virginia was not a separate state until 1863). The floor system of the Philippi bridge was the most elaborate part of its construction: it consisted of one set of diagonal timbers set between the beams, a layer of diagonal planking set at right angles to the timbers, and a top layer of transverse planking. Yet when the bridge was finally replaced in 1934, it was discovered that the flooring was the weakest part of the structure. The deck gave way as the result of horizontal shearing at the ends of the diagonal timbers.

Another variation on the arch-and-truss was introduced by George W. Thayer into a highway bridge over the Delaware River at Narrowsburg, New York (1859). He used the double arch rib of the White River span and further strengthened the truss by adding horizontal struts, called straining pieces, between the posts immediately below the top chord and above the bottom chord, near the points where the diagonals were joined to the posts. Thayer took out a patent on this truss system in 1845.

Indiana seems to have been the home of the last of the Burr bridges: they were built in that state up to 1890 and possibly later. The bridges in the Ohio Valley and Great Lakes regions were usually built of yellow poplar or walnut rather than the pine so common in the East.

14. *A Treatise on Bridge Architecture* (New York: Alexander Niven, printer, 1811), title page.

15. Ibid. p. xv.

16. Ibid. p. 281, 11. 1–4.

17. For the cantilever bridge, see pp. 152–62.

18. The bridge that has also been known as the Economy Bridge was built in 1811 over Frankford Creek at Bridgeburg, Pennsylvania. The center span was a movable one hinged at one end and raised at the other by chains.

19. An unprecedented feature of the New Hope bridge was that the arch ribs rested on the top of the abutments rather than in the masonry. Wernwag was able to provide a reaction to the horizontal thrust of the arch by the curious device of connecting the lower chord of the truss to a system of wrought iron plates to which the ends of the arch were fixed. These plates, which must have been bolted together, were thus subjected to the tension produced by the opposing horizontal thrusts at the ends of the arch. It seems reasonable, then, to regard this bridge as a primitive tied arch, the first of its kind in the United States. Wernwag's patent drawing (1829) showed wrought iron diagonals like those of the New Hope bridge.

20. The success of the Monoquay span led the company to entrust him with a much larger task, the construction of the long bridge over the Potomac River and the Chesapeake and Ohio Canal at Harper's Ferry (1836). There is little information on this bridge, which lasted only 16 years, beyond that it was covered and had seven spans. The first of six bridges built successively by the B. and O. at Harper's Ferry, it was replaced by a Bollman truss in 1852.

21. The two outer trusses of the Camp Nelson bridge curved outwardly toward their ends for greater resistance to wind loads. They thus formed horizontal arches whose lateral thrusts were sustained by tie rods under the deck. The truss was essentially a six-ply laminated arch rib braced laterally and vertically by stiffening trusses with posts and double diagonals. The posts in the line of the arch were set normal to the arch curve—typical of Wernwag bridges—and spaced equally along the arch. Lateral tie rods under the floor beams and the anchor ties at the abutments were wrought iron. All connections were wood except the suspender bolts of the floor beams.

---

The quantitative results of the 1927 stress analysis are as follows:

| | |
|---|---|
| Total compression in arch, dead load | 259,000 lbs. |
| Total compression in arch, uniform live load | 164,000 lbs. |
| Maximum compression in arch | 467,700 lbs. |
| Maximum unit compression in arch | 1,080 lbs./sq. in. |

| | Upper chord | Lower chord | Main diagonal | Counter diagonal | Post |
|---|---|---|---|---|---|
| Maximum tension, lbs. | 46,200 | 19,500 | 0 | 0 | 31,000 |
| Maximum compression, lbs. | 15,600 | 43,600 | 13,700 | 17,000 | 0 |
| Max. unit tension, p.s.i. | 386 | 136 | 0 | 0 | 408 |
| Max. unit compression, p.s.i. | 130 | 304 | 214 | 618 | 0 |

(From Nelson J. Bell and J. K. Grannis, "Stress Analysis of 90-year Old Bridge," *Engineering News-Record*, 100:6 (Feb. 9, 1928), pp. 234–5.)

---

The distribution of tensile and compressive stresses showed that the diagonals were compression members, the verticals tension, and the arches under compression. It is questionable, however, whether the distribution of forces on the posts and diagonals would have remained constant under a moving load. All stresses acted with the grain, and unit stresses were well within the limits of the strength of timber.

22. The bowstring truss is one in which the bottom chord is horizontal and the top chord is bowed upward from the ends of the lower member. Such a truss may under certain conditions function partly as an arch, which is what a number of builders, including Whipple, intended.

23. The top chords of the Chillicothe bridge were built up of 10 boards of oak, each 2 × 10 inches, spiked and bolted together every 5 feet. The bottom chord was a massive built-up piece 10 × 24 inches in section. The posts measured 10 inches square in section. The most inexplicable feature of the bowstring truss was the failure to carry one diagonal in each of the center panels to the joint made by the post and the top chord. This had the effect of adding another and unnecessary pair of joints and making even more difficult an estimate of the stresses in the various members.

## III, 3. TOWARD MATURE FORMS OF THE WOODEN TRUSS: THE WORK OF TOWN AND HOWE

1. Perhaps the best known of the Town bridges was the Tucker Bridge, over the Connecticut River at Bellows Falls, Vermont (1840). Its two main spans, each 131 feet long, were roofed but uncovered at the sides. It was replaced in 1930 as a result of the failure of a decayed bearing block, which caused irreparable damage to one truss. The longest bridge composed of lattice trusses crossed the James River at Richmond, Virginia (1838). Nineteen spans, most of them 152 feet 6 inches long, a few 140 feet, gave it a total length of about 2,820 feet between abutments. The disasters of war cut its life to a quarter of a century: it was destroyed by Confederate troops during the evacuation of Richmond in 1865. The longest single Town truss carried the center span of Blenheim Bridge over Schoharie Creek, North Blenheim, New York (1853). Its clear length was 228 feet, near the common maximum length for wooden spans at the time. The timbers of this bridge were entirely hand hewn, although sawing had by then become universal for large-scale timber construction.

    In 1859 Town's invention was adapted to iron construction, in which form it enjoyed a long life on the railroads, and was not finally abandoned until the early years of the present century. For the iron form, see p. 134.

2. A truss is redundant and hence indeterminate if it contains more members than are necessary for rigidity. A truss resting on more than two supports or containing more than one diagonal in each panel is redundant.

3. When the two diagonals are present, only the main diagonal is regularly stressed. The counter is stressed only under certain eccentric live loads.

4. Quoted in Stephen P. Timoshenko, *History of Strength of Materials* (New York, McGraw-Hill Book Company, 1953), pp. 191–2. Culmann's study of American bridges was published as a series of articles in *Allgemeine Bauzeitung*, 1851–52.

5. By the time Howe began his career as an inventor of bridge trusses, a number of European and American works on bridge construction were available to the builder. The chief source of all these early publications was Emiland Gauthey's *Treatise on the Construction of Bridges* (1809–13), published posthumously with extensive notes by his nephew Louis Marie Navier. Gauthey's theory of bridge trusses rested on two principles, which he called "equilibrium of position" and "equilibrium of resistance." In the former he considers the relative position of the truss members with respect to the load and to each other, and hence the distribution of forces among them. He regards the various members as rigid levers and calculates the forces on them by means of the laws of statical equilibrium and the resolution of forces into horizontal and vertical components, a mode of analysis first developed in the sixteenth century by Simon Stevin (the idea of resolution has Hellenistic antecedents). Gauthey's method was much oversimplified and not always reliable.

    The internal properties of wood and the presence of external moving loads led

Gauthey to realize that the second principle is as essential as the first in timber framing. Navier's notes carried application of the principle much further than his uncle was able to do. The fundamental point is that for the equilibrium of the structure, the internal stress in a member—that is, its resistance—must balance the external load on the member. Since wood is an elastic substance, this principle required the introduction of the theory of elasticity into the analysis of trusses, which in turn involved a more advanced level of mathematics than that required by the first principle (differential equations rather than elementary trigonometry).

The calculus was beyond most American engineers around 1835, and the work of the French authorities would have remained little known at the time if it had not been for the publication in the United States of several more elementary treatises, some of which contained simple epitomes of the Gauthey-Navier theory. The first of these was Jacob Bigelow's *Elements of Technology,* whose second edition (Boston, 1831) provided a general, nonanalytical treatment of truss bridge construction. More advanced and thus more useful was James Renwick's *Elements of Mechanics* (Philadelphia, 1832), which included an exposition of the Gauthey-Navier principles on both truss and suspension bridges. The most complete presentation of the French work appeared in an influential British publication, Thomas Tredgold's *Elementary Principles of Carpentry* (London, 1820), published in the United States in 1837. Tredgold introduced his own method of subdividing complicated trusses into simple systems for purposes of analysis. The American treatise which was based in good part on Tregold's work was Dennis H. Mahan's *Elementary Course of Civil Engineering* (New York, 1838), a volume developed largely from Mahan's lectures to the cadets of the United States Military Academy at West Point. But the work was seriously defective in the absence of analysis of most of the American truss bridges which had been built up to that time. All these works, together with Long's description of his truss, were undoubtedly known to Howe and formed the antecedents of Squire Whipple's more widely read treatise (see pp. 114–15).

6. The Western Railroad later became a part of the Boston and Albany, which has now lost its separate identity through merger with the New York Central.

7. The South Side Railroad was later absorbed by the Norfolk and Western Railway.

8. The total length between abutments of the Farmville bridge was 3,400 feet. The individual spans were about 160 feet long and 25 feet deep. The track level was 100 feet above mean water level in the river.

9. The Buffalo and New York City is now the Buffalo branch of the Erie Railroad.

10. The linear dimensions of the Portage bridge do not suggest a bridge of great size, but its unusual height and its timber bents required an unprecedented quantity of wood. The over-all length was 800 feet, the individual trusses being 50 feet long and 14 feet deep. The maximum height of the timber bents, between top of masonry footing and bottom of truss, was 190 feet. The footings were 30 feet high. The bridge contained 1,602,000 board feet of timber, 109,000 pounds of iron bolts, and 9,200 cubic yards of masonry.

11. Later extensions of the Rock Island company led the owners to adopt the present name of Chicago, Rock Island and Pacific, but the lines do not reach the Pacific coast.

12. For the Warren truss, see pp. 117–18, 304.

13. Each of the fixed spans of the Rock Island bridge was 250 feet long and the swing span 285 feet. The total length of the bridge proper was 1,535 feet. (The width of the Mississippi at this point was increased by subsequent construction of a roller dam. The present bridge is thus much longer than the original.) The materials of the bridge reached a total of 1,000,000 board feet of timber, 220,000 pounds of cast iron, 400,000 pounds of wrought iron, and an unknown but unparalleled amount of stone masonry for the piers. Iron was used only for fastenings.

14. It is not clear what McCallum's intention was in the design of this truss. It was not a bowstring truss, since the arched top chord did not spring from the ends of the bottom chord but was bowed up between the end posts, and hence it could not have functioned in any way as an arch. The chief ground for the arched form is that the maximum bending moment is at the center of the truss, the minimum at the ends, and consequently the depth of the truss may diminish from center to ends. In McCallum's patent drawing the arched chord is intermediate between the horizontal top and bottom chords. This extremely redundant form really represents the superimposition of one kind of truss on another, but the design does suggest that McCallum thought of the change in bending moment as an important determinant.

15. The two companies eventually formed most of the Chicago and North Western Railway's main line between Chicago and Omaha. The Galena company was the first railroad to serve Chicago, having been opened in 1848.

16. The diagonal stays in the swing span of the Clinton bridge extended from the upper corners of the truss outward and downward to the panel points along the bottom chord. Since a center-pivoted swing span is, when open, a pair of balanced cantilevers, its action is different from that of a simple truss. The cantilever is deflected downward at the free end. The radiating diagonals thus served to take some of the tensile stress in the top chord.

17. The railroad company later became a link in the Pennsylvania's main line between New York and Washington.

18. The last of the long bridges with Howe trusses was built by the North Coast Railway over the Columbia River at Kennewick, Washington (1909–10). Its total length, including approaches, was 2,542 feet. The river crossing included eight fixed spans of 150-foot length and one swing span of 240 feet. The trusses were fabricated on the ground near the site and floated into place on barges carrying falsework. The North Coast Railway later became a part of the Oregon-Washington Railroad and Navigation Company, which had previously been leased to the Union Pacific.

19. The rise of the arch in the Cascade Bridge was 50 feet. The over-all width of the deck was 24 feet. The arch ribs were 24 inches square in section at the center and 24 × 48 inches at the spring line.

20. The different companies and the years in which the respective bridges were opened were the following: Boston and Maine Railroad Extension Company, 1844; Fitchburg Railroad, 1847; Eastern Railroad, 1853; Boston and Lowell Railroad, second bridge, 1856.

21. The vertical lift bridge had to wait for steel construction. The first in the United States was built to carry South Halsted Street over the Chicago River in Chicago (1894). Designed by J. A. L. Waddell, the bridge spanned 130 feet clear.

## Chapter IV—THE IRON BRIDGE TRUSS

### IV, 1. THE FIRST IRON BRIDGES

1. Since Paine's project and the Brownsville bridge were arch structures, they are treated in detail in the chapter on iron arch bridges.

2. The illustration of this bridge is not clear, but the historian of American railroad bridges, Theodore Cooper, who knew it at first hand, has a detailed description of it:

    "The truss was a combination of the truss and suspension principles, and was formed of—first, seven cast-iron sections or panels of about 11 feet in length and 7 in depth, cast solid, each segment consisting of an upper chord, a pair of diagonal braces and half of a hollow cylindrical post at each end, except that the end segments had full cylindrical posts at the abutments. These semi-cylinders, being bolted or clamped together in series, formed full cylindrical posts, which were flanged at the bottom, and through which were passed vertical bolts securing them to wooden transverse floor beams. Second, two wrought-iron suspension rods (1½ inches in diameter) attached to the top end of the posts, and sagging in a parabolic curve, so as to pass under and support the two centermost floor beams, and under lugs cast at proper elevations upon the posts intermediate between the centermost and the end posts, whereby such intermediates were supported. Cross-sections of chords and diagonal braces were of the +-formed section." (Theodore Cooper, "American Railroad Bridges," *Transactions of the American Society of Civil Engineers,* vol. 21, pp. 14–15. By "+-formed" Cooper meant a cast bar in the form of an equilateral cross in section.)

3. For the Finley suspension bridge, see pp. 163–6.

4. One truss of Osborne's Manayunk bridge has been preserved by the Smithsonian Institution, where it is now a permanent exhibit.

5. The Baltimore and Susquehanna later became the Northern Central Railway, which is now the line of the Pennsylvania between Baltimore and Harrisburg, Pennsylvania.

6. Each pair of plate girders in the Bolton bridge were joined together and stiffened by staybolts set in cast iron sleeves. The paired girders were then braced in both the horizontal and vertical planes by transverse and diagonal members set in the 3-foot 10-inch space between the pairs. The girders were 6 feet deep and were built up of riveted ¼-inch wrought iron plates. The feature which most set them apart from modern bridge girders was the absence of top and bottom flanges. The transverse timber beams were 12 inches square in section, and the transverse wrought iron bars of the bracing were ¾ × 5 inches in section. The staybolts were set on 12-inch centers along the horizontal and vertical lines. The total weight of Milholland's bridge was a small fraction of the estimated total load which the span could sustain. The ultimate strength of the girders was calculated at 500,000 pounds of uniformly distributed load, while the total dead weight of the bridge was only 28,000 pounds. In 1864 Milholland's design was adapted to use on double-track lines and survived until 1882, when it was superseded by the modern flanged girder.

7. Milholland's invention raises the question of British and American precedence in this form. William Fairbairn patented a plate-girder bridge with lateral bracing between girders in 1846. It seems likely, however, that the American and British engineers worked independently of each other. Stephenson and Fairbairn's famous Britannia Bridge (completed 1850) was a derivative from the simple plate-girder span. The iron spans of this bridge have the form of a great box tunnel of through girders roofed and floored with parallel lines of contiguous girders forming cellular iron structures which support the greater part of the load. Britannia Bridge was widely and immediately known; yet it had little influence in England or the United States. James Hodges in 1850 proposed a double-deck rail and highway bridge over the Niagara River which was to be a counterpart of the English structure. He designed it as a continuous tubular bridge of three 550-foot spans resting on two high, slender piers of stone masonry. The girders were to be braced partly by a system of diagonal struts set between them and partly by the transverse beams that would have supported the two decks, the upper for the railroad, the lower for the highway. Hodges' project was never built, nor was anything like it. The simple girder span and the truss proved more useful.

8. The New York and Harlem Railroad is now the Harlem Division of the New York Central, and the New York and Erie was the original main line of the Erie Railroad, which extended from Jersey City to Dunkirk, New York.

9. For the Whipple and Post trusses, see pp. 114–15, 117, 145.

10. The results of Hodgkinson's experiments on the bending of cast iron beams were published in book form in 1846. These experiments conclusively demonstrated the inadequacy of cast iron members in tension. The use of wrought iron in the Britannia and Conway bridges, together with Hodgkinson's tests on wrought iron plates (published in 1849), greatly stimulated the enthusiasm for wrought iron in trusses, all members of which may be subjected to deflection.

11. The Cleveland, Painesville and Ashtabula was merged in 1869 with several other companies to form the Lake Shore and Michigan Southern Railroad, which was later absorbed by the New York Central and now forms the main line of that company from Buffalo to Chicago via Cleveland.

## IV, 2. PRATT AND WHIPPLE TRUSSES

1. There were several minor variations on the iron Pratt truss, the earliest of which was patented by Stephen H. Long about 1850. He built a small bridge on this design to carry De Milt Avenue over the Bronx River in what is now New York City (1853). The bridge spanned 70 feet clear and carried a 14-foot roadway and two 5-foot sidewalks. Although the bridge survived for nearly sixty years, Long seems to have made a less exact calculation of the distribution of stresses than Pratt. In 1912 bridge engineers of the New York Central and Hudson River Railroad made a stress analysis of the bridge in connection with a line relocation project. They discovered that the members were so unequally stressed as to subject some to loads far above the allowable working limits at the time. As a consequence, they demolished the bridge instead of moving it to a new location, as they originally intended.

2. The over-all length of the Portage bridge between abutments is 818 feet, divided as follows: ten spans at 50 feet, two at 100 feet, and one at 118 feet. The bents measure 20 × 50 feet at the top, with a maximum height of 203 feet 8 inches above the masonry footings. The horizontal members of the bents are set 25 feet on centers.

3. The trusses of the Portage bridge were designed to carry a live load of 3,000 pounds per lineal foot, and the bents a live load of 5,400 pounds per lineal foot. In addition, the latter were built to sustain a wind load at right angles to the bridge of 30 pounds per square foot of the area between posts. The design of members was based on a maximum tensile strength in the bottom chord of the truss of 10,000 pounds per square inch and a maximum compressive strength in the cast iron posts of 6,600 pounds per square inch. The strength of the metal is well above these comparatively low limits, which accounts for the fact that the bridge is still in use.

4. Another important bridge in which the Pratt truss was used for the approach spans was the Cincinnati Southern's Ohio River bridge at Cincinnati (1876–77), which included the longest single truss span built up to that time.

5. For details of Murphy's design, see pp. 114, 133.

6. For progress in stress analysis up to the development of Whipple's method, see pp. 297–8.

7. To Whipple the basic principle of all bridge construction is the idea of supporting a load by members inclined to the horizontal or vertical. In his own words:
   "The body [to be sustained] can only be prevented from falling by *oblique* forces; that is, by forces whose lines of action are neither exactly horizontal, nor exactly perpendicular. . . . Here, then, we have the elementary idea—the grand fundamental

principle in bridge building. Whatever be the form of structure adopted, the elementary object to be accomplished is, to sustain a given weight in a given position, by a system of *oblique forces,* whose resultant shall pass through the centre of gravity of the body in a vertically upward direction, in circumstances where the weight can not be conveniently met by a simple force, in the same line with, and opposite to, that of gravity. . . . It is not necessary that the [load] be at the angular point . . . of the braces or chains, but it may be sustained by simple suspension . . . below, or simple support . . . above, and such obliquity may be given to the braces or chains as may be most economical." (From *An Elementary and Practical Treatise on Bridge Building,* New York, D. Van Nostrand Company, 1872, pp. 2–3. This work is a revised and enlarged edition of Whipple's *A Work on Bridge Building.*)

8. Whipple's method of explaining resolution into components is worth quoting at length, I think, as an example of nontechnical presentation of the trigonometric operations for the bridge builder untrained in mathematics:

"The sustaining of weight by oblique forces gives rise to horizontal forces, for which it is necessary to provide counteraction and support, as well as for the weight of the structure and its load. Two equal and equally inclined braces, . . . in supporting a weight . . . , act in the direction of their respective lengths, each with a certain force, which is equivalent to the combined action of a vertical and horizontal force, which may be called the horizontal and vertical *constituents* of the oblique force. These two constituent forces bear certain determinate relations to one another, and to the oblique force, depending on the angle to which the oblique is inclined.

"Now, we know that the vertical constituent alone contributes to the sustaining of the weight, and consequently must be just equal to the weight sustained. . . . We know, moreover, from the principles of statics, that three forces in equilibrio, must have their lines of action in the same plane, and meeting at one point; and must be respectively proportional to the sides of a triangle formed by lines drawn parallel with the directions of the three forces; and that each of the three forces is equal and opposite to the resultant of the combined action of the other two. . . .

"The horizontal thrust of an oblique brace, equals the weight sustained, multiplied by the horizontal and divided by the vertical reach of the brace; and the *direct* thrust (in the direction of its length), equals the weight sustained multiplied by the length and divided by the vertical reach of the brace." (Ibid. pp. 6–7.)

9. Ibid. p. 143.

10. Ibid. p. 143.

11. The Rensselaer and Saratoga Railroad later became a part of the Delaware and Hudson Company, which began its long history in American transportation as a system of canals.

12. The Troy bridge was a single-span structure 146 feet long between abutments. The truss was 22 feet 9 inches deep overall, and the posts were spaced 10 feet 6 inches on centers. Whipple designed the truss for a rolling load of 2,000 pounds per lineal foot. Common locomotive weight at the time was 35 tons.

13. What may have been the last of the Whipple trusses in their original form was the wrought iron, wooden-deck structure built to carry McMillan Street over Reading Road in Cincinnati, Ohio (1899). A single span 115 feet long, its three parallel trusses carried a double roadway and two streetcar lines. It was replaced in 1937 by a steel span.

14. Actually it is not possible to make a precise statement about the distribution of tensile and compressive stresses in the Warren truss, since such distribution changes with the changing position of a moving load. Thus any one diagonal may be subjected first to tension and later to compression.

15. Whipple, op. cit., p. 69. His statement is ambiguous. He may have meant that he knew of Warren's invention and gave it its first practical demonstration in the United States.

16. In the Tyrone bridge the top chord consisted of a group of parallel I-beams held together by a plate riveted across their upper flanges. The bottom chord and the diagonals were made up of a series of wrought iron eye-bars. The truss was laterally braced with transverse and diagonal members in both the top and bottom planes. In the Blue River bridge, whose span length was 126 feet 10½ inches, there were vertical tension members in alternate panels. The vertical and diagonal members were wrought iron, the chords timber. The Tyrone bridge was pin-connected, but the use of wood in the Blue River span required bolted connections.

   The North Street (now Guilford Avenue) bridge over the Pennsylvania Railroad tracks in Baltimore (1880) was a highly ornamental cast and wrought iron Warren truss of two spans, each 173 feet 9 inches in length. The top chord was a hollow cast iron tube of octagonal section, the other members being wrought iron. The bridge was laterally braced with transverse members only. The absence of diagonal sway bracing led to excessive vibration from streetcars. This, together with the corrosive action of locomotive smoke, required continual repairs until the bridge was replaced in 1937 (by which date the Pennsylvania line through Baltimore had been electrified).

## IV, 3. BOLLMAN AND FINK TRUSSES

1. For a discussion of Latrobe's bridges, see pp. 242–305.

2. The idea of radiating members was not original with Bollman. They were then being proposed by Roebling for suspension bridges and had appeared as braces nearly a century before Bollman's invention. Jean Ulrich Grubenmann's famous Rhine bridge at Schaffhausen, Switzerland (1757), had a complex system of upward-

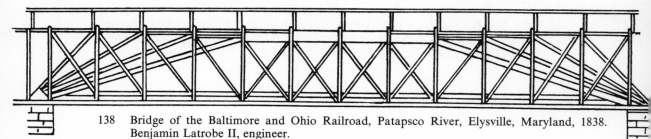

138 Bridge of the Baltimore and Ohio Railroad, Patapsco River, Elysville, Maryland, 1838. Benjamin Latrobe II, engineer.

radiating braces extending from the piers. Much like it was the timber bridge built by Benjamin Latrobe in 1838 to carry the Baltimore and Ohio line over the Patapsco River at Elysville, Maryland (fig. 138). This bridge was a modified Howe truss with a similar system of radiating braces extending upward and outward from each pier.

3. In the Bollman system the chief characteristic of the action was that most of the load on each panel was transmitted through the radiating bars directly to the end posts, the action of the truss being somewhat like that of the stiffening truss in a suspension bridge. Since the radiating members transmitted nearly all of the load to the top of the end, or portal, posts, the top chord was subjected to compression while the bottom chord was very nearly unstressed.

4. The first of Bollman's bridges to cross a large stream was the multispan structure built across the Potomac River and the Chesapeake and Ohio Canal at Harper's Ferry (1851–52) to replace Wernwag's bridge of 1836. The trusses, each 124 feet in length, had cast iron top chords, posts, and portal towers in the form of hollow hexagonal members bolted together. The numerous diagonals and radiating members were wrought iron rods. Bollman designed the truss on the basis of a maximum tensile strength in the wrought iron of 16,000 pounds per square inch, a figure much lower than the manufacturer's claim, which the engineer wisely declined to accept. The Harper's Ferry bridge was used by the railroad until 1894, when it was converted into a highway span and used as such until floods destroyed it in 1935.

5. For discussion of other Ohio River bridges, see pp. 124, 141–2, 144, 146, 149–51, 181.

6. The division of truss types and their lengths in the river crossing of the Bellaire bridge were as follows: nine Bollman deck trusses, varying in length from 107 to 125 feet; three Whipple deck trusses, from 211 to 214 feet in length; two Whipple through trusses, respectively 242 and 348 feet long. The total length of iron spans, including those in the approaches, was 3,916 feet, and the over-all length, including approaches, 8,566 feet. The track stood about 40 feet above mean low water.

7. For a fuller description of the Bellaire viaduct, see p. 339.

8. There were three bridges with Bollman trusses on the Valley Railroad, all in Virginia: at Mt. Crawford (1872), two spans, respectively 98 feet 6 inches and 148 feet 9 inches, the latter possibly the longest single Bollman truss; at Cave Station (1873), two spans, respectively 63 feet 5 inches and 98 feet 7 inches; at Verona (1874), four spans, the three Bollman trusses each 98 feet 7 inches, the Whipple truss, 147 feet. All were deck trusses.

The only Bollman truss bridge which, to my knowledge, is still in existence is a small two-span iron structure of through trusses on a branch line of the B. and O. at Savage, Maryland, near Baltimore. The bridge was built originally in 1852 for two tracks but now carries a little-used single-track line. The external appearance of the iron suggests that the metal is still sound.

Bridges designed by Bollman and Fink were not confined to the United States. Their trusses were used on a number of spans erected in Latin America during the latter half of the century.

9. Dimensions of the trusses in the Fairmount bridge were as follows: length, 205 feet; depth, 22 feet 6 inches; transverse spacing, 16 feet on centers.

10. Of the five spans in the Green River bridge, three were 208 feet long, and two, at the ends, 181 feet. The rail stood 115 feet above the bed of the shallow river.

11. For the trusses of the channel spans in the Louisville bridge, see pp. 146–8.

## IV, 4. SPECIAL INVENTIONS:
### TRUSS FORMS AND STRUCTURAL DETAILS

1. All the Douglas bridges were built by the Berlin Iron Bridge Company of East Berlin, Connecticut, between 1880 and 1895. Most of them were located in New York and New England, the longest, with a span of 205 feet, having been built at Waterbury, Connecticut.

2. The first American all-steel bridge was built in 1879; see pp. 143–4.

3. For Roebling's Pittsburgh bridges, see pp. 174–5; for detailed discussion of the three-hinged arch, pp. 190–91.

4. For the Long truss, see p. 93; the Pratt truss, pp. 110–11.

5. The first of Lowthorp's bridges (1856–57) in the form of the patent design was a large structure for the mid-century decade. Built for the Catasauqua and Fogelsville Railroad (later absorbed by the Lehigh Valley) near Allentown, Pennsylvania, it was 1,120 feet long overall and was divided into 11 equal spans with a truss depth of 16 feet. Its piers were cast and wrought iron bents resting on masonry footings and varying in height from 30 to 45 feet. The success of this bridge started Lowthorp on an active career: for the next twenty years he built a large number of railroad bridges in Pennsylvania and New Jersey.

6. The Pittsburgh, Fort Wayne and Chicago was later leased to the Pennsylvania Railroad and now comprises that company's main line between Pittsburgh and Chicago.

7. At least one steel lattice truss, built in 1911, is still in use, carrying a double-track freight line of the Chicago and North Western Railway over the Milwaukee Railroad near Glenview, Illinois.

8. The first indication of an understanding of the action of a continuous truss in the United States appears to have been a bridge designed by C. N. Beckel to carry a railroad line across Saucon Creek near Bethlehem, Pennsylvania (1870). There were two spans of Pratt trusses each 51 feet 10 inches long and 7 feet 10 inches in depth. The posts and top chord were cast iron members of octagonal section, the bottom chord a series of square-section eye-bars. What is important about this otherwise commonplace structure was that Beckel thought of the trusses as behaving like the spans of a continuous truss: that is, a single truss extending over several intermediate supports rather than being divided into a series of separate end-supported units. This initial step was certainly a hesitant one: it consisted merely in doubling

the diagonals sloping in one direction in the center panels of each span. But the presence of these additional members suggests that Beckel regarded the bridge not as having two separate trusses subjected only to downward deflection, but rather as a single unit deflected downward at the mid-span points and upward at the piers. On the other hand, the bottom chord of the Bethlehem bridge was treated as a tension member in all panels, which would not be the case in a continuous structure. A true continuous truss is an indeterminate structure, regardless of the disposition of individual members.

9. The New York, Lake Erie and Western was the corporate title of the Erie Railroad during one of its many receiverships.

10. The truss of the Marmaton River bridge, 200 feet long, was divided into seven panels with double diagonals only in the three center panels. The truss depth varied from 24 feet at the ends to 38 feet 9 inches at the center. The bridge was designed for a dead load of 350,000 pounds and a live load of 3,000 pounds per lineal foot (sufficient for a train with two locomotives).

11. For a discussion of the St. Louis station, see pp. 219–21.

12. For special long-span railroad trusses, see pp. 141–52.

13. The Cincinnati Southern is the only railroad built and retained as a municipal enterprise. It was constructed from Cincinnati to Chattanooga during the 1870's by the city of Cincinnati and in 1880 leased for operation to the Cincinnati, New Orleans and Texas Pacific Railway. This company is owned in major part by the Alabama Great Southern, which in turn is controlled by the Southern Railway. These complex arrangements are still in effect. For discussion of Bouscaren's bridges on the Cincinnati Southern, see pp. 142, 155–6. Louis Frederic Gustave Bouscaren was born in 1840 in the French West Indies. After a wide-ranging education, which included study at St. Xavier College, Cincinnati, Georgetown College, Kentucky, the Lycée St. Louis and the École Centrale des Arts et Manufactures, Paris, he held various positions in the engineering departments of several Ohio valley railroads, eventually becoming chief engineer of the Cincinnati Southern Railway. He established an independent practice as consulting engineer in Cincinnati in 1884, which he continued until his death in 1904.

14. Cooper, op. cit., p. 24.


IV, 5. LONG-SPAN BRIDGES

1. For cantilever bridges, see pp. 152–62.

2. The P. C. C. and St. L. Railroad originally included the lines of the Pennsylvania Railroad lying for the most part within the triangle whose corners are Pittsburgh, Cincinnati, and Indianapolis. It later acquired the Vandalia Railroad and thus secured entry into St. Louis. All the properties were eventually leased to the Pennsylvania.

Linville later developed his own variation on the Whipple truss, which he first used for the channel span of the Pittsburgh and Lake Erie's Ohio River bridge at Beaver, Pennsylvania (1877).

3. The Quincy span began a heroic age of iron bridge construction on the Eastern and Midwestern rivers, with the Whipple truss standard for all crossings over the big waterways. Within the year after the Quincy bridge was started, the Burlington began construction of its second Mississippi crossing, at Burlington, Iowa (1867–68). A nine-span bridge, it was virtually identical with its predecessor except that the bottom chord of the trusses was wood rather than wrought iron. Neither the Quincy nor the Burlington bridge had adequate wind or sway bracing between top chords, the stiffening system consisting entirely of a set of transverse rods with short diagonal struts at their ends. This defect constituted an invitation to disaster in a region where tornadoes are common. When the bridge at Burlington was replaced in 1895, six spans were bought by the town of Cicero, Illinois, and used to carry 52nd Avenue over the Burlington freight yard. This bridge survived until 1955, when it was replaced by the present concrete structure.

   A Whipple truss of record length for the time carried one span in the Ohio River bridge of the Baltimore and Ohio at Bellaire, Ohio (1868–71). Five of the 14 river spans were made up of Whipple trusses, one of which reached the length of 348 feet.

   The Burlington Railroad used Whipple's invention again for the first Missouri River crossing, at Kansas City (1869). The Wabash Railroad adopted it for its Mississippi bridge at Hannibal, Missouri (1876), and the Northern Pacific for its Missouri River bridge at Bismarck, North Dakota (1882). The Northern Pacific commanded the best engineering talents available when it commissioned George S. Morison and Charles C. Schneider as designers.

4. It was in connection with the construction of the Cincinnati bridge that Bouscaren introduced competitive bidding and precise train load calculations in specifications. See pp. 140–41.

5. The Alton, after several transformations, is now that part of the Gulf, Mobile and Ohio Railroad extending from Chicago to St. Louis and Kansas City.

6. For a complete discussion of Eads Bridge, see pp. 185–90. In the use of steel European builders enjoyed a 40-year lead over the American. The first European bridge with steel members was built by Ignaz van Mitis in 1828 to span the Danube Canal at Vienna. The structure was a suspension bridge the eye-bar chains of which were steel.

7. The total length of the Glasgow bridge was 3,574 feet, divided as follows: river crossing, five (three through, two deck) Whipple truss spans at 314 feet each, 1,570 feet; wooden trestle approach, 864 feet; iron deck truss approach, 1,140 feet. The depth of the Whipple trusses was 40 feet. The bridge was designed to carry two 65-ton engines followed by a load of 1,820 pounds per lineal foot of deck.

8. The extensive use of steel marked the most ambitious bridge project of the decade, the proposal by the engineering firm of Anderson and Barr to bridge the Hudson

River between Hoboken and Manhattan Island. Their plan called for 16 spans of Whipple trusses carrying two decks, one for railroad and the other for vehicular traffic. The three main river spans were each to be 500 feet in length. The grand scale of this project was matched only by its folly: a truss bridge thrown against the dense river traffic at this point would have been intolerable. The movable spans would have been rarely closed. A Hudson River crossing at New York City was not realized until 1931, when George Washington Bridge was completed.

9. A typical truss of one of the river spans in the Cairo bridge was 518 feet 6 inches long, 61 feet deep, and measured 30 feet 5¾ inches from center to center of posts. The spans were 25 feet wide overall. The total weight of a single river span was 2,055,200 pounds.

10. The Atlantic and Great Western was later absorbed by the Erie Railroad, and the Grand Trunk was taken over by the Canadian government to form the nucleus of the Canadian National Railway. The present International Bridge is used jointly by the C. N. R. and the New York Central (Michigan Central District).

11. International Bridge was divided into two parts by an island, the longer portion lying on the western, or Canadian, side. It consisted of seven spans of double-diagonal Warren trusses without posts and with vertical end frames. They were 250 feet long and 23 feet 6 inches deep. The bridge was built for a double-track line but the second track was never laid. The great quantity of ice in the Niagara River required extremely massive reinforced piers with heavy protective armor. The portion of the pier under water consisted of a huge timber crib inside of which were four hollow wrought iron cylinders set on a line transverse to the length of the bridge. The entire volume within the crib but outside the cylinders was filled with broken rock. The cylinders were filled with ashlar blocks. Above the water line the pier was a solid mass of ashlar masonry laid in mortar. The cutwater was a wedge-shaped crib again filled with broken stone and cased in stout planking further protected at the angles by wrought iron plates. The over-all height of the pier was 63 feet. The wrought iron cylinders were 8 feet in diameter. The quantity of material in a single pier indicates its great size: ashlar masonry, 1,865 tons; broken stone, 2,852 tons; timber, 535 tons; wrought iron, 65 tons. Pier construction of this kind is actually rather primitive, though it represented a step in the progress from the original loose heap of rubble masonry supporting piles to the solid and carefully shaped pier of cut stone or concrete built up in a water-tight caisson.

    The longest Warren truss built before the end of the century is the 350-foot span in the Memphis bridge. See pp. 159–60.

12. When the original Grand Central Terminal in New York was built (1869–71), Post trusses were used to carry 44th Street over the station approach tracks (fig. 113). The trusses differed from the standard form in that there were two systems of diagonals in addition to the inclined posts. And to make the structure even more redundant, the heavier diagonals crossed two panels, while the lighter, or counter, diagonals crossed only one. The 44th Street bridge was demolished during construction of the present terminal (1903–13). For a description of the whole Grand Central project, see pp. 210–13.

13. The length of the Omaha bridge was divided as follows: east approach, 2 miles, timber deck-girder trestle; river crossing, 2,750 feet, eleven 250-foot Post-truss spans; west approach, 729 feet, another timber deck-girder trestle. The rails stood 60 feet above mean low water.

14. For the evolution of drum piers like those of the Omaha bridge, see pp. 229–30.

15. The popularity of Post's invention during the 1870's was clearly demonstrated when it was chosen for one of the most heavily traveled bridges in the United States, the Harlem River crossing of the New York and Harlem, the New York Central and Hudson River, and the New York and New Haven railroads (1875). The second bridge at this site, it was built to carry the approach tracks of the recently opened Grand Central Terminal into the Park Avenue cut in New York. The four-span, double-track structure lasted about twenty years before it was replaced by one of steel. The later bridge served the railroads well for sixty years under the enormous traffic load of the great New York terminal, but it eventually had to be replaced by the present lift spans (1954–56).

16. In the Louisville bridge a typical panel of the 400-foot truss, which was 48 feet in over-all depth, measured 56 feet 7¼ inches from center to center of posts and was divided into four sub-panels each 14 feet 2 inches in length. Within the panel there were, in addition to the three vertical members, two full and two half-length diagonals. The top chord, posts, and main diagonals were made up of paired cast iron cylinders whose dimensions varied with the location of the individual member and hence with the compressive stress it carried. Half-diagonals and intermediate verticals were composed of four parallel wrought iron bars, counter-diagonals of eight bars, and bottom chord of sixteen bars, the variation again based on their respective tensile stresses. There was a complete system in both top and bottom frames of sway and wind bracing consisting of laterals and double diagonals. As near as one can tell from the plan and elevation of the truss, Fink used individual pieces of fifteen different cross-sectional sizes, an extravagance which would be intolerable to the contemporary bridge designer. The subdivisions of the panels were introduced to reduce the load of the compressed top chord on the main members by distributing part of it to the intermediate pieces. The design of this truss depended on a thorough knowledge of advanced theory in stress analysis.

    The first truss in the United States with subdivided panels was the spandrel truss of the Pennsylvania Avenue arch bridge over Rock Creek in Washington, D. C. (1858). For a full description of this bridge, see pp. 184–5.

17. For discussion of the bowstring, lenticular, and McCallum trusses, see pp. 98, 113, 125–8, 299.

18. For the Pegram truss, see pp. 137–8.

19. The company which financed and carried out construction of the Cincinnati bridge was a subsidiary of the railroad with the forbidding title of the Covington and Cincinnati Elevated Railroad and Transfer and Bridge Company. Many large railroad bridges were built by separate but subsidiary corporations such as this, and title to the property was often retained by them throughout the life of the structure.

20. William H. Burr was one of the engineers who helped to raise the level of American building technology to the status of exact science. As the author of *Stresses in Bridge and Roof Trusses* and *Elasticity and Resistance of the Materials of Engineering*, he played a valuable role in propagating European theory in the United States.

21. For each track of the C. and O. bridge the live load was established at 119,000 pounds for the engine followed by a uniform train load of 2,500 pounds per lineal foot. The live load for the highway was fixed at 960 pounds per lineal foot for each truss; in addition, the dead load was fixed at 30,000 pounds uniformly distributed over alternate 10-foot lengths. Then, presumably to balance moving loads outside the trusses, a uniform load of 80 pounds per square foot was imposed before and after each of the dead load areas. In spite of all these complications, the resulting truss was a precise and simple design: under the polygonal top chord each panel, subdivided into two parts, contained an intermediate vertical member, a full-length and a half-length diagonal, and—original with this bridge—a half-length horizontal strut in six of the sub-panels. All members of the truss were steel; all those of the sway bracing in top and bottom frames were wrought iron.

22. The masonry of the river piers in the C. and O. bridge was laid up on concrete-filled cribs built up of $12 \times 12$-inch pine timbers to a height of 35 feet, the cribs, in turn, resting upon caissons of similar construction except for their oak cutting edges. The caissons were driven through river sediments and gravel to bearing strata of shale and limestone located at a maximum depth of 54 feet below low water level. For pier construction of Brooklyn Bridge, see pp. 177, 317; of Eads Bridge, pp. 188–9.

23. The C. C. C. and St. L., commonly known as the Big Four, was later leased to and merged with the New York Central Railroad.

24. Untitled editorial on the collapse of the L. and J. bridge, *Engineering News,* vol. 30 (December 28, 1893), p. 515.


IV, 6. THE CANTILEVER BRIDGE

1. The action of a cantilever differs substantially from that of a simple beam or truss, and this must be fully understood for proper design of the truss. Since a cantilever is supported at only one end, it must either be fixed rigidly to its masonry abutment or anchored by a truss extending from the abutment in the opposite direction from the cantilever. Because it is in some way tied or anchored at the pier or abutment, it is subject to maximum bending and shearing stresses at the point of support rather than at the free end. In a simple span maximum bending occurs at the center, midway between supports. As a result of this condition, the distribution of stresses in the top and bottom chords of the cantilever is the reverse of what it is in the simple truss: in the former the top chord is in tension and the bottom in compression. When the cantilever bends downward, its upper surface is convex, which is opposite to the shape assumed by a simple beam or truss under deflection.

Any movable span other than a vertical lift is a cantilever in the open position, a fact recognized by the engineers of iron bridges and embodied in certain details of its design, but of course the span does not carry a load in this position.

2. For a discussion of Pope's work, see pp. 86–7.

3. Wilson introduced the three-hinged arch in the United States for both bridges and trainsheds.

4. The 40th Street bridge was 60 feet wide and 328 feet long overall. Its length was divided into a 189-foot center span, made up of two cantilevers, and two anchor spans each 69 feet 6 inches long. The trusses carried a 40-foot roadway between them and two 10-foot sidewalks set outside them on extensions of the transverse floor beams.

5. The cantilever system of the 40th Street bridge consisted of sets of rigid eye-bar chains of wrought iron radiating downward from near the tops of the towers to the underframing of the deck. For the purpose of maintaining rigid straight lines in the radiating members and the deck a supplementary flexible chain of small eye-bars was hung between the towers and anchored in the abutments. From this chain a set of vertical suspenders, also of eye-bars, dropped down to the pinned joints of the rigid members.

6. For Roebling's projected bridge at Dixville, see p. 316.

7. The proposal to use hinges in a continuous beam or truss was first made by Karl Culmann in his *Graphical Statics* (1866). The introduction of hinges and the resulting transformation of the parts of the beam on either side of the support into cantilevers has the consequence that the action of the member more nearly conforms to the theoretical curve of stress distribution, or stress trajectory, as it is sometimes called. The first large cantilever bridge whose design seems clearly to have been influenced by Culmann's theory was Heinrich Gerber's bridge over the Main River at Hassfurt, Germany (1867). The structure excited wide interest and was very likely known to Bouscaren and Smith.

8. It is interesting to note that although the trusses of the 1911 bridge at Dixville were nearly twice the depth of the original ones and were built of steel, their form closely followed that of the original Whipple truss. It was very likely the last application of Whipple's invention to railroad service.

9. The over-all length of the Michigan Central bridge of nearly 900 feet was divided into two anchor spans of 200 feet each, two 175-foot cantilevers, and one suspended span of 120 feet. Thus the clear span over the river was 470 feet. The base of rail stood 239 feet above the water surface. The cantilever and anchor spans were composed of modified Whipple trusses, while the floating span was a Pratt truss with double diagonals in the center panels. The individual members, however, were very much heavier than those in previous trusses of these types.

10. The Hartford and Connecticut Western is now that line of the New York, New Haven and Hartford Railroad which extends from Danbury, Connecticut, to May-brook, New York.

11. The over-all length of the Poughkeepsie bridge, including approaches, is 6,767 feet, divided as follows into three major parts: the Poughkeepsie approach, four deck-girder and 21 Warren deck-truss spans, 2,640 feet; river crossing, seven deck-truss spans, 3,094 feet; Ulster County approach, nine Warren deck-truss spans and one deck-girder, 1,033 feet. The minimum clear height, between mean high water and the bottom of the deepest truss, is 130 feet, while the total height from foundation to base of rail is 342 feet. The seven trusses of the river crossing are arranged symmetrically about a central pair of cantilevers and a suspended span, the three together having a length of 546 feet. From end to center span on each side there are, in order, an anchor span 201 feet long, a pair of cantilevers and a floating span together 548 feet long, and a connecting simple span 525 feet long and 88 feet deep.

12. The pier foundations rest on bedrock, above which lie 70 feet of alluvial mud and sand and 60 feet of water. The foundation is an immense chambered crib of massive timbers, whose interior spaces are filled with concrete. Above this a stepped pyramid of cast iron carries a grillage of $12 \times 12$-inch timbers, which in turn support the pier.

13. The great advantage of the route via Poughkeepsie bridge is that it bypasses the New York terminal region. Operation of this line requires the participation of as many as six railroad companies: the Baltimore and Ohio, Western Maryland, Reading, Central of New Jersey, Lehigh and New England, and New Haven. The last company is the present owner of the bridge.

    Two years after completion of the Poughkeepsie bridge the Atlantic and Pacific Railroad built its first steel bridge over the Colorado River near Needles, California, 1890 (the railroad later formed the lines of the Santa Fe system in Arizona and California). Designed by J. A. L. Waddell, the author of a widely read treatise on bridge engineering, it was a cantilever structure whose main span reached a new record of 660 feet in length. The total length of 990 feet was divided into two cantilevers each 165 feet long, two anchor spans of the same length, and a floating span 330 feet long. The cantilever trusses differed from their predecessors in their over-all profile: both top and bottom chords were inclined respectively downward and upward, thus giving the cantilever and anchor spans together the shape of a flattened hexagon, like those of the celebrated Firth of Forth bridge in Scotland. This angularity made for an awkward form, with the result that the bridge was most unattractive in general appearance. The piers at the ends of the cantilevers were stone masonry, while those at the very ends of the whole structure were concrete. The Santa Fe replaced the Needles bridge with a continuous series of deck trusses in 1948.

14. The subsidiary corporation was the Kansas City and Memphis Railroad and Bridge Company. The Fort Scott company is now the Kansas City-Memphis line of the St. Louis-San Francisco Railway, commonly known as the Frisco. The Memphis

bridge was built to serve all the railroads entering the city from the west, which at the time of its completion were the following: Kansas City, Ft. Scott and Memphis; Kansas City, Memphis and Birmingham (Frisco); St. Louis, Iron Mountain and Southern (Missouri Pacific); Little Rock and Memphis (Rock Island).

15. The high bluff along the Memphis side of the river fixed the elevation of the deck at 110 feet above mean low water. A wide expanse of low-lying marshy land on the west, subject to inundation during floods, required the long west approach, whose individual spans are 150 feet long. Between this approach and the river's edge there is a 350-foot Warren deck truss. The river crossing is made up of three spans, two at 621 feet each, and a channel span of 791 feet. Between the Memphis pier and the top of the east bank an anchor span of 175 feet balances the east cantilever. The maximum truss depth is 120 feet. The over-all length of trussed spans is 2,597 feet.

16. The Galveston, Harrisburg and San Antonio Railway is now part of the Texas and New Orleans, which comprises most of the lines of the Southern Pacific Railroad between El Paso and New Orleans.

17. The total length of the Pecos River bridge was 2,080 feet, its height to base of rail above mean low water 328 feet. The main span, 217 feet 6 inches long, contained two unequal cantilevers respectively 85 feet and 52 feet 6 inches in length and a floating span of 80 feet. Except for the anchor spans, which were equal to the cantilevers in length, the rest of the bridge was made up of 35-foot girder and 65-foot lattice truss spans.

18. The most common type of cantilever bridge at the end of the century was the movable steel bascule bridge, in which the bottom chord is continued back through a circular toothed segment to engage the rack on which the span rotates. The greatest number of these bridges was built in Chicago, of which the first carried Van Buren Street over the Chicago River (1895). It was replaced in 1956 by a wider and heavier structure.

19. "Architectural Effects in the Construction of Metallic Bridges," *Engineering Record,* 30:9 (July 28, 1894), p. 133.

20. For further discussion of architecture and the new structural techniques, see pp. 265–73.

## Chapter V—THE SUSPENSION BRIDGE

### V, 1. THE PIONEER WORK OF FINLEY AND ELLET

1. James Finley, "A Description of the Patent Chain Bridge," *The Port Folio,* vol. 3 (June 1810), pp. 445–6.

2. A suspension bridge ordinarily consists of a main span between towers flanked by two anchor spans. The cables are anchored in masonry at the end of the anchor span, the latter playing no structural role other than to bridge the portions of the

waterway between shore and tower. The action of a suspension bridge is comparatively simple: the load imparted to the cable by the vertical suspenders subjects it to tension, which is sustained by the anchoring device (usually plates imbedded in masonry). The reaction of the tower meets the vertical component of the cable load, while the two horizontal components, acting in opposite directions, balance each other. Because of the extremely slender proportions of its chief structural members, a large suspension bridge must be carefully designed for aerodynamic stability. A nonrigid structure, it may be subjected to extreme vibrations as the result of sway induced by wind loads.

3. See Kirby, Withington, Darling, and Kilgour, *Engineering in History,* pp. 234–5.

4. Drawings based on Finley's patent drawing suggest that the chains of his suspension bridges were not continuous between anchors but were divided at the saddles between main span and anchor spans. The connection at the saddle was a heavy wrought iron bar slightly curved into a circular segment with an eye at either end. A stout pin was fitted into each eye, and the last link of the chain was made to fit over the projecting portion of the pin. The curved connecting bar appears to have rested directly on a heavy wooden block at the top of the tower framing, but it is possible that this block was cast iron.

5. Ellet was the author of two books, *Physical Geography of the Mississippi Valley* (1849) and *The Mississippi and Ohio Rivers* (1853), which proved to be the only works that survived him intact. In the latter he first proposed the now universally accepted method of controlling floods in major streams by impounding tributary waters in upland storage reservoirs. The method was not adopted in the United States until the Army Engineers built the present system of dams in the upper tributaries of the Ohio River following the floods of 1913.

6. The engineering press at the time attributed the collapse of the Wheeling bridge to the failure of the wrought iron, about which, it is true, there was little reliable knowledge. An eye-witness account of the bridge's behavior during the storm, however, indicates that a major factor in the destruction was the extreme oscillation of the deck resulting initially from the wind load. These oscillations, reflected from the towers, reinforced themselves until they built up to waves of such amplitude that the cables and suspenders could no longer sustain the impact of the plunging deck. In short, the bridge as Ellet designed it lacked sufficient aerodynamic stability. One could hardly blame Ellet, however, since it was precisely this defect that led to the violent destruction of Tacoma Narrows Bridge on November 7, 1940. On the other hand, Roebling seems clearly to have recognized the existence of the problem and known what to do about it. As early as 1846, in connection with preliminary discussion of a Niagara suspension bridge, he pointed out the necessity of opposing vibrations of the deck by means of stiffening trusses and a system of radiating stays extending outward and downward from the tops of the towers to the transverse beams under the deck. In his own words, "To counteract the pliability of a cable, stays must be applied, by which a number of points,

which must necessarily correspond with the knots of vibration, are rendered stationary, and so that the stays and cables act in concert in supporting the bridge." (Quoted in David B. Steinman and Sara Ruth Watson, *Bridges and Their Builders,* New York, G. P. Putnam's Sons, 1941, p. 218.) For Roebling's Niagara bridge, see pp. 174–5.

## V, 2. FROM THE ROEBLINGS TO THE END OF THE CENTURY

1. The span length of the Allegheny aqueduct was 162 feet. The cable, 7 inches in diameter, contained 1,900 wrought iron wires of ⅛-inch diameter. The flume was trapezoidal in cross section, with an upper width of 16 feet 6 inches, a lower of 14 feet, and a depth of 8 feet 6 inches. Filled to capacity, its total water load was 4,600 tons, or a unit load of slightly over 4 tons per lineal foot.

2. The wooden aqueduct in the United States had a fifty-year history behind it before Roebling built the Allegheny span. The first one was built for the Middlesex Canal in eastern Massachusetts (1794–1803). This waterway enjoyed a prosperous existence until 1846, when it was killed by the competition of the Boston and Lowell Railroad. The aqueduct was originally a heavily-braced flume of thick wooden planking, but around 1800 trusses were introduced into the floor and side walls to carry the water load. Span length, of course, was severly limited. In some cases the flume was suspended from the bottom chords of the trusses. One such aqueduct, at Metamora, Indiana, has been completely restored. Its chief supporting members are arch-reinforced Howe trusses protected by a gable roof.

3. While engaged on his bridge and aqueduct projects of the 'forties, Roebling developed the method of manufacturing wire rope which became the basis of the modern industry. Demand for it led him to establish his own business in 1849 at Trenton, New Jersey, close to Peter Cooper's Trenton Iron Works. The John A. Roebling's Sons Corporation, as it is now known, remains a flourishing enterprise. For the present Smithfield Street bridge, see p. 127.

4. Quoted in David B. Steinman and Sara Ruth Watson, *Bridges and Their Builders* (New York, G. P. Putnam's Sons, 1941), p. 220.

5. While the Niagara span was under construction Roebling was associated with an abortive project in Kentucky. In 1853 the directors of the Lexington and Southern Kentucy Railroad commissioned him to build a suspension bridge over the Kentucky River at Dixville, the site of Smith and Bouscaren's cantilever bridge. The masonry footings were completed in 1854, when the railroad ran out of funds and abandoned the project. Part of the right-of-way was acquired by the Cincinnati Southern, along with the tower footings, which the two engineers used twenty-two years later for the abutments of their own bridge.

   On the question of rail traffic on suspension bridges, electric rapid transit cars can be carried satisfactorily on the larger structures, as they are on the Delaware River bridge at Philadelphia and were until April 1958 on San Francisco Bay bridge.

6. The fame of the wire-cable suspension bridge reached the Pacific coast scarcely after the wooden truss arrived. In 1862 the engineers of the Auburn-Coloma Road built a suspension bridge over the American River in Placer County, California. Although the bridge had a main span of only 258 feet, its careful builders suspended the deck from cables with a diameter of 11¾ inches. The wrapping wire was coated with tar, a protective measure that seems to have been used on this bridge for the first time. The material of the rest of the structure was wood. It stood for about 65 years, and when investigated in 1925 was still in sound condition.

A second Niagara River suspension bridge, for highway traffic only, was completed in 1868. The span was about 800 feet, but it was naturally a much lighter bridge than Roebling's, which stood close by downstream. As originally built, the towers and trusses were wood, but this was replaced by iron in 1887–88. Even with the heavier material, however, the bridge was too light under high wind load: a storm broke the deck stays of the span in January 1889 and dropped it into the river. The structure was rebuilt in three months during the same year, but was eventually demolished and never replaced.

7. For the European background of construction in a pneumatic caisson and its initial use in the United States on Eads Bridge, see pp. 188–9.

8. The Brooklyn caisson was a great hollow chamber 102 × 168 feet in plan, its side walls built up of 12 × 12-inch yellow pine timbers. The base area was divided by 24-inch partitions into six working compartments each about 50 feet square. The working chamber was 9 feet 6 inches high and was covered by a solid timber roof 15 feet thick. Below the working floor the side walls were tapered to an iron-shod cutting edge to penetrate the mud, sand, and clay of the river bed. The joints of the timber walls were calked with oakum and the inside surfaces were lined with pitch. The New York caisson was identical in construction with the Brooklyn, but was 4 feet longer and had a roof 22 feet thick. Cylindrical wrought iron shafts were introduced into the working chambers for the passage of men and supplies and the removal of excavated material. In addition there were a number of small pipes for gas, water, compressed air, and for blowing out sand by means of the high pressure within the caisson (the "sand pump" invented by James B. Eads). Maximum working pressure in the caissons was 23 pounds per square inch above atmosphere, or a total of about 38 pounds. Illumination in the working chambers was provided by calcium lights, gas burners, and candles.

9. The length of the main span of Brooklyn Bridge between towers is 1,595 feet 6 inches, the anchor spans 930 feet each, the roadway 85 feet in over-all width. The towers stand 271 feet 6 inches above mean high water, with the cable saddles at 266 feet. Set within the grooved cableways are wrought iron rollers which materially reduced lateral stresses in the towers induced by moving and unbalanced loads. (These rollers, however, long ago froze with rust and no longer function.) Immediately below the saddles are the wrought iron eye-bars which hold the radiating stays (26 on each side of the tower) that are attached to the girders below

the deck at 15-foot intervals for a distance of 390 feet out from the towers. The suspenders are set 16 feet center to center. The cast iron anchor plates, curved into an elliptical surface, weigh 23 tons each and measure $16 \times 17$ feet 6 inches in over-all profile. The 19 strands of a single cable are fastened to wrought iron eye-bars, in turn fixed to the anchor plates. Each of the four cables is 15¾ inches in diameter and contains 5,434 galvanized steel, oil-coated wires of ⅙ inch diameter and 160,000 pounds per square inch tensile strength. The cables take nearly all the load, the remainder falling on the radiating stays, which function partly to aid the stiffening trusses in opposing deflection of the deck near the towers as a result of moving loads and partly to counteract oscillations of the deck produced by wind loads. They are thus important in providing the bridge with aerodynamic stability, a necessity which Roebling clearly understood in connection with his reconstruction of the Wheeling bridge. Since the wires of the Brooklyn cables were spun straight and bound close, they are subject only to tension, without torsional or shearing stresses. Splice joints in the wires were coated with molten zinc. The cables can sustain a dead and live load of 37,000 tons without permanent deformation.

10. In Schuyler's *American Architecture* (New York, 1891), pp. 68–85.

11. Montgomery Schuyler, "The Brooklyn Bridge as a Monument," in Lewis Mumford, ed., *The Roots of Contemporary American Architecture* (New York, Reinhold, 1952), pp. 161, 167–8.

12. Lewis Mumford, *The Brown Decades* (New York, Harcourt, Brace, 1931), pp. 104–6.

13. The rigid suspension bridge found little favor in the United States, although it was once used in the post-Roebling period. Edward Hemberle adopted it for his design of the Point Bridge over the Monongahela River at Pittsburgh (1876–79). In this unique structure the suspension member consisted of a pair of shallow wrought iron Howe trusses joined to the towers and to each other in the form of an inverted three-hinged arch. The bottom chord was a stiff eye-bar chain of parabolic form, while the top chord was made up of two continuous rigid beams joined at the hinge. The clear span between the towers was 800 feet. The towers were hollow wrought iron posts resting on masonry footings. The Point Bridge never performed satisfactorily, and in 1903 it showed such clear signs of failure that it had to be extensively rebuilt. Its architectural treatment was worse than its engineering: an offensive mixture of Gothic revivalism and the then fashionable cult of personal idiosyncrasy sometimes known as the cult of ugliness.

Suspension bridges with flexible chains of wrought iron eye-bars survived until the last decade of the century. Two late structures were Gustav Lindenthal's 7th Street bridge over the Allegheny River at Pittsburgh (1884) and Carl Gayler's Grand Avenue bridge over the Terminal Railroad Association line at St. Louis (1890).

The success of the long-span bridges at Cincinnati and New York led to the first proposal for bridging the Detroit River by a suspension bridge between Detroit and Windsor, Ontario. It was submitted *c.* 1890 by Gustav Lindenthal, who made a preliminary design for a bridge with a main span of 1,095 feet, anchor spans of 787 feet each, and an over-all tower height of 395 feet. The bowed deck was to provide the standard 135-foot clearance above water level, a figure fixed by the U. S. Army Engineers and later prescribed for every bridge over a navigable waterway. The Detroit River project was not realized until 1929, when the present Ambassador Bridge was completed. As a matter of fact, the Detroit River, like the Hudson at New York, was crossed by a tunnel before it was spanned by a bridge. Lindenthal estimated the cost of his Detroit project at $6,500,000 exclusive of land, a figure whose magnitude effectively discouraged the building of many long-span suspension bridges. The total cost of Brooklyn Bridge came to $9,000,000 for construction and $7,000,000 for land, and to raise this enormous sum required heroic efforts on the part of even the New York financiers. The big railroad companies at the time were in the best position to afford them, but the experience with Roebling's Niagara span made the builders realize that the form was radically unsuited to the traffic loads that were the rule around 1890.

14. The channel span of the Rochester bridge is 800 feet long and its anchor spans respectively 400 and 416 feet. The stiffening trusses have a uniform depth of 18 feet throughout most of their length, but they expand abruptly near the towers to a depth of 28 feet. They are steel Howe trusses whose individual pieces are thin bars of T-section.

15. The stiffening trusses of the East Liverpool bridge are double-diagonal Warren trusses of uniform depth throughout the length of the bridge. There is lateral bracing between the trusses at both top and bottom chord. The main span of the East Liverpool bridge is 705 feet long, the anchor spans respectively 360 and 420 feet. The roadway is 22 feet wide, but the cable saddles are set 30 feet on centers, thus giving the cable a curvature in both the vertical and horizontal planes.

The last suspension bridge to be started in the nineteenth century was the second East River crossing at New York, Williamsburg Bridge (1897–1903), designed by Leffert L. Buck. With a span length of 1,600 feet, it attained a new record, but in the general character of its design it looked back to an age that had all but passed. The Williamsburg span is extremely overbuilt, a feature clearly exhibited by its heavy and awkward form and by the 40-foot depth of its lattice stiffening trusses. The truss depth is thus $\frac{1}{40}$ of the span length, the highest depth-span ratio ever used. Each of the four cables of Williamsburg Bridge is 18⅝ inches in diameter and composed of ungalvanized steel wires. The steel towers, bents of steel posts and open trusswork, stand 335 feet above mean high water, and the clear height of the deck is 117 feet above high water. Construction of the big and ungainly bridge was interrupted by a lurid fire that occurred on the night of November 10, 1902. Fed by paint, oil, and lumber at the west end of the bridge, it turned the Matnhattan tower into an enormous torch.

## Chapter VI—THE IRON ARCH BRIDGE

1. Theodore Cooper, "American Railroad Bridges," *Transactions of the American Society of Civil Engineers,* vol. 21, p. 14.

2. Quoted in Cooper, op. cit., p. 14.

3. The Brownsville arch, which spanned 80 feet clear between abutments, was made up of five parallel tubular ribs, each cast in nine segments bolted together through flanges at their ends. The 45 segments were identical in their curvature and in their length of 14 feet. The level deck was supported on radiating cast iron posts, on the English precedent, and both posts and ribs were tied together by transverse bars.

4. D. M. Strickland, "Pure Iron in Early American Bridge," *Engineering News-Record,* 87:20 (November 17, 1921), p. 819.

5. The arches of the Pennsylvania Avenue bridge were unusually flat, with a rise of 20 feet for the span of 200. The inside diameter of the arched mains was 4 feet, and they were built up of plates 1½ inches thick. Since the tubular form represents the most efficient distribution of material in a structural member, the arches of the bridge were nicely adapted to both of their functions. Tubular arches are the primary structural members of Eads Bridge. See pp. 189, 321.

   The roadway above the mains had an over-all width of 28 feet. The load of the deck was carried to the mains by a pair of wrought iron spandrel trusses consisting of posts set on radial lines, double diagonals, and half-length radial members extending from the intersection of the diagonals to the transverse beams under the deck. The joints of the truss appear to have been cast iron discs to which the wrought iron pieces, all of I-section, were in some way fastened, probably by being fitted into slots cut in the castings. The half-length posts made the spandrel system a truss with subdivided panels, the first of its kind in the United States. The shorter posts acted to carry the deck load between main posts to the intersection of the diagonals. Trusses with subdivided panels became common in the long-span railroad bridges. See pp. 146–51.

6. The structural system of the Pennsylvania Avenue bridge was tested for a uniform deck load of 125 pounds per square foot of roadway, which, together with the water load, produced a unit compressive stress in the mains of 4,000 pounds per square inch of cross-sectional area of metal. In addition, there was a tensile stress in the cast iron induced by a water pressure of 300 pounds per square inch.

7. A cast iron bridge of much greater total length than the Pennsylvania Avenue span was built to carry Chestnut Street across the Schuylkill River in Philadelphia (1861–66). The bridge was 400 feet long between abutments and was divided into two rather flat segmental arches of 185-foot span. The arch structure was made up of six parallel ribs, each cast in a number of separate segments. It was described as the largest wholly cast iron bridge in the United States at the time. Since all structural members in such a bridge are theoretically subject only to compression, it was possible to use the cast metal throughout. The bridge was built without falsework because of the river traffic, the individual segments having been placed in position from barges. (The method of cantilevering arches out from the piers was to come with the construction of Eads Bridge at St. Louis.) The Chestnut

Street span marked a considerable advance over previous iron arches in the United States. The deck of the bridge was carried by closely ranked cast iron posts, all set vertically, a system which made it essentially similar to the steel arch at the end of the century.

8. On the South Pass jetties, see p. 228.

9. Quoted in Steinman and Watson, *Bridges and their Builders,* p. 175.

10. For the initial uses of steel in other kinds of structures, see pp. 46, 52–5, 143–4, 177–80. For its physical properties, see pp. 286–7.

    The original iron and steel contractor for Eads Bridge was the Keystone Bridge Company, whose president, ironically enough, was Jacob H. Linville and its vice-president Andrew Carnegie. During construction Carnegie founded the Carnegie-Kloman Company, which became the iron subcontractor.

11. Each arch of Eads Bridge consists of eight tubes, four in parallel on each of the two levels, which are separated by a vertical distance of 12 feet. The two groups of four are laced together by diagonal bracing in the pattern of the Warren truss in both vertical and transverse planes. The individual tube, which is 18 inches in outside diameter, is built up of lengths of six 12-foot cylindrical segments bound together like the staves of a barrel. There are 6,000 such staves in the 24 arch tubes that constitute the primary structure. The individual pieces were rolled and machined from the chromium-steel alloy that Eads finally insisted upon after the original cast steel failed in the testing machines. The alloy tested to an elastic limit of 50,000 pounds per square inch and an ultimate strength of 120,000 pounds per square inch. Under maximum theoretical load Eads and Chauvenet calculated the compressive stress in the arch tube at 27,500 pounds per square inch. The wrought iron couplings with which the tubes are fitted tested to a tensile strength of 40,000 pounds per square inch.

12. The chief figure in the development of adequate methods of stress analysis for fixed and two-hinged arches was Jacques Antoine Bresse, the first edition of whose *Applied Mechanics* was published in Paris in 1859.

13. "Pennsylvania Railroad Bridge over Thirtieth Street, Philadelphia," *Engineering,* vol. 10 (July 22, 1870), p. 69.

14. The span of the arch over 30th Street was 64 feet 1 inch, the width 110 feet, giving a spacing of the ribs of 10 feet center to center. The rise from spring line to crown was 11 feet 11¾ inches. The bridge was designed for a total load per lineal foot of each rib, projected on a horizontal plane, of 2,000 pounds, divided between a dead load of 500 pounds and a live load of 1,500.

15. The Forbes Street bridge was 250 feet in total length and 40 feet in over-all width. The center span was a 150-foot arch made up of three parallel arched trusses with diagonal bracing only, as in the Warren truss. Beyond the masonry skewbacks toward the ends, the deck was carried by wrought iron bents and by inverted bow-

string deck trusses with a span of about 40 feet. The deck rested on wrought iron spandrel posts which were braced in the transverse plane, as were the arched trusses.

16. Fixed arch girders or ribs in the form of a long arcade appeared in the first, and abortive, New York subway. The initial project for a railway line under the street was proposed by the Arcade Railway Company in 1869. Its directors planned to construct a subway several blocks long under lower Broadway but were unable to find backers to finance construction. A second organization, founded by the inventor Alfred Ely Beach, had better luck and was able to open a line for a distance of 296 feet under Broadway from Warren to Murray Street on February 26, 1870. The track of the subway was laid on the floor of a tunnel driven by Beach's patented tunnel shield. Such construction is possible only on lower Manhattan, where the depth of alluvial gravel and sediments overlying the rock is sufficient to allow the usual method of tunnel driving. The vaulted roof of Beach's subway was carried on three parallel rows of cast iron columns connected by transverse and longitudinal wrought iron arch girders. Shorter transverse girders spanned the platforms between the outer columns and the vertical brick walls of the tunnel. Infilling, or webbing, of the vault between girders was also brick. The Broadway subway, which lasted only a few years, was the only one built until the present system was begun in 1900. The structural system of the original company was in part the precedent for the later method of construction in New York: roofed cuts in which street and overburden are carried on a closely ranked array of steel columns and shallow arches or beams. New York subways can seldom be built by mining, the conventional method of tunnel construction, because of the dense igneous rock that makes up most of Manhattan Island.

17. A large proportion of bridges of three-hinged arch construction in the East was built by the Baltimore Bridge Company, which grew out of the partnership of Charles and Benjamin Latrobe (grandsons of the architect) and C. Shaler Smith. The bridges of this company regularly attracted favorable attention in the engineering press for their "structural beauty." The best of them, perhaps, and most typical of the roadway bridge of intermediate span, was the three-hinged wrought iron arch in Baltimore known as Jones Falls Bridge (1890–91). The main span, 150 feet in length, consisted of three parallel ribs set 12 feet center to center and carrying the usual spandrel posts with transverse diagonal bracing. The roadway was flanked on either side by a sidewalk carried on brackets cantilevered out from the posts.

18. The span of the approach arches in Panther Hollow Bridge is 28 feet. The main arch ribs are set 12 feet 6 inches on centers and span 360 feet with a rise of 45 feet. At the crown the arch stands about 120 feet above the stream at the bottom of the ravine. The steel spandrel posts are braced in the vertical longitudinal plane with single diagonals and transversely with lateral and diagonal members. The posts carry a 40-foot roadway and two 10-foot sidewalks on cantilevers extending outward from the posts. The arch ribs are braced on the transverse line by double diagonals set between the ribs.

19. For Clarke's project, see pp. 248, 340.

20. In 1897 the Grand Trunk Railway completed the double-deck rail and highway span over the Niagara River at the Falls which took the place of Roebling's suspension bridge. The arch is built up of fixed steel girders 550 feet in clear span. The bridge is used today for highway traffic and the trains of the Canadian National Railway.

21. The rise of the arch in Buck's Niagara bridge was 137 feet and the truss depth 26 feet at the crown, a depth which was uniform throughout most of the length but was contracted sharply to a point at the hinges. The approaches beyond the ends of the arch rested on inverted bowstring deck trusses of parabolic form, one at each end, with a span of 214 feet. The total length of the bridge was 1,268 feet between abutments of the bowstring trusses. Its 49-foot roadway stood 170 feet above the surface of the water.

## Chapter VII—THE RAILWAY TRAINSHED

### VII, 1. THE ORIGINAL FORM OF THE RAILWAY STATION

1. The Boston and Lowell Railroad was one of the many companies later merged to form the Boston and Maine system.

2. The Boston and Worcester Railroad became the eastern end of the Boston and Albany, now merged with the New York Central.

3. The freight station and warehouse of the Boston and Providence Railroad (later part of the New Haven system) at Providence, Rhode Island (1849), was probably the largest enclosed gable shed before the mid-century, measuring 80 × 300 feet in plan. The side walls were long brick arcades between which the two tracks passed by means of 70-foot arched openings in the end walls. The roof was supported on 24 parallel queen-post trusses in the form of a shallow trapezoid with two posts. They were made up of heavy timbers except for a pair of wrought iron diagonal rods between the posts.

4. The Cleveland, Painesville and Ashtabula was merged in 1869 with a number of other railroads to form the Lake Shore and Michigan Southern, which was eventually acquired by the New York Central. The Cincinnati, Columbus and Cleveland became a part of the Cleveland, Cincinnati, Chicago and St. Louis, commonly known as the Big Four Route, subsequently leased to the New York Central.

5. Though not a station, the railroad engine house, or roundhouse, was a special form that involved peculiar framing problems. The common form of the roundhouse throughout much of the nineteenth century was a circular wall surmounted by a conical or pyramidal roof framed either with radial trusses or beams. The forerunner of all them appears to have been the octagonal engine house of the Boston and Albany Railroad at Worcester, Massachusetts (1847). The building probably had a

pyramidal roof. The turn table as well as the engine stalls were thus under the roof, and there was usually only a single door for the engine house lead. The exception to the common type was the original Michigan Central roundhouse at Detroit (1858). It was a circular building with masonry walls surmounted by a hemispherical dome which rested on a radial system of wooden trusses. Timber truss construction remained throughout the life of the steam engine roundhouse because of the corrosive action of locomotive smoke on iron members. The enclosed circular structure, however, proved to be awkward for the movement of engines in and out of the stalls, and as a consequence, some time before the end of the century, the familiar ring surrounding an outdoor turn table was substituted for the original form. The roundhouse is nearly a thing of the past, since the diesel engine has almost universally replaced steam power on American railroads. An enclosed roundhouse with a 16-sided double pyramidal roof still survives (1959) on the Baltimore and Ohio Railroad at Martinsburg, West Virginia. The roundhouse was built in 1866 to replace an earlier structure destroyed by Confederate troops during the Civil War.

6. The Great Western became the middle portion of the Erie Railroad, the lines in Ohio, Pennsylvania, and western New York. A good part of the earlier company was built with British capital.

## VII, 2. THE SEPARATE GABLE SHED

1. The Old Colony Railroad later became a part of the New York, New Haven and Hartford system.

2. For a description of South Station, see pp. 221–2.

3. The practice of parking idle cars was standard in terminals up to the last quarter of the century. By that time the volume of rolling stock had grown to such a point that the separate coach yard with its service facilities had to be built as an adjunct to the terminal station.

4. By the time the last La Salle Street Station was completed, the Northern Indiana Railroad had been absorbed into the Lake Shore and Michigan Southern. The Chicago and Rock Island was the predecessor of the present Chicago, Rock Island and Pacific. For the 1903 station, see pp. 330–31.

5. The Potomac company later became the Baltimore-Washington line of the Pennsylvania Railroad.

6. For Wilson's Philadelphia stations, see pp. 215–17, 329.
   Similar to the Washington shed was that of the Union Station at Worcester, Massachusetts (1875–77). At the time of its construction the Worcester station served the Boston and Albany, Boston and Maine, Fitchburg, New York and New England, and New York, New Haven and Hartford railroads. The Fitchburg was later absorbed by the Boston and Maine, and the New York and New England by the New Haven. The shed at Worcester, 450 feet long and spanning six tracks, was carried on wrought iron trusses with arched bottom chords, the ends of which rested

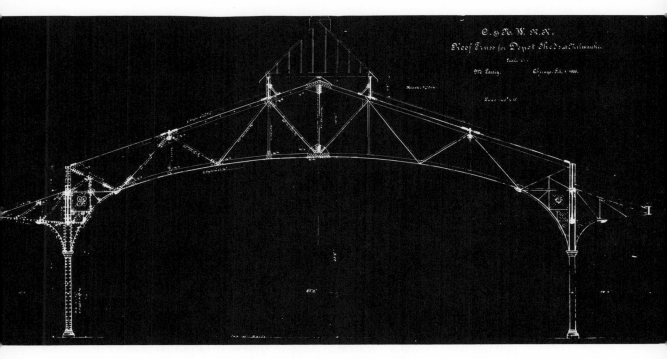

139    Station of the Chicago and North Western Railway, Milwaukee, Wisconsin, 1889. Cross section of the trainshed.

on massive stone walls. The tracks passed through huge segmental arches in the end walls of the shed enclosure. The whole structure, designed by Ware and Van Brunt, was a particularly fine example of the Romanesque station with a high slender tower.

7. Chicago Union Station was built by the Pittsburgh, Fort Wayne and Chicago Railroad but served in addition the Pittsburgh, Cincinnati, Chicago and St. Louis; the Chicago and Alton; the Chicago, Burlington and Quincy; and the Chicago, Milwaukee and St. Paul. The Fort Wayne and the P. C. C. and St. L. were later leased to the Pennsylvania Railroad, which is still the proprietary company of the present Chicago Union Station (1916–25). Trains of the Milwaukee railroad entered the station from the north; the other companies used the south approach.

8. The Chicago and North Western station in Milwaukee (1889), which stands in use today unchanged from its original design, has a gable shed supported on Warren rather than Pratt trusses (fig. 139). Four longitudinal trusses, or purlins, span the length of the shed to provide wind bracing. The over-all dimensions in plan are 75 × 440 feet.

For the Bush trainshed, see p. 222.

9. In the St. Paul shed the central gable, which spanned 165 feet 10 inches, rested on trusses extending across the two cantilevered sheds as well as the central roof and set 33 feet 6 inches on centers. The trusses were 6 feet deep at the ends and 23 feet at the center and had polygonal bottom chords which were raised at the center 10 feet above the ends. Top chord, posts, counter-diagonals, eye-bars, and pins were steel, the rest of the members wrought iron. A curtain wall of wooden planking at the open end of the shed matched in its profile that of the trusses and gable.

10. The successive union stations at St. Paul have always provided terminal facilities for all the railroads entering the city. At present these are the Burlington, Chicago Great Western, Great Northern, Milwaukee Road, Minneapolis and St. Louis, North Western (through a subsidiary, the Chicago, St. Paul, Minneapolis and Omaha), Northern Pacific, Rock Island, and Soo Line (Minneapolis, St. Paul and Sault Ste. Marie).

11. Dearborn Station was built by the Chicago and Western Indiana Railroad, a terminal company organized and owned by the railroads which use the station. At the time of its construction these were the following: Chicago and Atlantic (Erie); Chicago and Eastern Illinois; Grand Trunk Junction (Grand Trunk Western); Louisville, New Albany and Chicago (Monon); Wabash, St. Louis and Pacific (Wabash). In 1887 the Chicago, Santa Fe and California (Atchison, Topeka and Santa Fe) became a tenant. For a short time the Chesapeake and Ohio used Dearborn Station but later moved to Central Station. In spite of the unusual number of different railroads using it, traffic at Dearborn Station amounts to only 58 trains a day at present (1959).

12. The roof of Central Station at Chicago was a high, steep gable with a length of 610 feet and an over-all width of 180 feet, including the cantilevered extensions at the sides. The central gable spanned 108 feet and covered six tracks, while the side extensions each spanned 36 feet over two tracks. The roof formed a continuous cover over the side extensions and the main gable, and the cantilevered trusses formed an integral part of the arched members. For the first Illinois Central station at Chicago, see p. 327; for the three-hinged arch, pp. 190–91, 214–19.

13. Carroll L. V. Meeks, *The Railroad Station, an Architectural History* (New Haven, Yale University Press, 1956), p. 108.

14. The tenant companies of Central Station were originally the Big Four, Chesapeake and Ohio, and Michigan Central. The C. and O., however, later abandoned passenger service on the Chicago-Cincinnati line, and in January 1957 the New York Central transferred the trains of its Michigan Central District to La Salle Street Station.

15. The shed of North Station, which covered nearly four acres, was 491 feet 8 inches long and spanned 339 feet 1½ inches at its open end and 352 feet 3⅛ inches at the concourse. Under it there were 10 platforms and 23 tracks. The station building was equally generous in size, having a frontage on Causeway Street of 680 feet. The

vast trainshed was divided by intermediate lines of steel columns into nine parallel gables carried on light triangular trusses of steel. The span of the individual gables varied considerably: there were six at 39 feet 10½ inches, and one each at 23 feet 8½ inches, 32 feet 9½ inches, and 41 feet 7½ inches.

16. The curtain wall of North Station was fixed to a framework of light hangers suspended from the bottom chord of a series of Warren trusses. The columns were set 32 feet on centers and were connected by shallow Warren trusses of uniform depth running longitudinally through the length of the shed. The monitors were carried on a framework of light steel angles in the form of trusses with semicircular bottom chords. The unusual feature of the monitors was that the tops rather than the sides were glass. The steel members and iron roofing, which totaled 3,200,000 pounds in weight, were manufactured and erected by the Pennsylvania Steel Company.

## VII, 3. THE BALLOON SHED

1. The railroad company became a part of the Pennsylvania in 1881.

2. The presence of a single platform for so many tracks resulted from the early use of the station tracks as a coach yard, which was later separated from them.

3. The shed of the Illinois Central's Great Central Station in Chicago (1855–56) reached a new record in size but managed to hold it for only ten years. The station, designed by the German-born architect Otto Matz, stood at the lake shore on South Water Street. Its approach tracks rested on a pile-and-beam trestle over the water at some distance from the shore line along Michigan Avenue (now the site of Grant Park). The trainshed, enclosed in massive walls of irregular limestone masonry, was 504 feet long and spanned eight tracks with its width of 166 feet 6 inches. The arched Howe trusses of wood rose 36 feet above their spring line, their ends resting on 25-foot sidewalls. Horizontal wrought iron rods between the ends of the arches, suspended from central hangers, acted as ties. The end wall of the shed contained three openings under semicircular arches through which the trains entered and departed. Great Central Station burned in the fire of 1871. Rebuilt as a temporary structure of wood in 1872, it burned again in 1874. Another makeshift, which was little more than a set of platforms between blackened walls, served until the present Central Station was constructed (1892–93). In the words of a contemporary history, "The directors were satisfied with its ruins for depot purposes up to 1891." (*Industrial Chicago*, Chicago, Goodspeed Publishing Co., 1891, vol. I, p. 97.)

4. The 18 wooden-arched Howe trusses, set 20 feet center to center, rest on the 16-inch side walls at a height of 25 feet. The horizontal thrust of the arch is taken by a 1¼-inch wrought iron tie rod suspended from five ½-inch wrought iron hangers. A monitor skylight 12 feet wide runs the length of the shed at the center line.

5. The roof of the Grand Central shed embraced 60,000 square feet of glass and 90,000 square feet of corrugated iron, but in spite of this great area, the total quantity of structural iron was relatively small, 350 tons of cast and 1,350 tons of wrought iron.

There was no special provision for wind bracing in the huge shed, but the construction of the arches in the curtain wall may have offered some protection in this respect.

6. The next balloon shed to follow the model of Barlow's St. Pancras Station was that of Park Square Station, Boston, of the Boston and Providence Railroad (1872–74), one of the many companies later merged to form the New Haven system. The shed was 600 feet long and spanned five tracks and three platforms with its 125-foot width. The roof was constructed of wooden sheathing covered with tarred roofing paper and rested on a system of wooden joists and 21 wrought iron arched Howe trusses which came to a blunt point at the crown, in the form of a flattened Gothic arch. The spring line of the bottom chord was at the platform level, but the top chord ended at the top of the brick side walls. The walls, however, were little more than rows of brick piers, each bay being opened into a pair of large arched windows. The open end of the shed was partly covered by a masonry wall above a wide arch through which the trains passed. The upper part of the archway was screened by a glass curtain set in an iron frame. Construction of the Park Square shed was in general less advanced than that of Grand Central Terminal, but the later structure was better illuminated because of the extensive openings in the side and end walls. The Park Square terminal was demolished on completion of South Station in 1899. See pp. 221–2.

7. The sheds of Broad Street Station could easily have been supported on the arch ribs. The web members of the truss functioned chiefly as wind bracing, while the cambered bottom chord acted as a tie to take the horizontal thrust at the ends of the arch. A similar construction and form characterized the shed of the Pittsburgh, Cincinnati, Chicago and St. Louis station at Cincinnati (1882), with the difference that the arch ribs were built up of tin-covered wooden members. Trusses of this kind actually belong to the simpler and less advanced structural system of the gable shed. The prototype of the shed on pointed-arch ribs was probably that of the station at Middlesbrough, England (1875–77), in which the rib stood by itself without any associated trusswork. The P. C. C. and St. L. station was demolished shortly after completion of the present Cincinnati Union Terminal (1929–33).

8. The over-all dimensions of the Jersey City shed, which spanned 12 tracks, were 256 × 652 feet 6 inches. The clear height at the center line was 86 feet, and the total height to the top of the monitor 110 feet. The glass-and-iron roof rested on 24 wrought iron arched Howe trusses which were tied at the lower hinges by an I-beam set one foot below the base of rail in a continuous wooden box filled with gravel and pitch. At the end of the shed there was a glass curtain wall in an iron frame the bottom of which was held rigid by a horizontal wind truss. Further wind bracing was provided by longitudinal trusses running the length of the shed.

9. The Chicago-St. Paul connection was never completed, and the bulk of the traffic during the early history of Grand Central came from the two tenant companies, the Wisconsin Central and the Chicago, St. Paul and Kansas City (later Chicago

Great Western Railroad). The properties of the Chicago and Northern Pacific Railway were eventually acquired by the Baltimore and Ohio Chicago Terminal, which is now the proprietary company. The present tenants are the Wisconsin Central (part of the Soo Line) and the Chesapeake and Ohio.

10. The roof of Grand Central Station, made of galvanized corrugated sheet steel, is 560 feet long by 119 feet wide and rests on 15 arched trusses. There are six tracks under the main vault of the shed and an additional one on each side sheltered by a cantilevered overhang extending outward 11 feet 9 inches beyond the springing points of the arches. Foundation work of the trainshed is unusual in several respects. The abutments of the arches are of coursed stone set at an angle to the vertical so that the axis of the footing block is in line with the thrust of the inner chord of the arch. The load of the arch is in part carried to the footing by an additional compression member which extends along the inner arc to a point 8 feet above the springing. The tracks of the station are set on concrete foundation walls carried on footings of broken stone.

11. The tin-covered wooden roof of the Reading shed spans 259 feet over 13 tracks, extends 506 feet in length, and rises to 88 feet at the crown. A center skylight in a monitor and four flanking skylights run the length of the shed. The roof, a somewhat flattened segmental vault, rests on three-hinged arched trusses of wrought iron which are grouped in pairs, each pair being laced together by light diagonal members. At the rear, or open, end of the shed there is an armature of iron hangers and horizontal bars which originally functioned as the support for a glass curtain as well as wind bracing. The glass was subsequently removed, leaving the open framework of iron. A similar glass curtain still remains at the station end of the shed.

12. The span between hinges of the Broad Street shed was 300 feet 8 inches, its over-all length 598 feet, and the height above track level of the center hinge 108 feet 6 inches. The plank roof rested on 10 pairs of three-hinged wrought iron arched trusses, the members of each pair spaced 9 feet on centers. The spacing of the paired trusses ranged from a minimum of 56 feet 4 inches to a maximum of 67 feet 1 inch. The truss depth varied from 7 feet 1¾ inches at the center pin to 16 feet 1⅞ inches, measured radially, at the knee. A curious feature of the truss was that the bottom chord was a succession of segments, laid out in a continuous curve, with seven different radii. Maximum allowable stresses in the individual members of the truss were 20,000 pounds per square inch in tension and 27,000 pounds in compression. The arches were tied between the lower hinges by steel beams set below the track level of the station. (For the buildings of the Chicago World's Fair, see pp. 218–19, 330.)

13. Joseph M. Wilson, "The Philadelphia and Reading Railroad Terminal and Station in Philadelphia," *Transactions of the American Society of Civil Engineers*, vol. 34 (1895), pp. 135–6.

14. Walter G. Berg, *Buildings and Structures of American Railroads*, (New York, John Wiley and Sons, 1893), p. 356.

15. The first building to embody the main structural features of the trainshed was the Armory of the Seventh Regiment, Park Avenue at 66th Street, New York (1877–80). The roof of the drill hall rested on 24 three-hinged wrought iron arched trusses spaced 12 feet on centers and spanning 187 feet 4 inches overall.

16. Machinery Hall measured 390 × 741 feet in plan. The three vaults were each carried on a series of 14 semicircular three-hinged arched trusses with a span of 121 feet 10 inches. Since the bottom hinges stood nearly 35 feet above the floor level, the maximum clear height inside was 94 feet 2 inches. The arches were of uniform depth throughout, 6 feet 8 inches.

17. The central roof of the Manufactures Building was glass set in a steel framework. Its over-all dimensions in plan were 385 × 1400 feet. It was framed like a hipped roof with curving intersections, the main structural elements being 18 arched trusses with a span between hinges of 368 feet and a clear height to the center hinge of 200 feet 4 inches. Longitudinal wind trusses with parallel chords extended between the trusses.

18. Two balloon sheds built simultaneously in Pittsburgh at the turn of the century marked the end of hinged-arch construction for railroad terminals. The one built by the Pennsylvania Railroad for itself and its affiliated companies (1898–1901) was comparable in size to the sheds of the new Philadelphia stations. The shed spanned 16 tracks and measured 255 × 555 feet in plan. The roof, a nearly semicircular vault, was carried on 24 arched trusses spaced 9 feet and 40 feet 6 inches alternately and rising to a clear height of 87 feet at the center hinge. Purlins in the form of shallow trusses extended throughout the length of the shed to function as wind bracing. There was a glass curtain wall at both ends set in a steel framework with the usual wind truss along the bottom. The peculiarity of truss construction in the Pennsylvania station was that the hinge at one end of each truss was left free to move to take up the effects of thermal expansion and contraction. The engineer of the shed and track facilities was W. H. Brown, then chief engineer of the Pennsylvania Railroad, and the architects of the station building were D. H. Burnham and Company. The shed survived until 1947, when it was replaced by platform canopies.

    The other Pittsburgh station was built by the Pittsburgh and Lake Erie Railroad (1899–1901). With only six tracks to cover, the size of the shed was relatively small, 120 feet in span and 500 feet in length. It was unusually light and graceful in form, a consequence of the widely spaced three-hinged arches, the open sides, and the glass curtain wall at the open end. In 1934 the volume of through traffic at the station was greatly increased when the Baltimore and Ohio Railroad began to operate its through trains over the P. and L. E. tracks between Newcastle and McKeesport, Pennsylvania. At the same time the handsome little trainshed was replaced by the usual platform canopies.

    The last of the balloon sheds, built for the present La Salle Street Station in Chicago (1901–03), marked a return to a primitive form of construction. The roof was a half-cylinder of circular section carried on steel bowstring trusses, the ends of which rested on steel columns imbedded in the brick piers of the side walls. The roof was 578 feet long and was supported by 20 pin-connected trusses, which spanned 11 tracks and 6 platforms and had an over-all length of 212 feet. The trusses were set 30 feet 3 inches on centers and provided a clear height of 21 feet above the track level. Light monitors in the roof ran transversely, following the curve of the shed, one between each pair of trusses. Since the track level at La Salle Street Station was elevated 16 feet above the street grade, the track and platform area is carried on steel girders and columns. The trainshed lasted the conventional thirty years: it was replaced in 1934 by a flat concrete slab hung from overhead trusses which span between the original wall columns. La Salle Street Station was built jointly by the Lake Shore and Michigan Southern and the Rock Island railroads. The present owners are the New York Central and the Rock Island, the New York, Chicago and St. Louis (Nickel Plate Road) being a tenant.

The maximum length of the balloon shed rarely exceeded 600 feet. With the rolling stock and motive power now common on American railroads, this length would accommodate a four-unit diesel locomotive and four cars, or seven cars without an engine. Since the current practice is to operate long trains, the consequence has been that platforms and platform canopies had to be built well beyond the end of the shed, in some cases at a length greatly exceeding that of the original structure.

19. The maximum number of companies served by St. Louis Union Station was once 19 but was subsequently reduced to the following 16 by mergers: Baltimore and Ohio; Chicago, Burlington and Quincy; Chicago and Eastern Illinois; Chicago, Rock Island and Pacific; Gulf, Mobile and Ohio; Illinois Central; Louisville and Nashville; Missouri-Kansas-Texas; Missouri Pacific; New York Central; New York, Chicago and St. Louis (Nickel Plate Road); Pennsylvania; St. Louis-San Francisco (Frisco); St. Louis Southwestern (Cotton Belt Route); Southern; Wabash. The C. and E. I., Rock Island, and Southern have abandoned passenger service into the city.

20. For the Pegram truss, see pp. 137–8.

21. The shed of the St. Louis station measures 601 × 700 feet in plan and stands 75 feet above the track level at the crown. The span lengths between rows of columns are as follows: two side, each 90 feet 8 inches; two intermediate, each 139 feet 2 inches; center, 141 feet 3½ inches. The trusses supporting the roof are inverted, their bottom chords bowed downward, and inclined so that their long axes are parallel to the tangents to the vault curve at the center points of the spans. The top chords of the trusses are slightly curved so that all of them together conform exactly to the profile of the roof. The shed and the light monitors required a total of 110,000 square feet of glass, 424,000 square feet of tin, and 1,000,000 board feet of planking. The supporting framework required 5,500,000 pounds of steel.

22. Quoted in an editorial on the St. Louis station, *Engineering News,* vol. 27 (April 2, 1892), p. 322.

23. At the time of the terminal's construction these were the Boston and Albany, Boston and Providence, New England, New York, New Haven and Hartford, and the Old Colony. Subsequent mergers reduced these to the Boston and Albany and the New Haven.

24. The shed of South Station was 570 feet wide and 602 feet long. The roof framing was divided into three spans, the central one 228 feet 6 inches across, the two at the sides each 165 feet 9 inches. The supporting trusses, which had upward curving bottom chords, were actually combinations of cantilevers and floating spans. The trusses were set 60 feet on centers and were tied together longitudinally in pairs. The roof was composed of tongue-and-groove hard pine sheathing covered with layers of roofing paper and tar. At the open end of the shed there was a single wind truss with flat bottom chord which spanned the entire width of the track area and supported the usual glass curtain wall. The wet and compressible soil under the track area and the proximity of Fort Point Channel required unusual methods of foundation construction. All excavation had to be done inside a cofferdam, and the granite footings, 20 feet high and 18 feet square at the base, had to be supported on spruce piles 25 to 40 feet long.

## Chapter VIII—CONCRETE CONSTRUCTION

### VIII, 1. PLAIN CONCRETE IN WALLS AND BUILDINGS

1. White's water lime was an impure hydraulic lime—that is, a quicklime (calcium oxide) mixed with oxides of aluminum and silicon which will set under water. It was derived from so-called cement rock, a Silurian limestone common in New York and Pennsylvania which is a clayey magnesian limestone containing varying proportions of the oxides of aluminum, iron, and silicon. The natural cements of New York differ from the artificial variety chiefly in the relatively small proportion of lime, the relatively high proportion of aluminum and iron oxides, and the presence of impurities. Lime for cement may also be manufactured from various clays, marl, and oyster shell.

2. In 1829 the builders of the Louisville and Portland Canal at Louisville, Kentucky, turned up a local deposit of natural cement along the route of the canal. They founded their own mill and immediately put the product to use for lock walls. The builders of the Illinois and Michigan Canal used it for retaining walls beginning in 1838, when a cement mill was established along the canal route, probably in La Salle County, Illinois, where there are deposits of an appropriate limestone. The new material was introduced into the Chesapeake and Ohio Canal in 1839, and into the Miami and Erie sometime around the mid-century. In at least one place, about eight miles southeast of Hamilton, Ohio, the original concrete lock walls of the Miami and Erie Canal still remain, but they were built some years after the Dayton-Cincinnati portion of the canal was completed in 1828.

3. For Saylor's invention, see p. 227.

4. A novel form of concrete block construction in the early period was used at Fort Sumter for the embrasures of the gun openings in the walls. The exact date on which the concrete was placed in the walls is difficult to determine. Construction of the fort began in 1829 and continued until 1838, but the walls had risen to a height of only 2 feet by that time. Litigation over title to the land held up further progress until 1841, when construction was resumed. The fort was completed in its original form in 1860. The gun emplacements and openings were probably built shortly after 1841. The individual opening is a narrow slot surrounded by six wedge-shaped blocks forming an oblong embrasure in the 5-foot wall. The concrete is a crude mixture of an aggregate of shells and brick fragments in a matrix of cement, sand, and water. Five of these openings remain in the west wall of the fort, the rest of which was destroyed by Union artillery on Morris Island immediately to the south. The fort was not taken until Sherman occupied Columbia, South Carolina, early in 1865. The old fort was never rebuilt, with the consequence that full restoration is an archaeological job of digging up the buried rubble left from the Civil War action.

5. Horace Greeley may have been influenced by Fowler's thesis when he built a barn of concrete on his farm at Chappaqua, New York, in 1853. It was later converted to a residence, which stood throughout the remainder of the century. The idea took hold, and by 1860 concrete houses began to appear with growing frequency in a few of the Eastern cities and in Chicago. One of these, built about 1865 at Black Rock (now within Buffalo), New York, had monolithic walls the proportions of whose concrete mixture have been preserved—1½ parts of quicklime, 4 of sand, and 6 of gravel, with sufficient water for casting and proper setting. The house was built entirely of concrete except for the wooden joists and floor planking.

6. From *Frear's Patent Artificial Stone, Stucco, Mastic Cement, etc., and Pressing Machine,* Chicago, no date; quoted in "Frear Artificial Stone, Patented 1868," *Journal of the Society of Architectural Historians,* 13:1 (March 1954), pp. 27–8.

7. After Frear showed the way, a number of other manufacturers established businesses for the production of concrete block, or artificial stone, as it was usually known. The Chicago Composition Granite Company (founded 1869) went further than any of its competitors when it was given the contract to erect the entire front wall of a building at Adams and Wabash streets shortly after the fire of 1871. As the name of the company indicates, its concrete was made with an aggregate of broken granite in a matrix of sand and hydraulic lime or Portland cement.

8. For Ransome's work in reinforced concrete, see pp. 234–40.

9. An Eastern organization, the Schillingler Artificial Stone Company of New York, laid the first concrete sidewalk in Chicago in 1872. It was a strip 16 × 181 feet in area along the east side of the old Chamber of Commerce Building. The walk cost a little over $1,000, or 35 cents a square foot.

   The most extensive use of concrete block as a structural material appeared in the J. V. Farwell and Company warehouse, Chicago (1882). The first-story walls of the big building, which measured 360 × 400 feet in plan, were built entirely of precast blocks. They were treated exactly like stone masonry, having been dressed and finished with chamfered edges after casting. In spite of this additional expense, the cost was estimated to be about one-quarter that of limestone or sandstone.

10. "Artificial Stone as a Building Material," *American Architect and Building News,* vol. 13 (April 7, 1883), p. 159.

11. The manufacturer conducting the tests was probably the Middlesex Stone Brick Company, also founded about 1870. The results of compression to disintegration gave an ultimate crushing strength ranging from 5,000 to 10,000 pounds per square inch, with a maximum of 15,300 pounds for a sample with granite aggregate. The lower figure, however, was the general rule, the upper being much higher than was usually obtained with concrete. The wide range of the figures indicates the extreme lack of uniformity in a standard run of mixtures. After a year's exposure the ultimate strength of some of the samples with ordinary aggregates increased to 12,000 pounds per square inch, which would be expected with good mixtures. In its resistance to frost the concrete proved to be equal to natural stones with the exception of sandstone, the laminated and porous structure of which made it much inferior in this respect. The fire resistance of the artificial material, on the other hand, was distinctly below that of natural stone.

12. R. Lockwood, quoted in "Building Stones," *Van Nostrand's Engineering Magazine,* 8:52 (April 1873), p. 373.

An example in the East of an extensive application of concrete to ornamental as well as structural purposes is Dwight Place Church, New Haven, Connecticut (*c.* 1872), the walls of which were built entirely of concrete block. It provided a convincing demonstration of the claims for the new material, since it still stands in its original condition.

13. While Eads was working on his jetties, various engineers in the East were using precast blocks for docks and shore protection. The engineer Schuyler Hamilton first applied concrete to harbor works in salt water beginning in 1873 for the construction of docks and shore walls at New York City. He used blocks varying in weight from 13 to 60 tons, the material of which was Portland cement, seashore sand from the Staten Island kills, and broken traprock from the Hudson River palisades. Small sample blocks were submitted to exhaustive stress, slump, moisture, and temperature tests. Systematic testing of concrete such as this paralleled the methods of testing iron members which were being developed at the same time. In the case of concrete, such tests were even more imperative because of extreme variation at the time in successive barrels of both artificial and natural cements and the still experimental stage of proportioning the various ingredients.

There was some question of the effects of tidal currents on concrete, but the installations at New York Harbor held up well. This was not always the case elsewhere. A concrete pier built at Warren, Rhode Island, on Narragansett Bay (1883), was subjected to tidal currents carrying abrasive material. As a consequence, it was eroded so badly between high and low water that it had to be replaced in twenty-five years. On the other hand, concrete bridge piers exposed to the extreme tidal conditions in the Bay of Fundy showed little evidence of erosion in a similar period of time.

14. The Guaranty Loan Building in Minneapolis (1888–90), designed by E. Townsend Mix, included in its great variety of structural features floors composed of precast slabs laid on hollow-tile arches spanning between I-beams. The partitions of the building were built up of hollow tile covering a concrete core.

    The builders of two important commercial structures in Boston used concrete flooring in generous quantities. In the Chamber of Commerce Building (1890–92) the basement floor was a continuous 12-inch slab covered with a layer of tarred paper and a wooden floor. The boiler room floor, below the level of high water, was a 24-inch slab covered with brick, as were the boiler room walls. All other floors were built of precast slabs laid on steel beams with a finished flooring of wood laid on top of the concrete. The roof was constructed in the same way except for the familiar tar-and-gravel covering over the slab. The architects of the Chamber of Commerce Building were Shepley, Rutan and Coolidge, and the builders Norcross Brothers, who later received several patents in concrete construction. W. G. Preston's International Trust Company Building (1892–93) had floors of 6-inch slabs laid on steel beams and hollow-tile arches.

15. For a full discussion of Starrucca Viaduct, see pp. 244, 339.

16. The dimensions of the cylinder were as follows: diameter, 6 feet; length, 31 feet 6 inches; thickness, 1⅛ inches. The cylinder was built up of 7 ring sections, each 4 feet 6 inches long.

17. For a full description of the Omaha bridge, see pp. 145–6.

18. The foundation of the statue, a hollow truncated pyramid of concrete, is 52 feet 10 inches deep, 91 feet square at the bottom, and 65 feet square at the top. The central opening is 10 feet square. The top, or foot of the pedestal, stands 60 feet above mean high water. The concrete throughout the foundation depth is a mixture of 2 parts of cement, 2 of sand, and 7 of broken traprock, the cement being divided between the Rosendale and Portland varieties as follows: first 15 feet 8 inches, all Rosendale; intermediate 12 feet, half Rosendale, half Portland; final 25 feet 2 inches, all Portland. Compressive tests on the all-Rosendale mixture clearly indicated the growth of strength with increasing age. A test block in the form of a 12-inch cube yielded after aging 6 months at 813 pounds per square inch, and after 27 months at 1354.5 pounds per square inch. One cube, at the age of 28 months, held up to 1,452 pounds per square inch. The pedestal, 89 feet high, has the same form as the foundation, contracting from 65 feet square at the bottom to 43 feet 6 inches at the top. The opening is 27 feet square. The concrete core of the pedestal consists of 1 part Portland cement to 4 of traprock screenings. For the statue framing, see pp. 46, 287.

19. For a description of the Poughkeepsie bridge, see pp. 157–8.

20. The Omaha pier, which extended to bedrock, was a solid cylinder 134 feet 6 inches deep and 40 feet in diameter overall. An inner steel cylinder 20 feet in diameter contained a solid core of concrete up to the stone plate which carried the bearings of the truss. The inner and outer cylinders were rigidly joined by a system of radial braces in the space between the two. The remainder of the space was filled with concrete. The outer cylinder extended only up to the water line; above it the concrete was faced with stone masonry.


## VIII, 2. REINFORCED CONCRETE BUILDINGS

1. Plain concrete is essentially like stone in physical properties and structural behavior. It is thus a rigid substance which can only resist compression. If it is used as a beam or slab on isolated supports, however, it is subject to deflection, which places the concave surface of the deflected member in compression and the convex surface in tension. On a hypothetical surface between the two there lies the so-called neutral axis, which is the center line of the unstressed section of the member. Since only an elastic substance can absorb a tensile stress, it is necessary to introduce metal reinforcing into the concrete member in the region of tension. In the case of a simple beam, which is bent downward between its supports, the undersurface is subjected to maximum tension, and consequently the bulk of the reinforcing must be located as near that surface as possible. A continuous beam is bent downward between supports and upward in the neighborhood of the supports, and the reinforcing must be nearest the undersurface at the mid-point and nearest the upper surface at the support. Footings and floor slabs are subject to complex bending and shearing action, and the distribution of reinforcing is thus a more difficult problem. Arches under moving loads pose peculiar problems of their own. Reinforcing concrete not only vastly extended the range of its structural possibilities, but in transforming it into an elastic material, the new technique opened it, so to speak, to the sciences of elasticity, strength of materials, and stress analysis. Thus it became, in the two fundamental ways of nineteenth-century technology, a modern engineering material.

2. The first American step in the direction of reinforced concrete was a patent issued in 1844 to a mason named P. Summer for metal lathing to hold and to strengthen plaster and mortar. Many of the next group of patents were granted for reinforced pipe construction, but it was not until 1872 that J. A. Middleton patented the method of reinforcing pipe by imbedding wire mesh in the concrete. This was essentially Monier's technique and is now widely used for slabs laid on the ground, such as basement floors, driveways, and streets. The important patents between Summer and Middleton for reinforced pipe were the following: R. B. Stevenson (1854), for sheet metal pipe with an exterior coating of hydraulic cement mortar; Wyckoff (1861), for wooden pipe wound with iron wire and covered with mortar; Knight (1861), for sheet metal pipe covered inside and out with mortar; A. P. Stephens (1868), for corrugated sheet-iron pipe covered as in the Knight patent.

3. The first example of reinforced brick construction appears to have been the brick dome of the Georgetown Reservoir, Washington, D. C., built in connection with Montgomery Meigs's water supply system (1857–64). The dome was actually a dome-shaped ring with a bottom diameter of 120 feet and a top diameter of 80 feet. The reinforcing consisted of ¼ × 2-inch wrought iron straps imbedded in the mortar joints. The footing of the cylindrical reservoir was plain concrete.

4. Shearing stresses in footings and slabs offer a more complex problem than stresses in beams, but in general the solution is a matter of locating reinforcing members in such a way that the pressure of the columns is translated into tension in the iron rods rather than allowed to punch through the slab or footing.

5. Ward, an engineer and a wealthy manufacturer, was one of the founders of the Russell, Birdsall and Ward Screw Manufacturing Company of Port Chester. This well-known business still flourishes under its original name.

6. "Artificial Stone as a Building Material," *American Architect and Building News,* vol. 13 (April 7, 1883), p. 159.

7. J. B. Johnson, "Monier Construction," *American Architect and Building News,* vol. 69 (August 4, 1900), p. 37. The full title of Hyatt's book is *An Account of Some Experiments with Portland Cement Concrete, Combined with Iron, as a Building Material* (privately printed, 1877). In this work Hyatt described and analyzed all the basic modern techniques of reinforced concrete construction: correct location of bars in beams and slabs; the superiority of bent bars and bars with bosses; hoop reinforcing of columns and chimneys; coefficients of expansion and moduli of elasticity of concrete compared to iron; and tables of compressive and tensile strength of reinforced concrete.

8. The quantities of materials in the Ward house were as follows: 4,000 barrels of Portland cement imported from England, 8,000 barrels of sand, 12,000 barrels of machine-broken Hudson River limestone, and 12,000 barrels of white beach pebbles. The reinforcing elements, all of wrought iron, were ⅜-inch rods and rolled I-beams of various sizes.

9. The floor slab of the Ward house rested on I-beams surrounded by concrete and on a continuous bracket built out from the four walls of each room. The depth of the I-beams varied from 5 to 8 inches, depending on the size of the room. In the parlor, with a maximum span of 18 feet, the slab rested on 8-inch beams set 6 feet on centers. On a flat form of rough boards laid between the beams, the slab was poured to a depth of 1 inch. A course of ⅜-inch rods was laid on the concrete, the rods spanning laterally between the beams, and a second 1-inch layer of concrete was poured over the rods. A second course of rods was then laid on at right angles to the first and a final 2-inch layer of concrete was poured over them. This massive and elaborate construction formed only the sub-floor. The finished floor—most remarkable of all—was poured over inverted troughs which served as heating ducts connected with the furnace by means of

hollow spaces in the walls. This was a modern variation on the Roman method of heating by hollow chambers, or hypocausts, under the floor. The finished floor was hand-rubbed with stone and sand to give the appearance of polished sandstone. During the earlier period of construction (1871–72) Ward subjected his beams and slabs to extreme tests, loading them far beyond the allowable limits for iron at the time, and found only a negligible deflection.

10. The Mansard roof, like the floors, was cast in solid slabs reinforced with rods over I-beams set at varying distances, the maximum being 10 feet. Over each beam and hip rafter in the roof there was a shrinkage joint covered by a molded hip-roll with a layer of felt between the roll and the concrete. The cornice and the main roof gutters wer cast integral with the walls. The largest individual slabs in the house were those in the floor and roof of the veranda, some sections between shrinkage joints measuring 12 × 30 feet. The veranda columns were cast as hollow cylinders to carry off roof water and were reinforced with hoops of ⅜-inch rods. This reinforcing indicates that Ward must have anticipated Hyatt in an important discovery, namely, that although columns are subjected theoretically only to compression, the crushing force tends to rupture the outer surface and hence subjects that surface to tension. The chimneys of the house were cast as single pieces.

11. *American Architect and Building News,* vol. 2 (August 18, 1877), p. 267.

12. Unless the builder chooses to use a large mass of concrete, the reinforcing of a column footing is necessary to give the concrete sufficient resistance to the shearing or punching action of the column above the footing, along with upward bending of the raft-like slab.

13. The value of prestressing arises from an important discovery made by a number of European investigators in the strength of materials: that concrete under compression and iron and steel under tension are stronger than the same materials unloaded. The stresses, of course, must be below the crushing strength or elastic limit of the materials in question.

14. The invention of prestressing was not made practicable until 1927, when Eugène Freyssinet in France and Gustav Magnel in Belgium developed a high-tensile steel wire which retained its tension even after the concrete shrank to its minimum volume. Since then a number of methods have been developed for precompressing concrete and pretensioning steel cable by loading it with weights. These techniques have had revolutionary consequences for twentieth century building.

15. On the first reinforced concrete bridge, see pp. 248–9.

16. Ernest L. Ransome and Alexis Saurbrey, *Reinforced Concrete Buildings* (New York, McGraw-Hill, 1912), p. 10.

## VIII, 3. THE MASONRY ARCH BRIDGE: STONE AND CONCRETE

1. By the beginning of the new century masonry bridges of relatively large size could be built if capital was available to pay the costs. A good early example was Wit-

mer's Bridge over Conestoga Creek at Lancaster, Pennsylvania (1800). About 275 feet in over-all length, the bridge consisted of nine full-centered, or semicircular, arches varying in span from 23 to 25 feet. Only the voussoirs (the radial blocks that make up the ring of the arch) were dressed stone, the rest of the structure being rubble masonry laid up in mortar. The bridge was repaired with concrete in 1917 and continued a useful life for some time after that date.

2. For other achievements of Benjamin Latrobe as chief engineer of the Baltimore and Ohio, see pp. 118–19.

3. The exact length of Aqueduct Bridge was 1,197 feet, which was divided into 15 arches, six of 50-foot span on the Bronx side, eight at 80 feet over the river and on the Manhattan side, and another of 50 feet at the Manhattan end. The arches provided a clearance of 100 feet above mean high water, and the total height of the structure was 121 feet maximum. The arches supported an attic story which carried two 36-inch cast iron pipes laid in 1848 and one 90½-inch wrought iron pipe laid in 1864. The roof of the bridge, 21 feet wide, was used as a walkway.

4. The Western Railroad later became the western portion of the Boston and Albany, between Springfield and Albany. This line crosses the Berkshire Mountains, and as a consequence, Whistler and his assistants acquired a good deal of experience in the construction of bridges in hilly topography. Many of these structures were masonry arches, some of which, with repairs, survived until the mid-twentieth century.

5. The over-all length of Starrucca Viaduct is 1,040 feet, which is divided into 17 full-centered arches of 50-foot span. It stands 100 feet high from the top of the foundation to the base of rail and is 25 feet wide over the copings. The transverse faces of the piers are slightly battered—that is, lean inward from bottom to top. The depth, or thickness, of the pier is about 12 feet at the spring line of the arch.

6. The west approach of the Ohio River bridge of the Baltimore and Ohio between Bellaire, Ohio, and Benwood, West Virginia (1868–72), established a new record in size for masonry-arch construction. The approach, which lies above the streets of Bellaire, is built on a curve and is about 1,800 feet long overall. The deck stands on the average 45 feet above grade level and is carried by 43 full-centered arches with a span of 33 feet 4 inches. Although the iron trusses of the river crossing have been replaced, the masonry approach still stands, easily dominating most of the buildings of the town.

The only bridge of stone arches over the Mississippi is that of the Great Northern Railway at Minneapolis (1882–83). The 18-foot St. Anthony's Falls, close to the rail crossing, made navigation impossible at the site, so the company could use the multiple-arch form. The total length of 2,100 feet is divided into 23 arches. Those over the water have a span of 98 feet, which decreases to a minimum of 40 feet in the approaches, where the ground drops sharply to the water level. The maximum height from the foundation to the top of the coping is 76 feet, and the average width 27 feet. The voussoirs are granite, the rest of the masonry limestone. The bridge cost $690,000 at the time of its construction, which has been altered only by the addition of steel tie rods as arch reinforcing in 1907. The big structure continues to carry the traffic of the Burlington, North Western, and Northern Pacific railroads as well as that of the Great Northern.

7. For the action of the concrete arch and the function of reinforcing, see pp. 247–8, 340.

8. The proportions of concrete for the arch barrels of the Nashua Aqueduct were 1 part cement, 2 of sand, and 5 of broken stone. For the filling they were 1:3:6.

9. The history of bridges at the Rockville site nearly recapitulates the development of bridge construction throughout the century. The first, completed in 1848, was a wooden structure of Howe deck trusses. The secod (1876) was an iron bridge of Warren trusses with posts and subdivided panels, each having a half-length post extending from the top chord to the intersection of the diagonals. The third is the present stone and concrete viaduct. Its total length is 3,820 feet, divided into 48 arches of 70-foot span.

## VIII, 4. THE REINFORCED CONCRETE ARCH

1. Although the arch is theoretically subject only to compression in static equilibrium, the European theorists and engineers were the first to understand that this is not the case under certain conditions and hence to realize the necessity for metal reinforcing in the arch. In a properly designed arch the pressure line, or line along which the load acts, conforms in shape to the profile of the soffit and lies wholly within the arch. Under heavy moving loads, however, the pressure line may depart from the axis of the arch to such an extent that the arch is subjected to bending and hence tensile forces. These may be absorbed with a sufficient mass of material, but this would be a highly uneconomical and sometimes unsound way to build. Moreover, even if the arch is subject only to compression, the consequent deforming forces at the soffit may result in tensile stresses at or near the inner surface of the arch. Hyatt, as a result of his experiments, understood that this is also true of the outer surface of columns and chimneys and that as a result hoop reinforcing is a necessity under heavy loads. Ward and Ransome, as practical builders, recognized the same characteristic. Further, an arch in the form of a shell or a series of parallel ribs may be subjected to transverse bending and twisting from eccentric loads on the deck. Torsional forces of this kind are particularly high in bridges built on a skew or a curve. Again, with solid masonry, such forces might be absorbed by the sheer mass of the material, but reinforced concrete, combining the virtues of both metal and stone, offered great economies of construction and made possible great increase in size of a single span because of the precise way in which it could meet the specific conditions imposed upon the structure.

2. For Washington Bridge as constructed, see pp. 194–5.

3. Clarke's reinforcing was apparently introduced solely for the purpose of adding to the total strength of the arch at the crown and the mid-points of the haunches. The fact that in a typical failure the arch breaks at these points had been known since 1732, when Danizy conducted the first series of experiments on models of arches.

4. The Housatonic bridge has a clear span of 100 feet with a rise of only 10, and an over-all width of 7 feet. The arch varies in depth from 9 inches at the crown to 30 inches at the abutments, a variation which is characteristic of the fixed arch. It is reinforced with four 7-inch steel I-beams bent in a slightly flatter curve than the soffit. It required only 22 cubic yards of concrete and cost the town $1,475, yet it easily sustained a test load of 25 tons.

5. The Eden Park bridge spans 70 feet for a rise of 10 and has an over-all width of 33 feet. The arch slab, 15 inches deep at the crown and 48 inches at the abutments, is reinforced with twelve parallel steel I-beams 9 inches deep.

6. The Michigan Central bridge carried seven tracks and had a clear span of 56 feet for a rise of 9 feet 6 inches. There were 24 parallel reinforcing trusses, each with a depth of 15 inches at the crown and 24 inches at the abutments. The proportions of the concrete were as follows: for the barrel of the arch, 1 part Portland cement, 2 of sand, and 4 of broken stone; for the spandrels, abutments, and foundations, 1:3:6, respectively.

7. Many of the Melan arches which followed the Detroit bridge were built by the Melan Arch Construction Company of New York, whose chief designing engineer was William Mueser. Two of these were notable for special characteristics of design or size. The bridge built to carry Mount Avenue over Grand in Atlantic Highlands, New Jersey (1896), though with a span of only 50 feet, was set on a skew of 53 degrees 8 minutes. A crossing at any angle between abutments other than 90 degrees subjects the bridge to torsional stresses, which require special reinforcing. In the Mount Avenue span the designers added three sets of transverse tie rods between the curving ribs of the arch, the rods thus acting to hold the ribs in place as well as to take transverse bending forces.

   The bridge over the Passaic River at Patterson, New Jersey (1896–97), was the longest of its kind at the time both in total length and individual span, respectively 295 feet and 80 feet.

   Franklin Bridge in Forest Park, St. Louis (1898), with its 60-foot span, was typical of most Melan arches (fig. 132).

8. "'Monumental' Engineering," *The Architectural Record,* 11:2 (October 1901) p. 632.

9. The third Goat Island Bridge at Niagara Falls (1900–1), for example, was built of Melan arches with a span of 103 feet 6 inches; yet its designers felt obliged to use limestone ashlar for a facing. Even when the concrete surface was exposed, it was usually scored in such a way as to simulate stonework (at least at a distance). The most conspicuous example of this is the enormous Tunkhannock Creek Viaduct of the Lackawanna Railroad at Nicholson, Pennsylvania (1912–16).


VIII, 5. THE MASONRY DAM: STONE AND CONCRETE

1. A gravity dam is one which opposes the pressure of the impounded water by the sheer mass of the material of which it is composed. The dam must rest on stable and impervious rock formations and the joint at the base must be tight enough to prevent excessive seepage of water under high pressure.

2. The specific problem in determining the form of a dam is to prevent the overturning of the structure—that is, to meet the overturning moment exerted by the pressure of the water on the upstream face. Since water pressure varies directly with the depth, the level at which the force produces the maximum overturning moment is somewhat below the mid-point of the depth. For greatest stability the resultant of the line of action of the water load and the downward or gravitational thrust of the dam's weight must fall within the middle third of the base divided longitudinally. In addition the mass and solidity of the dam must be such as to resist sliding of the whole mass and crushing of the toe—that is, the downstream edge of the base. A dam is subject to tension on its upstream face and compression on the downstream, and the form must in part be determined by the need to avoid excessive stresses at these locations. Not all of these characteristics of dam action were understood at the time Croton Dam was built.

3. New York built its second water supply dam in the Bronx River (1881–82) to impound Kensico Reservoir. Within a few years, however, need again outgrew supply. Another dam, known as Quaker Bridge, was planned in 1888 to increase the size of Croton Reservoir, but the project was abandoned two years later for an even larger structure. The latter, or new Croton Dam, was built in two sections (1893–1901, 1902–6) in the same way as the original—granite facing over a rubble core. When it was completed old Croton Dam was wholly submerged by the deeper reservoir. The new structure is a large dam for the eastern United States: it is 1,760 feet long, stands 291 feet high above the foundation, and varies in width from 216 feet at the base to 18 feet at the top.

   The original Croton Dam provided the model for a number of municipal water supply dams in the East built during the middle third of the century. The most notable of these are Lake Cochituate Dam, Boston, 1848; Mill River Dam, New Haven, Connecticut, 1862; and Druid Lake Dam, Baltimore, Maryland, 1871 (the last is actually a dike forming one wall of a reservoir).

4. South Fork Dam was 840 feet long, 72 feet high at the maximum, and varied in width from about 200 feet at the base to 10 feet at the top. The mass was divided into two parts down the center: the upstream half consisted, from surface to interior, of loose stone facing, earth fill, and slate core; the downstream half was mostly rubble masonry of large, or Cyclopean, pieces. (The term Cyclopean comes from an early Hellenic folk-tale which said that the Cyclopes built the Mycenaean tombs and other structures, some of which were constructed of extraordinarily large blocks of stone.) Extending through the dam at the base was a sluiceway of stone masonry set in mortar, the entrance of which could be closed by a gate operated from the top of a masonry tower near the upstream face.

5. A mill dam at Blackstone, Massachusetts (1880), was built up of granite ashlar facing with a core of rubble masonry piled up in concrete. The significant characteristic of the dam was its construction on a curve, making it an arch-gravity structure.

It was only 11 feet high, with a chord length of 140 feet. A similar dam was built at Westville, Massachusetts (1881), for the same purpose. Both of them were designed by S. B. Cushing and Company of Providence, Rhode Island. Another of the same construction but much larger in size was built across the Hudson River at Mechanicsville, New York, by the Hudson River Water Power and Pulp Company (1882). It was 16 feet high and 795 feet long, a relatively large size for a power dam at that date.

6. The arch-gravity dam combines both mass and the efficient shape of the arch to withstand the water pressure. The form is virtually mandatory for all dams of relatively great height compared to their length, and is hence the natural choice for narrow canyons. In an arch dam the water pressure on the upstream face acts in the same way as does the vertical load on an arch bridge: the water pressure gives rise to compressive stresses in the dam and thus forces the dam against its abutments in the canyon walls. For this reason it is essential that the rock in the side walls be solid and impervious. On very large dams there are also torsional and shearing forces which must be compensated for in the design of the finished structure.

   The construction of a concrete dam the size of San Mateo requires special care in providing water-tight anchorage in the walls and floor of the canyon, which can be done only by working inside cofferdams. The major problem arises from pouring the immense mass of concrete in sections, each of which must be allowed to set and cool before the adjacent one is poured. The need to dissipate the heat generated by the setting of great volumes of concrete meant that construction was an extremely slow process until the method was developed at Hoover Dam of imbedding pipes carrying refrigerated water in the body of the dam.

7. The original hydroelectric installation was placed in service at Minneapolis in February 1882, but it made use of the natural drop in the water at St. Anthony's Falls. The Appleton plant went into service on September 30 of that year.

## Chapter IX—AN ARCHITECTURAL APPRAISAL

1. Carroll L. V. Meeks, *The Railroad Station* (New Haven, Yale University Press, 1956), p. 44.

2. From a paper read before a meeting of the American Association for the Advancement of Science, May 1854; quoted in *Scientific American,* 190:5 (May 1954). p. 14.

3. "Modern Architecture: the Office of Art in Engineering," *Van Nostrand's Engineering Magazine,* 1:2 (February 1869), p. 148. For a comprehensive source book in the growth of modern functionalist and organic theory in the United States, see Lewis Mumford, ed., *The Roots of Contemporary American Architecture* (New York, Reinhold, 1952).

4. From Dankmar Adler, "The Influence of Steel Construction and Plate Glass upon Style," 1896; quoted in Mumford, op. cit., p. 249.

5. *The Autobiography of an Idea* (New York, Press of the American Institute of Architects, 1922), pp. 82–5.

6. Ibid. pp. 246–8.

7. Ibid. pp. 313–14.

# BIBLIOGRAPHY

The major part of the following bibliography consists of books and general articles which are largely secondary works rather than source documents. I have divided them according to the main categories of the subject matter in this history. The bulk of it, however, is derived from special articles on individual projects which have been published in a large number of periodicals whose titles I have listed at the end of the bibliography. The most thorough and trustworthy of these are the technical journals, which I have marked with an asterisk. Since the original drawings and specifications are for the most part lost, such journals constitute the main repository of source material.

Chapters I, II: WOOD AND IRON FRAMING

Allen, Zachariah, *Diaries, 1853–75.* Unedited mss. in the possession of the Rhode Island Historical Society, Providence, Rhode Island.

Badger, Daniel D., *Illustrations of Iron Architecture, Made by the Architectural Iron Works of the City of New York.* New York, 1865.

Bagnall, William R., *Sketches of Manufacturing Establishments in New York City, and of Textile Establishments in the Eastern United States.* Bound typescript, dated 1908, in the possession of the Baker Library, Harvard University.

Bannister, Turpin C., "Bogardus Revisited," *Journal of the Society of Architectural Historians,* 15:4 (December 1956), pp. 12–22; 16:1 (March 1957), pp. 11–19.

Bannister, Turpin C., "The First Iron-framed Buildings," *Architectural Review,* 107:640 (April 1950), pp. 231–46.

Birkmire, William H., *Architectural Iron and Steel, and its Application in the Construction of Buildings.* New York, 1898.

Birkmire, William H., *Skeleton Construction in Buildings.* New York, 1897.

Blake, William P., ed., *Reports of the United States Commissioners to the Paris Universal Exposition, 1867.* Washington, 1870.

Bogardus, James, *Cast Iron Buildings: Their Construction and Advantages.* New York, 1856.

Condit, Carl W., *The Rise of the Skyscraper.* Chicago, 1952.

Damrell, Charles S., *A Half-Century of Boston's Building.* Boston, 1895.

Field, Walker, "A Re-examination into the Invention of the Balloon Frame," *Journal of the Society of Architectural Historians,* vol. 2 (October 1942), pp. 3–29.

Fitch, James M., *American Building; the Forces that Shape It.* New York, 1948.

Gallagher, H. M. Pierce, *Robert Mills, Architect of the Washington Monument.* New York, 1935.

Giedion, Siegfried, *Space, Time and Architecture,* 3rd edition. Cambridge, 1954.

Gilchrist, Agnes, *William Strickland, Architect and Engineer.* Philadelphia, 1950.

Haupt, Lewis W., *A Manual of Engineering Specifications and Contracts.* Philadelphia, 1878.

Haviland, John, *An Improved and Enlarged Edition of Biddle's Young Carpenter's Assistant.* Philadelphia, 1833.

Henrici, Olaus M. F. E., *Skeleton Structures, especially in their Application to the Building of Steel and Iron Bridges.* New York, 1867.

Hitchcock, Henry-Russell, *Architecture, Nineteenth and Twentieth Centuries.* Baltimore, 1958.

*Industrial Chicago.* Chicago, 1891.

Larkin, Oliver, *Art and Life in America.* New York, 1949.

Morrison, Hugh, *Early American Architecture.* New York, 1952.

Morrison, Hugh, *Louis Sullivan, Prophet of Modern Architecture.* New York, 1935.

Mumford, Lewis, *The Brown Decades.* New York, 1931.

Mumford, Lewis, ed., *The Roots of Contemporary American Architecture.* New York, 1952.

Mumford, Lewis, *Sticks and Stones.* New York, 1925.

Randall, Frank A., *History of the Development of Building Construction in Chicago.* Urbana, 1949.

Real Estate Record Association of New York, *A History of Real Estate, Building, and Architecture in New York City.* New York, 1898.

Schuyler, Montgomery, *American Architecture.* New York, 1891.

Sturges, W. Knight, "Cast Iron in New York," *Architectural Review,* 114:682 (October 1953), pp. 233–7.

Sullivan, Louis H., *The Autobiography of an Idea.* New York, 1922.

Sullivan, Louis H., *Kindergarten Chats.* New York, 1947.

Tyrrell, Henry G., *The Design and Construction of Mill Buildings.* Chicago, 1911.

Weisman, Winston, "New York and the Problem of the First Skyscraper," *Journal of the Society of Architectural Historians,* 12:1 (March 1953), pp. 13–21.

## Chapters III, IV: BRIDGE TRUSSES

Allen, Richard S., *Covered Bridges of the Northeast.* Brattleboro, Vt., 1957.

Bigelow, Jacob, *Elements of Technology,* 2nd edition. Boston, 1831.

Bishop, J. Leander, *A History of American Manufactures from 1608 to 1860.* Philadelphia, 1861–66.

Brock, F. B., "Truss Bridges," *Engineering News,* vol. 9 (1882), pp. 371 *et seq.,* and vol. 10 (1883), pp. 5 *et seq.*

Calhoun, Daniel H., *The American Civil Engineer, 1792–1843.* Unpublished doctoral dissertation, Johns Hopkins University, Baltimore, 1956.

Clarke, Thomas C., "American Iron Bridges," *Scientific American,* Supplement No. 32, August 5, 1876.

Cooper, Theodore, "American Railroad Bridges," *Transactions of the American Society of Civil Engineers,* vol. 21, pp. 1–60.

Culmann, Karl, "Der Bau der eisernen Brücken in England und Amerika," *Allgemeine Bauzeitung,* vol. 16 (1851), pp. 69–129, and vol. 17 (1852), pp. 163–222.

Edwards, Llewellyn N., "The Evolution of Early American Bridges," *Transactions of the Newcomen Society of England,* vol. 13, pp. 95–116.

Fletcher, Robert, and J. P. Snow, "A History of the Development of Wooden Bridges," *Trans. A. S. C. E.,* vol. 99, pp. 314–408.

Galloway, John D., *The First Transcontinental Railroad.* New York, 1950.

Haupt, Herman, *The General Theory of Bridge Construction.* New York, 1851.

Henrici, Olaus M. F. E. See under chaps. i, ii.

Hungerford, Edward, *The Story of the Baltimore and Ohio Railroad, 1827–1927.* New York, 1928.

Kirby, Richard S., and Philip G. Laurson, *The Early Years of Modern Civil Engineering.* New Haven, 1932.

Kirby, Richard S., Sidney Withington, Arthur B. Darling, and Frederick Kilgour, *Engineering in History.* New York, 1956.

Knight, E. H., *Knight's American Mechanics' Dictionary.* New York, 1874–76.

Mahan, Dennis H., *An Elementary Course of Civil Engineering,* 2nd edition. New York, 1838.

Mehrtens, Georg C., *Vorlesungen über Ingenieur-Wissenschaften,* Part II, *Eisenbrückenbau.* Vol. 1, Leipzig, 1908; vol. 2, Leipzig, 1920.

Morison, George A., *George Shattuck Morison, 1842–1903, a Memoir.* Peterborough, N. H., 1940.

Morison, George S., *Bridge Construction.* Ithaca, 1893.

Morison, George S., *The Memphis Bridge; a Report to . . . the Kansas City and Memphis Railway and Bridge Company.* New York, 1894.

Pope, Thomas A., *A Treatise on Bridge Architecture.* New York, 1811.

Renwick, James, *The Elements of Mechanics.* Philadelphia, 1832.

Smith, C. Shaler, *A Comparative Analysis of the Fink, Murphy, Bollman, and Triangular Trusses.* New York, 1865.

Stevenson, David, *Sketch of the Civil Engineering of North America.* London, 1838.

Stuart, Charles B., *Civil and Military Engineers of North America.* New York, 1871.

Timoshenko, Stephen P., *History of Strength of Materials.* New York, 1953.

Town, Ithiel, *A Description of Ithiel Town's Improvements in the Construction of Wood and Iron Bridges.* New Haven, 1821.

Tyrrell, Henry G., *The History of Bridge Engineering.* Chicago, 1911.

Watkins, J. Elfreth, *History of The Pennsylvania Railroad Company, 1846–1896.* Philadelphia (?), 1896.

Whipple, Squire, *An Elementary and Practical Treatise on Bridge Building.* New York, 1872.

## Chapters V, VI: SUSPENSION AND ARCH BRIDGES

Bishop, J. Leander. See under chaps. iii, iv.

Culmann, Karl. See under chaps. iii, iv.

Ellet, Charles, *Report and Plan for a Wire Suspension Bridge . . . across the Mississippi River at St. Louis.* Philadelphia, 1840.

Ellet, Charles, *Report on a Railway Suspension Bridge across the Connecticut River at Middletown.* Philadelphia, 1848.

Ellet, Charles, *Report on a Suspension Bridge across the Potomac, for Rail Road and Common Travel.* Philadelphia, 1852.

Farrington, E. F., *Concise Description of the East River Bridge, with Full Details of Construction.* New York, 1881.

Farrington, E. F., *A Full and Complete Description of the Covington and Cincinnati Suspension Bridge, with Dimensions and Details of Construction.* Cincinnati, 1867.

Jakkula, A. A., *A History of Suspension Bridges in Bibliographical Form.* State College, Texas, 1941.

Kirby, Richard S., and Philip G. Laurson. See under chaps. iii, iv.

Kirby, Richard S., Sidney Withington, et al. See under chaps. iii, iv.

Mahan, Dennis H. See under chaps. iii, iv.

Mehrtens, Georg C. See under chaps. iii, iv.

Renwick, James. See under chaps. iii, iv.

Roebling, John A., *Final Report . . . to the President and Directors of the Niagara Falls Suspension and Niagara Falls International Bridge Companies.* Rochester, 1855.

Schuyler, Hamilton, *The Roeblings: A Century of Engineers, Bridgebuilders, and Industrialists.* Princeton, 1931.

Steinman, David B., *The Builders of the Bridge.* New York, 1945.

Steinman, David B., and Sara Ruth Watson, *Bridges and their Builders.* New York, 1941.

White, Joseph, and von Bernewitz, M. W., *The Bridges of Pittsburgh.* Pittsburgh, 1928.

Woodward, Calvin, *A History of the St. Louis Bridge.* St. Louis, 1881.

## Chapter VII: RAILWAY TRAINSHEDS

Berg, Walter L., *Building and Structures of American Railroads.* New York, 1893.

Droege, John A., *Passenger Terminals and Trains.* New York, 1916.

Harlow, Alvin F., *The Road of the Century.* New York, 1947.

Harlow, Alvin F., *Steelways of New England.* New York, 1946.

Hungerford, Edward, *Men and Iron, the Story of the New York Central.* New York, 1938.

Hungerford, Edward, *Men of Erie, A Story of Human Effort.* New York, 1946.

Meeks, Carroll L. V., *The Railroad Station, an Architectural History.* New Haven, 1956.

## Chapter VIII: CONCRETE CONSTRUCTION

Emperger, Fritz von, "The Development and Recent Improvement of Concrete-Iron Highway Bridges," *Trans. A. S. C. E.,* vol. 31, pp. 438–88.

Fay, Frederic H., W. M. Bailey, M. C. Tuttle, and A. W. Woodman, "Brick and Concrete Metal Construction," *American Architect and Building News,* vol. 72 (April 20, 27, 1901), pp. 19 *et seq.*

Gillmore, Quincey A., *A Practical Treatise on Limes, Hydraulic Cements, and Mortars.* New York, 1863.

King, Charles, *A Memoir of the Construction, Cost, and Capacity of the Croton Aqueduct.* New York, 1843.

Lesley, Robert W., *History of the Portland Cement Industry in the United States.* Chicago, 1924.

Melan, Josef, *Plain and Reinforced Concrete Arches.* Translated by David B. Steinman. New York, 1917.

Radford, William A., ed., *Radford's Cyclopedia of Cement Construction.* Chicago, 1910.

Ransome, Ernest L., and Saurbrey, Alexis, *Reinforced Concrete Buildings.* New York, 1912.

Watson, Wilbur J., *Bridge Architecture.* New York, 1927.

Weymann, Edward, *The Design and Construction of Dams.* New York, 1899.


PERIODICALS

*American Architect and Building News**

*Architects' and Builders' Magazine**

*Architects' and Mechanics' Journal**

*Architectural Forum*

*Architectural Record*

*Architectural Review*

*Architectural Review and American Builders Journal**

*Art Bulletin*

*Arts and Architecture*

*Brickbuilder*

*Building**

*Building News**

*Bulletin of the Railway and Locomotive Historical Society*

*Carpentry and Building**

*Concrete**

*Engineer**

*Engineering**

*Engineering and Building Record**

*Engineering News**

*Engineering News-Record**

*Engineering Record**

*Harper's Weekly*

*Inland Architect and News Record**

*Journal of the Franklin Institute**

*Journal of the Society of Architectural Historians*

*Journal of the Western Society of Engineers**

*Land Owner*

*Magazine of Art*

*Mechanics' Magazine and Register of Inventions and Improvements**

*New York Illustrated News*

*Niles' Weekly Register*

*Port Folio*

*Railroad Gazette**

*Railway Age**

*Railway Review**

*Sanitary Engineer**

*Scientific American*

*Trains*

*Transactions of the American Society of Civil Engineers**

*Van Nostrand's Electric Engineering Magazine**

*Western Architect*

# INDEX

Bridges *(cont.)*

Britannia, 9, 185, 301

Brooklyn, 119, 153, 177–81, 286, 317–18, 319, fig. 93

Cabin John, Washington, D. C., 244–5

Carrollton, Baltimore, Md., 241–2, fig. 127

Cascade, Susquehanna, Pa., 101, 300

Catasauqua and Fogelsville R. R., Allentown, Pa., 306

Central Pacific R. R., Lower Cascade, Cal., 100

Charles River, Boston, Mass. (1786), 292

Charles River railroad, Boston, Mass., 101–2

Charles River, Cambridge, Mass. (1662), 76

Cheat River, Rowlesburg, W. Va., 294

Chestnut St., Philadelphia, Pa., 320–21

Chicago and North Western Ry., Glenview, Ill., 306

Cleveland, Painesville and Ashtabula R. R., Ashtabula, O., 108–9, fig. 41

Colorado River, A. and P. R. R., Red Rock, Ariz., 313

Colossus, Philadelphia, Pa., 87, 168, fig. 29

Columbia River, North Coast Ry., Kennewick, Wash., 299

Connecticut River, Bellows Falls, Vt. (1785), 77–8, fig. 23

Connecticut River, Middletown, Conn., project (1848), 168

Connecticut River, Orford, N. H., 91

Connecticut River, Western R. R., Springfield, Mass., 94–5

Conway, Wales, 9, 301

Croton Aqueduct, *see* Harlem River

Danube Canal, Vienna, Austria, 308

Dearborn St., Chicago, Ill. (1834), 101

Delaware and Hudson Canal aqueducts, Pa., 173

Delaware River, Easton, Pa., 82, 293, fig. 25

Delaware River, Narrowsburg, N. Y., 295

Bridges *(cont.)*

Delaware River, New Hope, Pa., 87, 295, fig. 29

Delaware River, Philadelphia, Pa., 316

Delaware River, Stockton, N. J., 84, 294

Delaware River, Trenton, N. J., 83–4, 294, fig. 27

De Milt Ave., New York, N. Y., 302

Detroit River, Detroit, Mich., project (*c.* 1890), 318

Dunlap's Creek, Brownsville, Pa., 104, 184, 320

Eads, St. Louis, Mo., 9, 143, 155, 156, 185–90, 193, 276, 286, 289, 320, 321, figs. 96, 97

East River, New York, N. Y., projects (1867, 1872), 154, fig. 79

Eastern R. R., Manchester, Mass., 102

Eden Park, Cincinnati, O., 250–51, 341

Erie Canal, Frankford, N. Y., 104, fig. 39

Erie R. R., Washingtonville, N. Y., 145

Evergreens Cemetery, East New York, N. Y., 246–7

Forbes St., Pittsburgh, Pa., 191, 321, fig. 99

Forth, Firth of, Scotland, 8, 159, 313

Fortieth St., Philadelphia, Pa., 154–5, 312, fig. 80

Forty-fourth St., New York, N. Y., 309

Frankford Creek, Bridgeburg, Pa., 295

Franklin, St. Louis, Mo., 341

Garabit, France, 194

Garonne Canal, Grisoles, France, 246

Genesee River, B. and N. Y. C. R. R., Portage, N. Y., 96, 298, fig. 36

Genesee River, Erie R. R., Portage, N. Y., 111–12, 302, fig. 45

George Washington, New York, N. Y., 195, 309

Glenmere Pond, Lynn, Mass. (*c.* 1800), 76

Golden Gate, 181

Grand Ave., St. Louis, Mo., 318

Great Salt Lake, S. P. R. R., 100